physical anthropology

an introduction

physical anthropology

an introduction

A. J. KELSO

UNIVERSITY OF COLORADO

J. B. LIPPINCOTT COMPANY

PHILADELPHIA   NEW YORK   TORONTO

To my wife, Mary,
and to my children, Colette and William

Acknowledgments

I AM GRATEFUL to several persons for their assistance and helpful suggestions. Professor Francis Johnston, University of Texas, and Professor John Greenway, University of Colorado, read the entire manuscript. Professors Newton E. Morton and Laurence E. Snyder, both of the University of Hawaii, and Dr. Stanley Wright, of the University of California at Los Angeles, read Chapter 3. Professor George Armelagos, University of Massachusetts, and Professors Alice M. Brues and David L. Greene, of the University of Colorado, each read several parts of the manuscript as it was in preparation. Professor Robert M. Adams, University of Chicago, read Chapter 5. Each of these persons offered useful and thoughtful suggestions on the content and organization of the material in the text.

Duane Quiatt kindly permitted me to draw heavily on material contained in his dissertation in preparing the section on primate behavior. Dr. Carleton S. Coon graciously supplied me with most of the "people pictures" contained in Part III. Dr. Theodore Grand, Oregon Regional Primate Research Center, supplied several of the photographs of living primates.

Miss Sue Ellen Jacobs and the late Miss Bonnie Deane Davis prepared the original drawings. Mr. Robert Burton did the photography on the fossil man casts.

Mrs. William Wade typed most of one draft, and Miss Paula Bogenschutz typed most of the final version.

These and many other individuals took time to help me, and I appreciate their courtesy. More indirect but certainly no less important is the debt I owe my teachers and my students. Among the former I would like particularly to acknowledge President Frederick P. Thieme, University of Colorado; Professor James N. Spuhler, University of New Mexico; Professor Leslie A. White, University of Michigan; and Professor Newton E. Morton, University of Hawaii.

Even with all this help I am aware of shortcomings and inadequacies in the text. These and any errors that may remain are, of course, my own fault.

A. J. K.

Contents

Illustrations

Tables

Preface

RECENT YEARS have brought extraordinary increases in anthropology course enrollments generally, and in only the past two years the increase has exceeded 100 percent at the author's school, compared with a 15 percent increase for the university as a whole in the same period. To the extent that this inflation reflects an accelerating interest in man, his evolution, his varied appearances, and his countless ways of doing things, it is most gratifying to one who has made the study of anthropology his life's work. But huge class enrollments bring penalties to student and instructor alike, as personal contacts become limited, and there is a danger that the student may leave the course with a few newly acquired facts but no real comprehension of the depth and breadth of a field that has been described as "the science of groups of men and their behavior and productions."

Crowded classes necessarily give the textbook (and complementary reading matter) a more important role in the teaching process than it might otherwise have. How well the textbook performs its role depends in large part on its content and organization; this book is organized in a way that the author hopes will display the factual information that must underpin knowledge, while at the same time providing the needed stimulus for that deeper appreciation that is the foundation of true understanding.

Broadly, this is a book about man's biological evolution and the significance of contemporary human biological variation. With respect to human evolution, the discussion focuses on the early record of man as shown in fossils: where they have been found, how old they are, what has been found with them, and what all this information implies concerning the probable course of our ancestry. The question of *how* human evolution takes place is covered indirectly through a discussion of the mechanisms that bring evolutionary change to all forms of life.

With the introduction of the phrase *human heterography*, the distinct character of this book will be evident to the professional. It is hoped that the student will find the study of the significance of today's biological variation among human populations from this new perspective a clearer and simpler introduction to a complex field that continues to develop and change in response to research findings. Since this approach makes no assumptions about the way in which human variations should be grouped together, the common racial classifications are ignored.

Acquiring some knowledge of physical anthropology is largely a mechanical exercise that can be done with or without a textbook. Achieving understanding is a more complex process, and it is hoped that this book may contribute to that process by facilitating the essential interaction between student and teacher that makes all true learning a revelatory experience.

A. J. KELSO

Boulder, Colorado
April, 1970

PART I

Background to Physical Anthropology

ANTHROPOLOGY IS A SCIENCE. Its subject matter is man, and its major objective is to provide an understanding of human variability. However, since there are endless ways in which human beings differ, anthropology must by necessity focus its attention on particular kinds of variation. Thus, anthropology deals with two major ways in which human beings differ: culturally and biologically.

Culture is the basic unifying concept of anthropology. To study man without a consideration of culture is analogous to studying fishes without an understanding of the properties of water. Culture is the medium in which man resides. It presents simultaneously its own adaptive challenges and also the primary means by which the human species meets these challenges and others provided by the environment. Yet, in spite of its obvious importance, anthropologists disagree on the correct definition of culture. For example, A. L. Kroeber and Clyde Kluckhohn (1952) compiled 161 definitions of culture from the writings of anthropologists and other scientists over the eighty-year period from 1871 to 1951. Why is it that anthropologists are unable to define culture with sufficient "accuracy"? Because defining culture is not a problem of accuracy or precision.

1

It is a matter of convenience and usefulness. How, then, does one decide upon the most useful definition? This depends on the problem at hand.

To the physical anthropologist, it is practical to use the term *culture* to designate that which man employs in adapting to the requirements of his environment. Like other animals, man is readily able to adapt to a restricted range of environmental conditions by drawing upon nothing more than his biological resources. But unlike other animals, only man is able to use an enormously diverse range of things over and above his limited biological resources. He makes tools, builds houses, wears clothing, lives in socially organized groups, joins churches, forms corporations, establishes armies, devises legal codes, and believes in a life after death. These and many other conditions and events have enabled human beings to adjust to a wide variety of environmental circumstances. Collectively they are the conditions and events referred to by the term *culture*, and they constitute the primary subject matter of cultural anthropology.* Since culture is man's primary means of adjusting to his environment, one might anticipate that within anthropology the most interesting and fully developed sector of the field would be the part that integrates the cultural and biological spheres. However, such is not the case; anthropology lacks the theory needed to join together these two realms. That cultural evolution has had a profound effect on man's biological evolution is basic anthropological doctrine, but precisely how this occurs remains vague and uncertain. Thus, even though it is clear that both cultural and biological factors are significant to the anthropologist, it continues to be necessary to discuss them separately.

Physical anthropology investigates man's biological variability, but the structure of the field is not as clearly defined and agreed upon as is the structure of cultural anthropology. Students in an introductory course are likely to get the impression that physical anthropology is either hopelessly complex or distressingly disorganized. Often in one semester they move through mammalian-primate-human morphology, fossil ancestors of man and the primates, evolutionary mechanisms, genetics, contemporary human biological variation, the classification of human variations, the measurement of man, growth, physiological adaptation, constitution, and applied physical anthropology. The only feature common to all of these is the fact that each is concerned, at least in part, with man. Beyond this the field is structurally undifferentiated.

There are several useful ways to order physical anthropology, but the one used in this book divides the field along the same dimensions (i.e., time and space) that provide the basis for the subdivisions of cultural anthropology. *Human paleontology* investigates variability among man's an-

---

* *Archaeology* investigates the forms of cultural variability along the dimension of time; *ethnology* investigates them among contemporary peoples, and thus primarily along the dimension of space.

cestors; hence its primary data are obtained from fossils. This material is discussed in Part II. *Human heterography* investigates biological variation among living populations. It would be in some ways more logical to refer to this part of physical anthropology as human biography, but because of the already well-established use of the word *biography, heterography* will be used here. This subject is considered in Part III.

Before dealing with human paleontology and heterography, some essential preliminary topics must be considered. These constitute Part I, and they are: 1) a history of physical anthropology, 2) man's place in nature, and 3) some background in genetics.

REFERENCES AND SUGGESTIONS FOR ADDITIONAL READING

KELSO, A. J.
  1966 The subdivisions of physical anthropology. *Current Anthropology* 7:315–319.
KROEBER, A. L., AND CLYDE KLUCKHOHN
  1952 Culture: a critical review of concepts and definitions. *Papers of the Peabody Museum of American Archaeology and Ethnology* 47.
SPUHLER, J. N.
  1959 Somatic paths to culture. *Human Biology* 31:1–13.
WASHBURN, S. L.
  1953 The strategy of physical anthropology. In *Anthropology today: an encyclopedic inventory,* ed. A. L. Kroeber, pp. 714–727. Chicago: University of Chicago Press.

CHAPTER 1

HISTORY OF PHYSICAL
ANTHROPOLOGY

Introduction

The history of physical anthropology is the history of man's concern with problems of human evolution and human variation. Insofar as these general problems indicate an interest in man's origin and development, they are problems that have interested man from his beginning. The following is directed at the development of our present attitudes about the problems of human evolution and human variation within the general context of scientific inquiry.

Origins (1600–1859)

Before the publication of *The Origin of Species* in 1859, physical anthropology had not yet emerged as a separate, self-conscious, independent discipline. There was, however, a great deal of concern with the problems that were ultimately to form the central questions of the field, and many attitudes toward these problems were firmly held. These attitudes were based on the following: the Old Testament story of Creation, the presumption that the living animals always were and always will continue to be as they are, the belief that "life" had a special spiritual or unknowable quality, the reckoning of the earth's antiquity in terms of a few thousand years, and an all-pervasive conceptualization of the real world in terms of the Platonic ideal types (Mayr, 1959).

There were, of course, many other elements of the ideology of the times preceding Darwin that influenced the emergence and acceptability of an evolutionary theory. An evaluation of those listed above, however, is helpful in indicating the ideological context of the period from 1600 to 1850. While in many ways these attitudes seem to dominate this period, there were many discoveries made and new understandings reached during this same time that ultimately placed the dominant attitudes in a position of secondary importance. Perhaps the most far-reaching of the new understandings in terms of influence on modern science was the emergence of empiricism over a purely rationalistic approach to the understanding of problems arising out of our experience with the real world.

Rationalism and Empiricism

The rationalistic approach characterized the writing and thinking of many of the classical Graeco-Roman scholars and continued to exert much influence on thoughtful men throughout the seventeenth century. The movement was based particularly on the writings of Aristotle and is best represented in the work of Abelard, Thomas Aquinas, the scholastics of the thirteenth and fourteenth centuries, and later by Leibnitz and Descartes. The essential feature of the position taken by rationalists is that truths about the problems of man's experience can be reached by the power of reasoning alone. Thus, if one begins with self-evident premises, he might be able to string together a complete philosophical system of true propositions by correctly applying the rules of logic. Therefore, the rationalists regarded the checking of their conclusions against naturalistic observation as unnecessary.

As long as theological considerations remained the dominant concern, rationalists could draw upon the self-evident truths of revelation to arrive at proofs of theological dogma. In the thirteenth century, however, there began to appear elements which slowly brought about the decline of rationalism. Scholasticism, an extreme form of the rationalist approach that flourished in the thirteenth century, generated a revival of interest in the writings of the classical Greek and Roman scholars and directed attention to the problem of harmonizing the events of this world with those of the next.

A growing interest in the affairs of this world, the development of mathematics, and the secularization of scholarship within a growing middle class are among the most important factors that led to empiricism.

The empiricist is not fundamentally opposed to the rationalist, but rather insists on adding to correct reasoning the provision of empirical observation or, in short, the testing of the correctness of the reasoning process by recourse to sense experience. This empirical approach was exemplified in the work of Galileo, Boyle, Francis Bacon, and, most notably, Newton. It can be recognized as the basis of exploration in modern science.

Thus, the emergence of the empiricist approach provided a new means by which man could come to understand nature and his part in it. However, even more significant than this was the realization that the empirical approach actually worked, i.e., that it did in fact make it possible to predict with great precision the occurrence of events over which man exerted no direct control and which were previously thought to be capricious and undetermined. Such striking results, originally made in astronomy and later in physics, stimulated similar inquiries in other aspects of our experience with the real world. One area affected by this stimulus was the study of life—the science of biology.

Linnaeus and the Classification of the Varieties of Life

There are several landmarks in the history of biology during the seventeenth and eighteenth centuries that represent the products of herculean effort. One of the most notable of these serves as a reasonable beginning point in a discussion of the history of physical anthropology, and that is the work of Carolus Linnaeus (1707–1778), who set out to achieve no less than a classification of all living things. The importance of this work on the history of biology would be difficult to overemphasize; it is to biology what the periodic chart of elements is to physics and chemistry. Now having asserted that Linnaeus's work was of fundamental importance, how did it affect the development of biology? On one level his influence is obvious: he set forth rules for classifying the forms of life that remain the basic rules of taxonomy today. Moreover, he applied the rules to obtain a comprehensive classification which he believed reflected the rational plan of creation, and this had a more subtle, though perhaps more significant effect. In viewing the array of life forms as the fixed and immutable products of creation, Linnaeus established the antithesis that led eventually to the evolutionary synthesis. Once the rigid structure of the classification was established, some peculiar and unexpected patterns made it difficult to discern the anticipated rational order. For example, at some points in the classification there were many kinds of organisms that differed only slightly from one another, whereas at other points there were groups of organisms separated by wide gaps from any others in the classification. Moreover, remains had been found in the earth's strata of organisms that had no living representatives. How could these inconsistencies be explained? One answer is God, but if so, then it appears that God created

Figure 1-1. Carolus Linnaeus (1707-1778). (Courtesy The American Museum of Natural History.)

some forms of life and then obliterated them, and the anticipated reflection of the Creator's plan was not at all obvious from the classification. In this way, Linnaeus's work raised issues that gradually were formulated into questions to which answers were eventually offered. One such answer was evolution, which stated that groups of organisms are similar because they have descended from a common ancestor. At the outset, the evolutionary "answer" could be thought of only as speculative, for no one was able to explain satisfactorily how such similar groups (species) could have become different at all. This is the problem Darwin attacked, and it will be considered in detail later on in this chapter.

Selecting Linnaeus's work to begin a history of physical anthropology is largely a matter of convenience, for in the history of biology, he represents but one manifestation of the increasing interest and the rapid growth that can be detected clearly from the beginning of the seventeenth century. Between 1600 and the publication of *The Origin of Species* in 1859, an understanding of life was abetted by the rapid accumulation of data, its systematization into classifications, the development of laboratory instruments, and the validation of basic theories. To be more specific, consider the following important events: William Harvey (1578–1657) presented evidence that the blood circulates; John Ray (1627–1705) completed a monumental series of detailed descriptions of the various forms of life; Georges Louis Leclerc, Comte de Buffon (1707–1788), published his forty-four-volume *Natural History;* and the microscope was applied to the investigation of microanatomy, which led to an improved understanding of tissues and eventually to the cell theory.

Blumenbach and the Classification of the Varieties of Man

These and many other developments have had a lasting effect on biology. Likewise, one may see one specific consequence of the growing interest in description and classification that had a particularly important bearing on physical anthropology: the classification of man's biological variation. The problem of racial classification of man may be seen partly as the by-product of this interest in classification and partly as the by-product of a controversy over the origin of the varieties of man. One side of this controversy consisted of the view that all men share a common origin (*monogenesis*); opposed to this was the belief that the varieties of man had separate origins (*polygenesis*). The former view, that of the monogenists, was the more acceptable in the sense that it was consistent with the biblical account and further was held by most prominent scientists. This view, however, led to a problem: if all groups of man share a common origin, then how did the present types come into existence? Perhaps a proper classification would resolve the difficulty. The most notable and lasting of the early attempts to classify man was made by Johann F. Blumenbach (1752–1840), who classified man's variations into five groups: negroid (Ethiopian) or black, mongoloid or yellow, caucasoid or white, American Indian or red, and Malayan or brown. Then, as now, the classification appeared reasonably to represent the distribution of variation in the human species. To be sure, there were those who disagreed with Blumenbach, but their differences were based largely on the issue of accuracy. For example, Anders Retzius (1796–1860) of Sweden indicated that Blumenbach's classification was inadequate, for within the races there

Figure 1–2. Johann Friedrich Blumenbach (1752–1840). (Courtesy The New York Academy of Medicine.)

was far too much variability, particularly in head form, which, he claimed, should not be ignored. He invented the cephalic index as a way of expressing head form numerically (see Chapter 7). Likewise, as Darwin (1871) pointed out, "There is the greatest possible diversity among capable judges whether [man] should be classed as a single species or race, or as two (Virey), as three (Jacquinot), as four (Kant), five (Blumenbach), six (Buffon), seven (Hunter), eight (Agassiz), eleven (Pickering), fifteen (Bory St. Vincent), sixteen (Desmoulins), twenty-two (Morton), sixty (Crawfurd), or as sixty-three, according to Burke."* But in most important respects these differences are trivial in comparison with the broad area of agreement on the subject of race. One should keep clearly in mind that Blumenbach and the others were, like Linnaeus, attempting to reflect a natural order; moreover, they were trying to do this long before an understanding of evolution, and thus the classifications consisted of groupings of mankind that: 1) were presumed largely to be fixed, unchanging, and eternal, 2) were based on the assumption that one race differs from another by the possession of a particular cluster of attributes, 3) implied that the individual members of a race, while imperfect representations of the racial type, could be recognized as belonging to one or another by the possession of these attributes, and 4) drew the attention of early anthropologists to the problems of ascertaining and describing these races in as complete a manner as possible.

Possessing these implications, racial classifications are irreconcilable with an evolutionary approach. The most puzzling residue of this dilemma is the realization that both views are present among many modern anthropologists, reconciled apparently by compartmentalization; when on the subject of race, they lapse into typological thinking (see Mayr, 1959, 1963), but on the subject of genetics and evolution they think in terms of processes, mechanisms, and the dynamics of population changes. The problem will be discussed again in Chapter 9.

Other Advances in Science

Substantial refinements in science outside of biology were also paving the way for imminent advances in areas of central importance to physical anthropology. Among the most significant of the new discoveries were those being made by early geologists, paleontologists, and archaeologists. Geologists were beginning to find convincing evidence that the antiquity of the earth was not to be measured in a few thousands of years, but rather that the earth must have taken millions of years to form.

* From Charles Darwin, *The Descent of Man* (1871), quoted in Earl W. Count, ed., *This Is Race: An Anthology Selected from the International Literature on the Races of Man* (New York: Henry Schuman, 1950), p. 138.

That is, by observing the rate at which geological phenomena were going on at the present time and assuming that present rates are the same as those in the past (*uniformitarianism*), a geologist could conclude that it must have taken millions of years for the earth's crust to accumulate and form its present structure.

Early paleontologists were discovering fossil bones of animals very different from the ones living in the same zone today. Evidence of marine life and strange-looking large mammals and reptiles was found in fossilized form in Europe. In addition, the fauna of one layer of rocks was often quite different from that in adjacent layers. At the same time, archaeologists were finding evidence that Europe was once occupied by people whose way of life differed distinctively from that of modern man.

The evidence obtained in the times before Darwin from geology, paleontology, and archaeology can be seen to have made two major contributions: 1) the demonstration of the fact of great antiquity for the earth and for the life that occupies it, and 2) the presentation of conclusive evidence for earlier faunal and cultural variants that differed not only from modern forms in the same area, but also from forms known anywhere else in the world.

Taken as a totality, these advances can be seen as steps that made possible the formulation of new questions. Why are there so many species of one kind in Linnaeus's classification, whereas other genera have so few? Why do living forms seem to cluster in their similarities at some points in the classification, yet show sharp discontinuities at other points? How did the variation observed within modern species come about? More particularly, how and when did racial variation arise in the human species? What are the relationships between the fossil forms and modern fauna? Long before Darwin, there were many proposed answers which attempted to shed light on one or more of these questions. There were, of course,

Figure 1–3. Charles Darwin (1809–1882). (By permission of the Trustees of the British Museum, Natural History.)

obvious theological answers; any of these questions can be answered by claiming God's will. There were also many proposals suggesting that modern species are a consequence of evolution. That is, many authors long before Darwin saw the possibility of explaining many of these problems by calling upon an evolutionary explanation that claimed that today's fauna comprises the descendants of the fossil forms, and thus is the product of a long line of modifications. The deficiency of these early explanations was their inability to explain how it was that the modern forms differed from the evolutionary antecedents. What caused them to evolve? Darwin's work provided an answer.

DARWIN AND *The Origin of Species*

Consider for a moment that you have just been asked the question: How do species originate? What would your answer be, and how would you formulate it? One way to begin is to determine just exactly what the question means. It could mean, for example, that the questioner wishes to know how the first species came into existence; this is unlikely, however, for, if he were concerned with that, he would be more likely to ask about the origin of life. Thus, the question must mean something else—there are thousands of species in existence today and thousands more that existed in the past. What processes have been in operation that have, by their action, caused these species to appear? This is essentially the question which Darwin attempted to answer.

The Apparent Paradox

Darwin arrived at an answer to this question only after confronting a seemingly paradoxical situation which came to his attention through many years of careful study and observation. On the one hand, Darwin observed that all living organisms attempted to perpetuate their kind by means of a variety of reproductive processes, and that species in nature tended to produce many more offspring than necessary to maintain their numbers. Yet, on the other hand, Darwin observed that the actual numbers in terms of population for a particular species remained relatively constant over time. How can this contradiction be reconciled? In fact, the situation is relatively simple and obvious; many of the offspring produced by each generation simply do not survive. One need only go one step further and propose that there is a consistent difference between the offspring that survive and those that do not. A simple illustration may help: Suppose that a particular species of moth lives in an environment where dark individuals are less conspicuous than light ones, and thus less susceptible to attack from their natural predators. The environment acts as a selector, and thereby reduces the contribution of the lighter-colored moths to the next generation; a greater proportion of the lighter moths are caught and killed by predators before the completion of their reproductive life than is true of the darker variants. The darker forms therefore produce more offspring in the next generation than the lighter moths.

Natural Selection and Reproductive Isolation

Thus, the natural circumstances of the environment can be seen to operate in a selective way, reducing in number the poorer-adapted variants of species while increasing the proportion of the better-adapted variants. Darwin called this process *natural selection.* The idea of natural selection enables one to understand in a more profound way how a species can change over a period of time, but it is not immediately obvious how it relates to Darwin's primary concern with the origin of species. To comprehend this relationship one must consider another phenomenon, *reproductive isolation,* a situation in which one group of organisms either cannot or does not interbreed with another. Under normal circumstances reproductive isolation prevails between the members of any two species. Occasionally, one species becomes divided into two or more reproductively isolated subspecies. This might take place for any number of reasons. The separation may be abrupt and immediate—for example, as a result of an earthquake or a torrential rainfall. Such natural disasters as these often result in the subdivision of many of the species living in the affected areas. Or isolation may result from events that take a long time to occur in an environment, such as a drought, or a gradual reduction in the mean annual temperature, or the invasion of an area by a new species. With the appearance of man, many "artificial," or cultural, causes for reproductive isolation came into play. Cultural events affect not only man but other organisms as well (e.g., the building of a road or the burning of a field can upset the previous ecological balance and result in reproductive isolation among members of a species formerly able to interbreed). Whatever the cause, it is the results that are important. A group of organisms formerly consisting of one interbreeding unit is divided into at least two such units.

Once a species becomes subdivided into reproductive isolates, natural selection can cause these isolates to become progressively dissimilar. Since no two environments are identical, the differences that distinguish one from another, no matter how subtle, can be expected to be reflected in the adaptive requirements of the organisms that live within them. The final step is a relatively simple one. As the divergence continues, eventually the resulting forms become sufficiently dissimilar to be regarded as separate species. Thus, the description of the way in which one ancestral species can, by means of selection and reproductive isolation, give rise to two new species has answered the original question: How do species originate?

It is difficult to overemphasize the significance and impact of natural selection on the development of biology. The earlier concept—that species were essentially unchanging entities—had to be replaced by a view that emphasized continuous change and adaptation, and that regarded contemporary species as the products of a long succession of alterations brought about by natural selection operating on isolated units. In addition to this fundamental change in point of view, a number of more specific consequences also followed, among them the beginning of a deliberate search for fossil ancestors of modern forms, the focusing of attention on the processes of inheritance whereby one generation passes an inborn adaptive potential to the next generation, and the emergence of an entirely new set of interesting problems. These new concepts were not, of course, instantaneously accepted. Many scientists and most laymen rejected the notions of evolution and natural selection. Many reasons were given, but the strongest opposition came over the problem of whether or not man had evolved from some lower form.

While the theory of evolution was being developed and debated, anthropology, as a separate, distinct, and self-conscious discipline, began to make its appearance. The evolutionary view was an important part of the early development of scientific anthropology, although more so in cultural than in physical anthropology. There were many writers during the last half of the nineteenth century and in the early part of the twentieth century who applied the processes of evolution to the problem of understanding cultural growth, development, and variation.

The most important effect that Darwin and his work had on physical anthropology was to focus attention directly on the problem of human evolution. The question of whether or not man had evolved from some lower form caused an enormous controversy, which needed more than argument and analogy to be resolved. What was needed was evidence: fossil evidence of man's ancestors. In fact, a few fossils of man had been discovered prior to the publication of *The Origin of Species*, but it was not until after that point in time that the significance of these discoveries could be fully appreciated. The immediate effect of this evolutionary climate on the problems of interest to physical anthropology was the beginning of a deliberate search for fossils of man's ancestors. How the history of fossil man discoveries has affected the interpretation of human evolution is considered in Chapter 6.

MENDEL AND THE PARTICULATE THEORY OF INHERITANCE

One way of regarding natural selection, as Darwin had presented it, was to view it as a mechanism that brought about changes of improved adaptation from one generation to the next. Or, evolution can be defined as a selective accumulation of generational changes. This view suggests one obvious and particularly fruitful way of studying evolutionary change, and that is by determining and analyzing the manner in which one generation passes its characteristics on to the next generation. The modern science of genetics was not known to Darwin, although the work that laid the foundation for it was being done during his lifetime by an Austrian monk, Gregor Mendel. There were, indeed, a number of theories of inheritance available; among them the most prominent were the blending theory of inheritance and—the one most generally accepted by the scientific community of the time—the theory of the inheritance of acquired characteristics. The *blending theory* was essentially a simple, "commonsense" explanation of inheritance, which proposed that offspring were a blend of their parents in their characteristics. There is both evidence to support this view and data that are contrary or that constitute exceptions to it. On the one hand, one is usually able to draw on several instances among his own acquaintances in which the children of a couple tend to be an intermediate "blend" of the parents. On the other hand, there are many exceptions—instances in which a child is like one parent and not like the other, and many cases in which the child is unlike either parent in many characteristics. Although this theory has never been formulated in a systematic way and tested empirically, it is surprisingly common in our society today—to the extent that the multitudinous exceptions are regarded as *throwbacks, atavisms,* or *reversions.* These are all essentially synonymous terms implying that the person in question displays the characteristics of an ancient ancestor. Admittedly, this is no explanation, and the theory has never been taken seriously in modern science. It simply breaks down under the sheer weight of contrary evidence.

The theory of the inheritance of acquired characteristics proposes that the experiences an organism has during its lifetime shape its hereditary material in such a way that the offspring it produces are better able to cope with the same kind of experiences during their lifetime. This view has been argued for over a hundred years, and even today there are practicing biologists who subscribe to it. The history of experiments dealing with the theory would take a long time to relate; the essential point is that the theory has been discredited. Many an experiment has suggested that acquired characteristics can be passed on by inheritance; attempts to duplicate such experiments, however, have failed to verify the inheritance of acquired traits. In any case, this was the theory accepted by Darwin. It is usually associated with J. B. P. A. Lamarck, who did indeed put the theory explicitly in writing, but in fact only slightly modified versions of it had been implicit in the works of many scholars for centuries.

One of the most troublesome problems associated with the theory of the inheritance of acquired characteristics stems from the fact that the theory requires a mechanical transfer of the effects of the environment to the

Figure 1–4. Gregor Mendel (1822–1884). (Courtesy The New York Academy of Medicine.)

genetic material that is passed on from one generation to the next. That is, if the way of life that an individual leads modifies the heritable material, how does this modification take place? This question has never been satisfactorily answered, but one of the most notable attempts to do so was made by Darwin. He proposed the theory of *pangenesis,* which postulates the presence of particles called gemmules in all of the cells of the body which are modified or shaped by the way of life of the organisms. These gemmules then were believed to enter the circulatory system and eventually to combine with other particles present in reproductive cells and modify the nature of these cells accordingly. In effect, what this theory does is to recognize a logical necessity of the theory of the inheritance of acquired characteristics. There is, however, no empirical evidence to support the existence of such gemmules, and the theory of pangenesis has been discarded. The entire theory of the inheritance of acquired characteristics has been discarded by most of the scientific community. In recent times, it has enjoyed popularity among geneticists in the Soviet Union under the influence of Lysenko, but even there it now has been abandoned.

The theory of inheritance which forms the basis of modern views is the particulate theory, and, as mentioned earlier, the work that led to it was done during Darwin's lifetime but went unnoticed until the beginning of the twentieth century. The *particulate theory* of inheritance proposes that the inherited characteristics of one generation are transmitted to the next by means of particles (eventually called genes) and that these particles are present in pairs in individuals but present singly within sex cells. Thus any individual will receive half of his total number of genes from one parent and half from the other parent.

The experimental work that pointed to this theory is interesting and instructive. It was carried out by Gregor Mendel in the 1860's. His work started simply enough; Mendel kept a vegetable garden, and in it, among other things, he grew some peas. In caring for his plants he observed that the peas differed from one another in several characteristics, such as length and color of the stem, seed-coat color, shape of pod and seed, etc. He decided to investigate generational differences in some of these traits and proceeded to interbreed the plants. In all, he experimented with seven characters, each having but two modes of expression (see Table 1–1).

TABLE 1–1

MENDEL'S INITIAL CROSSES AND RESULTING HYBRIDS

Characters	Result in Hybrids (F_1 Generation)
1. Shape of seed wrinkled × round	all round
2. Endosperm color yellow × green	all yellow
3. Seed-coat color grey × white	all grey
4. Pod shape smooth × constricted	all smooth
5. Pod color green × yellow	all green
6. Position of blossoms axial × terminal	all axial
7. Length of stem long × short	all long

The evidence presented by the hybrid generation was in itself convincing evidence against the blending theory of inheritance, but more important to us is the conclusion Mendel reached concerning the relationship between the two modes of expression for each character. Since one and only one appeared in the hybrids (the F_1 generation), Mendel could distinguish the form that did appear as *dominant* and the one that did not as *recessive*. Had this been the end of his work, Mendel's contribution would have been considered substantial, but he continued his experiments.

Mendel took the hybrids that resulted from the first crossing and interbred them. His results are summarized in Table 1–2.

Such a splendid array of consistency in the results must have astounded Mendel. The appearance of the dominant varieties was no great surprise after the results of the first cross, but the consistent reappearance of the recessive forms could mean only one thing: the quality that determined the recessive character was present even though it was not expressed in the F_1 generation.

TABLE 1–2

RESULTS OF CROSSES IN THE F₁ GENERATION

F_1 Crosses	Approximate Ratios in F_2 Hybrids
1. round × round	3 round to 1 wrinkled
2. yellow × yellow	3 yellow to 1 green
3. grey × grey	3 grey to 1 white
4. smooth × smooth	3 smooth to 1 constricted
5. green × green	3 green to 1 yellow
6. axial × axial	3 axial to 1 terminal
7. long × long	3 long to 1 short

From these experiments Mendel concluded: 1) the inherited capabilities of one generation are passed on to the next by means of discrete particles that retain their potential effect even though their presence is not indicated by the appearance of the character; 2) that these particles are obtained in pairs, one from each parent, and passed on singly to the next generation. This is called Mendel's first law of inheritance (see Table 1–3).

TABLE 1–3

MENDEL'S FIRST LAW OF INHERITANCE

First generation "pure" bred crosses (paired units)	Round × Wrinkled (RR) (rr)			
Second generation (F_1) paired units inherited singly	Round Rr	Round Rr	Round Rr	Round Rr
Third generation (F_2) paired units inherited singly	Round RR	Round Rr	Round rR	Wrinkled rr

Mendel added another step to his investigation when he decided to examine pairs of characteristics—to cross plants dominant for two traits (e.g., round seeds and yellow endosperm) with plants recessive for the same traits (wrinkled and green). In the F_1 generation Mendel observed that all of the hybrids, as expected, were round and yellow, but the interesting question was, What happens to the particles (genes) when the F_1 hybrids are crossed? Do the genes for seed shape and endosperm color stay together from one generation to the next or do they assort independently of one another? Table 1–4 shows the results. From this experiment he concluded that different hereditary determiners assort independently in the process of inheritance. This is Mendel's second law.

As indicated earlier, even though the evolutionary view focused attention on the hereditary process, the significance of Mendel's work went un-

TABLE 1–4

SUMMARY OF MENDEL'S EXPERIMENT USING PAIRS OF CHARACTERISTICS

Generation				
Parental	Round-Yellow RRYY	×	Wrinkled-Green rryy	
F$_1$	Round-Yellow RrYy	×	Round-Yellow RrYy	
F$_2$	9 Round-Yellow RRYY (1) RRYy (2) RrYY (2) RrYy (4)	3 Round-Green RRyy (1) Rryy (2)	3 Wrinkled-Yellow rrYY (1) rrYy (2)	1 Wrinkled-Green rryy (1)

recognized for over thirty years, until 1900, when it was rediscovered. Mendel's work provides the foundation of the study of *genetics,* that aspect of modern science concerned with explaining and understanding how similarities and differences due to hereditary factors arise among individuals. In recent years, genetics has progressed rapidly and has diversified into many subdisciplines, becoming one of the most provocative and exciting areas in modern science. Physical anthropology has drawn heavily from genetics in recent years, particularly from population genetics, a branch of the science concerned with the genetic composition of breeding populations and the factors which cause these compositions to change. Population genetics will be discussed in some detail in Chapter 3.

MUTATION—THE SOURCE OF NEW VARIABILITY

One other important area of interest stimulated by the work of Darwin was the problem of explaining the origin (and maintenance) of variability in life forms. Natural selection could be seen to be a formative and creative process that could shape the variation of lines of descent within groups over a period of time in the direction of improved adaptation. Indeed natural selection can be seen as a mechanism that tends to weed out the less-well-adapted range of variation of each generation while favoring the better-adapted. It would seem that a process such as natural selection would eventually lead to uniformity among the members of a particular species. Yet, when one looks around him today, after a billion or more years of evolution, an enormous range of variations can be seen, both within and between species. Thus, if we accept the view that living forms reached their present condition by evolution from earlier forms by means of natural selection, then how did such variation arise? Where did it come from? The answer to this question is mutation, i.e., a change in the material of inheritance. A reasonably clear understanding of this did not come about until several years after Darwin's death.

An appreciation of the significance of mutation depended ultimately on the presence of four other understandings: 1) the evolutionary view that claimed that life changed by modification through natural selection (this was provided by the work of Darwin); 2) the knowledge that heredity in nature was controlled by particles (this was shown in the work of Mendel); 3) the observation that traits controlled by these particles could and did change abruptly from one generation to the next (this was made known by the experiments of a Dutch botanist, Hugo De Vries); and 4) an explanation as to how the particles of heredity could change—an explanation for the occurrence of mutations. It is clear now that several factors can generate new variability; the earliest cause of mutation to be identified was X-radiation.

The first three of these theories were known in 1900, but initially the significance of mutations and their relationships to Mendel's work and to the problem of explaining variation in the context of evolution was not clear. At first it appeared that the discovery of mutations negated the validity of natural selection. That is, if mutations were seen as abrupt changes between one generation and the next, then it appeared that evolution proceeded by these sudden "spontaneous" steps rather than by means of the gradual adaptive changes implicit in natural selection. This is where the work of Mendel was all-important in clarifying the point that there was no contradiction between the two factors. Mendel's work showed how abrupt qualitative changes between generations could occur naturally and regularly and along predictable lines. Thus, Mendel's experiments were enough to account for differences between one generation and the next, but where did *new* variation come from? With a particulate view of the process of heredity, one had only a short step to take to postulate that new variation could come about as a consequence of the alteration of the structure of genes, the particles of inheritance. This is, in fact, a reasonable definition of *mutation* in modern genetics—a change in the structure of a gene.

However, a problem is posed as this understanding is reached: What causes the structure of a gene to change? This pushes the problem back; if mutations give rise to new forms of a trait, then what is responsible for mutations? There was no simple answer to this question; it took over twenty-five years after the rediscovery of Mendel's work to obtain the necessary information.

During this time the common fruit fly became an important experimental animal in the study of genetics, and a large amount of information about the genetics of this lowly animal accumulated. One consistent observation on the fruit fly was the regular occurrence of a small proportion of mutant varieties in each generation no matter what the experiment, no matter how stringent the controls. These mutants interested H. J. Muller, who was concerned with the problem of the cause of mutation. He decided to see if he could affect the rate at which these mutant varieties occurred by varying environmental features. With this in mind, he proceeded to subject the fruit flies to a series of environmental changes. He introduced them to varied intensities of light and qualities of motion, to drugs and alcohol; in his words, the flies were "treated with everything except affection from generation to generation."* The result was always the same; the next generation showed the same regular but small proportion of mutant varieties. Eventually he experimented with variations in the intensities of X-radiations, and the results were most interesting; the generation of flies produced from the irradiated sample showed a substantial increase in the proportion of mutants. Furthermore, the relationship between the intensity of exposure to X-radiation and the proportion of mutants was highly correlated. That is, the greater the exposure, the more frequently the mutants occurred in the next generation. Thus, at least one answer to the question of the origin of mutations could be given: some were caused by radiation. In retrospect this makes sense, since all living organisms are continually subjected to small but regular doses of radiation. Thus, radiation could be seen not merely as a factor that could increase the ever-present low rate of mutation, it further could be regarded as the cause of that low rate as well.

Since Muller's discovery, a number of other mutagenic agents have been identified; these include specific chemical substances, such as caffeine and phenol, as well as other sources of high-energy radiation. Likewise, a few substances that reduce mutation rates have been identified. In general, the importance of X-radiation as a source of mutation has faded (Crow, 1959) to some degree as more factors have been identified. Though clearly some progress has been made, we remain today largely ignorant of the major causes of mutation, and the situation has become further complicated by the realization that some mutations themselves can influence the rates at which other genes mutate.

EVOLUTION, GENETICS, AND THE NEW PHYSICAL ANTHROPOLOGY

Thus far, the impact of Darwin has been evaluated, as well as contributions made to science by naturalists, botanists, and geneticists. By the

---

* Cited in Ruth Moore, *The Coil of Life* (New York: Alfred A. Knopf, 1961), p. 229.

time the nineteenth century came to a close, anthropology had established itself as a separate scientific discipline, and interests within the field had already separated along cultural and biological lines. Indeed, the separation was so sharp that the biological aspects of the field were taken over as the academic province of segments of medical school faculties (particularly in England and on the European continent), while the cultural aspects (known variously as ethnology, social anthropology, and cultural anthropology) remained within the social sciences. In the United States, anthropology received its academic start as cultural anthropology and, with only a few minor exceptions, very little physical anthropology was taught here until 1913, when E. A. Hooton initiated it at Harvard University.

While little physical anthropology was actually being taught, something was being accomplished in research. As already pointed out, the discovery of fossils stimulated various interpretations on the course through which man's ancestors may have passed. The collection of vast amounts of descriptive material on the morphological variation of living populations continued at an accelerating rate and eventually was supplemented by the collection of quantities of data on the blood group characteristics of the peoples of the world. Blood group studies brought about an important shift in emphasis that eventually was responsible for a major change in the scope and strategy of physical anthropology, particularly in the United States. The changes were sufficiently abrupt and striking that the field, since World War II, has often been called the "new physical anthropology" (see Washburn, 1951). In addition to its emphasis on problems of process and the application of experimental procedures, the new emphasis has caused physical anthropology to enter and explore areas formerly neglected or totally ignored (e.g., primate behavior and biochemical variation among human populations and between man and the other primates) and to stress the development of theory. In short, until recently, physical anthropology continued along relatively undifferentiated lines concerned almost exclusively with questions of historical and descriptive importance, such as: Where did X (a group or, in the case of a fossil, perhaps an individual) come from? How closely is it related to groups Y and Z? Has it been significantly influenced by migration?

Looking at the field today, one has the impression that it is undergoing a rapid expansion involving not merely new data, but the exploration of new problems requiring qualitatively different classifications and analytical procedures. It is difficult to trace the source of this new vitality, but it could well be that with its emphasis on dynamic interrelationships, process, structure, and function, physical anthropology is only beginning to feel the full impact of the evolutionary view.

REFERENCES AND
SUGGESTIONS FOR ADDITIONAL READING

BARNES, HARRY ELMER
    1965   *An intellectual and cultural history of the Western world.* 3d rev. ed. 3 vols. New York: Dover.

COUNT, EARL W., ED.
    1950   *This is race: an anthology selected from the international literature on the races of man.* New York: Henry Schuman.

CROW, JAMES F.
    1959   Ionizing radiation and evolution. *Scientific American* 201, September, pp. 138–160.

DARWIN, CHARLES
    1859   *On the origin of species by means of natural selection, or the preservation of favored races in the struggle for life.* London: John Murray.
    1871   *The descent of man.* In *This is race: an anthology selected from the international literature on the races of man,* ed. Earl W. Count, pp. 133–144. New York: Henry Schuman, 1950.

EISELEY, LOREN
    1960   *The firmament of time.* New York: Atheneum.

GREENE, JOHN COLTON
    1959   *The death of Adam: evolution and its impact on Western thought.* Ames: Iowa State University Press.

HOWELLS, W. W.
    1965   Some present aspects of physical anthropology. *Annual of the American Academy of Political and Social Science* 137:127–133.

HUXLEY, THOMAS H.
    1896   *Man's place in nature.* New York: Appleton.

KUHN, THOMAS S.
    1962   *The structure of scientific revolutions.* Chicago: University of Chicago Press.

MAYR, ERNST
    1959   Darwin and the evolutionary theory in biology. In *Evolution and anthropology: a centennial appraisal,* pp. 3–12. Anthropological Society of Washington.
    1963   *Animal species and evolution.* Cambridge: Harvard University Press.

MOORE, RUTH
    1961   *The coil of life.* New York: Alfred A. Knopf.

PENNIMAN, T. K.
    1965   *A hundred years of anthropology.* 3d ed., rev. London: Gerald Duckworth.

STEWART, T. D.
    1959   The effect of Darwin's theory of evolution on physical anthropology. In *Evolution and anthropology: a centennial appraisal,* pp. 11–25. Anthropological Society of Washington.

STURTEVANT, A. H.
    1965   A *history of genetics*. New York: Harper & Row.
TROTTER, MILDRED
    1956   Notes on the history of the AAPA. Presidential address to the 25th
            annual meeting of the American Association of Physical Anthro-
            pologists. *American Journal of Physical Anthropology* (n.s.)
            14:350–364.
WASHBURN, S. L.
    1951   The new physical anthropology. *Transactions of the New York
            Academy of Sciences*, ser. 2, vol. 13, pp. 298–304.
WENDT, HERBERT
    1956   *In search of Adam*. Boston: Houghton Mifflin.
WILSON, R. J., ED.
    1967   *Darwinism and the American intellectual: a book of readings*.
            Homewood, Ill.: Dorsey.

CHAPTER 2

MAN AND HIS RELATIVES

Introduction

Introductory courses in physical anthropology usually begin with a unit called "man's place in nature," "man as a member of the animal kingdom," or, here, "man and his relatives." The information presented under these headings generally consists of descriptive statements about the various taxonomic units to which man belongs, and that is the kind of information contained in this chapter. Since man is an animal, it is necessary to discuss, for example, the distinguishing characteristics of the animal kingdom, and, more particularly, since man is a primate, the distinguishing characteristics of the primates.

Why should this material be presented in a course in physical anthropology? One answer to this question is obvious; if you intend to take up the study of man's biological evolution and contemporary variability, you should certainly be informed that man is an animal, and that his closest living relatives are primates. But the information presented herein is intended to provide much more than merely a convincing argument that man is a member of specific taxonomic units. It is intended to provide one category of minimal information which must be mastered for the practice of physical anthropology. What problems, for example, immediately confront a student of human paleontology? He must be able to recognize significant fossil material; to interpret the significance of a discovery as it relates to others; and, on occasion, to reconstruct the significance of the morphology and ecological setting in which the newly discovered animal lived. Without an awareness of the "man's place in nature" material, a person would be unable even to recognize the significance of a fossil discovery. In short, to comprehend and appreciate the significance of fossil discoveries requires an awareness of the range of variability among living forms.

One caution should be mentioned before proceeding to the problems of zoological classification: the listing and discussion of characteristics that distinguish one grouping from another has the effect of making it appear that the groups and their distinctive attributes are fixed, immutable, and eternal. Keep in mind that the groups and their characteristics were brought about by evolutionary processes that operated not merely at some time in the distant past, but which continue to operate in the present and can be expected to give rise to new forms in the future. It is easy to forget the dynamic, formative, and systemic character of the evolutionary process when inspecting some of the minute details it has produced.

ZOOLOGICAL CLASSIFICATION

The most convenient way of presenting and summarizing the total range of variability within living animal groups, and further of showing how man fits into the animal kingdom, is by means of the already well established system of animal classification. The subdivision of zoology that is directly concerned with the application of this system is known as *systematic* or *taxonomic zoology*. The general outlines and the regulations governing the classification of living things were set forth by Linnaeus two hundred years ago. Both the system and the rules governing its formulation have changed in considerable detail since the time of Linnaeus, but the objective is the same now as it was then: to achieve a systematic classification that accurately reflects the true biological distance between and among the animal groups.

At first the problem may sound reasonably simple. A competent specialist should be able to examine an animal, note its features, and make a decision concerning its classification, just as a chemist might be given some material which he can analyze and determine whether it is gold, copper, zinc, or whatever. However, there are many pitfalls in this apparently straightforward procedure. Animals are classified most often by judging degrees of apparent similarity. Human beings always emphasize vision. There is no a priori reason why animals could not be classified by means of tactile, olfactory, or auditory similarities and differences, but they are not. They are classified largely on the basis of visually perceived similarities and differences. The fundamental regulating principle in zoological classification may be stated as follows: the greater the degree of similarity, the closer the degree of biological relationship. This is another deceptively simple proposition, for some similarities do indeed indicate close common ancestry and thus close biological relationship, but others are merely superficial. Those similarities which indicate close biological relationships are called *homologies*. Homologies can be recognized as detailed structural similarities built upon a basic pattern which presumably characterized the common ancestor. Superficial similarities that might lead one to think that two forms are closely related when in fact they are not are called *analogies*. Thus, the wings of a bat and the wings of a beetle are functionally similar, but structurally dissimilar; they are analogies. Whereas the wings of a bat and the forelimbs and extremities of rodents are functionally dissimilar but structurally similar; they are homologies.

So in deciding relationships among animals, the problem is not as simple as it might appear at first. In addition to distinguishing between homologies and analogies, a classifier must also make judgments about the relative importance of traits. This problem will not be discussed in detail here, since it is basically the specialist's problem, but it can be illustrated by the following question: When classifying a particular animal, is the fact that it has hoofs more important than the fact that it has antlers? Frequently the taxonomist just can't make a judgment on such a problem. This is one of the most frequent sources of disagreement among zoological classifiers.

Another problem area in animal classification is that of determining in how many ways two groups or specimens must differ before they are considered to be different units (e.g., species) in the classification. While attempts have been made to eliminate this problem by standardizing procedures, there continues to be an element of personal preference among qualified zoologists. Because of this unavoidable ambiguity, it is possible to recognize two major groups of classifiers: 1) those who regard either few or slight differences between the compared groups as significant (the *splitters*) and 2) those who regard few or slight differences as unimportant (the *lumpers*). This is of more than passing interest to the physical anthropologist. The catalogue of erect bipedal fossil forms, any one or all of them possibly in man's ancestral line, includes discoveries originally classified into more than a dozen different genera. In addition to this, the situation is further confused by those discoveries named for the place of their discovery. It is not difficult to see that the classification of man and his ancestors has been in a badly jumbled mess.

The problem of zoological classification, as we have seen, is by no means a simple one on methodological grounds alone. It is, however, further complicated by the fact that the actual evidence available to the classifier is often crude and incomplete. This is particularly true in the case of fossil animals, with very often the only evidence available consisting of little more than a few fragments of bone or possibly a single tooth.

Because of these difficulties particular classifications are often found to be in error and are thus the subject of more or less constant revision. Perhaps the classification of the future will be more stable and less subject to error. If so, this might be a consequence of a relatively recent trend in taxonomy, which is to employ more criteria than simply morphological attributes as bases of a classification. New criteria of classification have been derived from histological, biochemical, and behavioral studies. As applied to the primates, the new approaches have tended to confirm the validity of standard classification. The fact that these criteria have had little effect on old classifications may be due to the methodological problems associated with interpreting the taxonomic significance of the results, or simply because such studies are, like those based on anatomical characteristics, fundamentally morphological and thus can be expected to reflect the same kind of relationship. A complete classification of the many forms of life might involve the use of as many as twenty-one levels in the taxonomic hierarchy, but only seven of these are in frequent and regular usage. They are:

Kingdom
Phylum
Class
Order
Family
Genus
Species.

Man's Place in Nature

The physical anthropologist is interested in knowing not only in what category man belongs at each taxonomic level, but he is also interested in knowing the membership of the other categories, particularly within those levels that include his closest relatives. In the discussion that follows, the primate order and its subdivisions will be considered in some detail, whereas the higher taxonomic levels will be dealt with very briefly. In this way one may obtain at least a minimal understanding of man's place in nature.

Kingdom: Animalia

This is a major subdivision of life. The traditional way of dividing life is to divide it into two major categories: plants and animals. During recent years biologists have become less satisfied with this simple dichotomy for two main reasons: 1) many living organisms possess characteristics which simply do not qualify them to fit neatly into either the plant or animal kingdom (e.g., bacteria and protozoa), and 2) many organisms have attributes characteristic of *both* plants and animals. The dissatisfaction arising out of these difficulties has brought about a number of suggested changes at the kingdom level, but for present purposes the standard division of life into plants and animals will be adequate. Within the animal kingdom there is an enormous range of variation, and thus it is difficult to point to many common distinctive features. There are structural and functional characteristics that distinguish animals from plants, but in general, animals are capable of locomotion, and plants practice photosynthesis. (The process of photosynthesis is the means by which the sun's energy is converted into the energy of life.) However, there are exceptions that vex the classifiers. A few animallike organisms are photosynthetic, and a few plantlike organisms move about. And some plants lack the photosynthetic ability!

Phylum: Chordata

How many different kinds of animals are there? One answer might list and count everything identifiable as animal; that is to say, there are bears, spiders, geese, beetles, dogs, deer, oysters, and so on. This obviously is not too helpful; what is called for here is a grouping together of general categories of animals that share some fundamental similarity in organization of their body structures. Animals that share this basic similarity are said to be members of the same phylum. For example, insects and spiders are grouped together in the phylum Arthropoda; clams, oysters, and a variety of other shellfish are in the phylum Mollusca. Man belongs to the phylum Chordata.

Figure 2–1. *Amphioxus* dissected from the right side. Illustrates position of the notochord. (After P. D. F. Murray.)

The phylum Chordata includes an extraordinarily diverse group of animals all of which have, at least at some time during their life cycle, gill slits, a nerve, and an elastic tubular structure known as a notochord (see Figure 2–1) located along the back (or dorsal) surface. The notochord is the basic feature common to all members of the phylum Chordata. In some members the notochord is a lifelong trait. In one subphylum of the Chordata, the vertebrates, it appears during the embryonic stage and is ultimately replaced by a vertebral column, a more complex linear sequence of segments containing a spinal cord.

Class: Mammalia

There are eight classes of vertebrates: 1) the primitive jawless "fish" (Agnatha), 2) the primitive armored fishes (Placodermi), 3) the sharks and their relatives (Chondrichthyes), 4) the bony fishes (Osteichthyes), 5) the amphibians (Amphibia), 6) the reptiles (Reptilia), 7) the birds (Aves), and 8) the class to which man belongs, the mammals (Mammalia). The mammals occupy many different types of environments. Some spend much of their life underground, some fly, some live in the sea; but by far the majority live on land, and these are distributed over practically the entire surface of the earth. As might be expected from the diversity of environments they live in, mammals are highly varied; yet they share in common several characteristics of adaptive significance.

Basically mammals are a distinctive class of chordates because of the characteristics they share that are associated with reproduction and care of the young. All mammals conceive their young within the uterus of the mother and, after the offspring are born, nourish them by means of mammary glands. Among living mammals there are three basic variations in this process: 1) some, the Prototheria mammals (such as the duckbill platypus), like other vertebrates, lay eggs but feed their newborn by means of mammary glands, 2) others, the Metatheria, like the kangaroo and opossum, bear their young in an immature condition and permit their development in a pouch, and 3) in the most common group, and the one to which we belong, the Eutherian mammals, the mothers carry their young within the uterus until an advanced state of development is reached. This is made possible by the placenta, which connects the embryo to the wall of the uterus and enables nutrients and oxygen to get to the offspring and, likewise, provides a means for eliminating waste products.

Mammals are distinctive in other ways. For example, mammals have hair, are warm-blooded, have relatively large brains, and display a number of characteristics in their skeleton that, compared to other vertebrates, appear to be more efficient simplifications.

Clearly the mammals possess a range of features which is of enormous adaptive significance. The young are developed over a relatively long period of their total life within the highly protected environment of their mother's uterus. Once they are born, they are already well along in their developmental process, but even so, mammals are further protected and allowed to develop more fully before being confronted by the problems of food-getting and offense and defense by being provided with milk from the mother's mammaries. These attributes, those previously mentioned, and many others not mentioned enabled the mammals to replace the reptiles as the dominant vertebrates, a status they achieved about one hundred million years ago and which they continue to enjoy at the present time. The factor of dominance is determined largely by two measures: 1) the amount of influence over other forms of life, and 2) the range of different environmental zones occupied.

Until now, the discussion has been concerned with generalized characteristics common to mammals and the benefits they provide in meeting the requirements of survival. In a more specific context, some mammalian characteristics may be seen as facilitating the survival of man and his culture. The relatively long period of postnatal care, prolonged even further in man, facilitates the transmission of culture from one generation to the next by freeing the young from the rigorous requirements of survival during the period of life when they are able to learn quickly and with greatest ease. This period of becoming "cultural" is essential not only for the continuity of culture but for development and progress as well.

There are many other ways in which the fact that man is a mammal conditions the general character of culture. To be specific with regard to the cultural consequences of being a mammal is virtually impossible. However, one can begin to appreciate the significance of man's mammalian heritage by asking a few strategic questions such as: Would culture be different if man were cold-blooded? Or if his young were hatched from eggs? Or if mankind depended upon wind, birds, and insects as the mechanisms of fertilization? Clearly the answer is an emphatic *yes*. However, it would be impossible to know exactly how these factors would modify the details of culture. From these conditions one should be able to see that being a mammal is a prerequisite for man's having culture as we know it.

The mammals are comparatively recent arrivals on earth, appearing on the evolutionary scene probably no more than two hundred million years ago. At first they were small and inconspicuous when compared with the huge and magnificent dinosaurs that were beginning to dominate the landscape. But the reptiles, particularly the large ones, eventually found survival more and more difficult. Mountains were being built, causing major changes in the earth's topography; areas that were moist and swampy with ample food supply were beginning to dry up, and as they did, the large reptiles were more and more restricted in range and eventually reduced to a degree that doomed them to extinction. In fact, the early mammals may have helped to speed up the process by feeding on their eggs.

As the reptiles underwent the process of mass extinction, they left behind them vast evolutionary possibilities which the mammals began to

TABLE 2–1*

THE 32 ORDERS IN THE CLASS MAMMALIA

Orders	Families			Genera		
	Extinct	Living	Total	Extinct	Living	Total
MONOTREMATA	0	2	2	0	3	3
†MULTITUBERCULATA	5	0	5	35	0	35
†TRICONODONTA	1	0	1	8	0	8
†PANTOTHERIA	4	0	4	22	0	22
†SYMMETRODONTA	2	0	2	5	0	5
MARSUPIALIA	5	8	13	81	57	138
INSECTIVORA	12	8	20	88	71	159
DERMOPTERA	1	1	2	2	1	3
CHIROPTERA	2	17	19	16	118	134
PRIMATES	7	11	18	99	59	158
†TILLODONTIA	1	0	1	4	0	4
†TAENIODONTA	1	0	1	7	0	7
EDENTATA	7	3	10	113	19	132
PHOLIDOTA	0	1	1	3	1	4
LAGOMORPHA	1	2	3	23	10	33
RODENTIA	10	30	40	275	344	619
CETACEA	9	9	18	137	35	172
CARNIVORA	6	9	15	261	114	375
†CONDYLARTHRA	6	0	6	42	0	42
†LITOPTERNA	2	0	2	41	0	41
†NOTOUNGULATA	14	0	14	105	0	105
†ASTRAPOTHERIA	2	0	2	9	0	9
TUBULIDENTATA	0	1	1	1	1	2
†PANTODONTA	3	0	3	9	0	9
†DINOCERATA	1	0	1	8	0	8
†PYROTHERIA	1	0	1	6	0	6
PROBOSCIDEA	5	1	6	22	2	24
†EMBRITHOPODA	1	0	1	1	0	1
HYRACOIDEA	2	1	3	10	3	13
SIRENIA	3	2	5	14	2	16
PERISSODACTYLA	9	3	12	152	6	158
ARTIODACTYLA	16	9	25	333	86	419
TOTAL	139	118	257	1932	932	2864
PERCENT	54%	46%		67%	33%	

* Reprinted from Simpson's "Formal Classification of Mammalia," *Bulletin of the American Museum of Natural History*, 85 (1945): 35. Courtesy of the American Museum of Natural History.

† Indicates extinct orders.

take advantage of, resulting in rapid diversification within the class Mammalia. This diversification is reflected in the number of mammalian orders. Simpson (1945) classified mammals into thirty-two orders, eighteen of which still have living representatives. Table 2–1 is taken from Simpson and lists the thirty-two orders, indicating the number of extinct and living families and genera known for each. From this, one may see that while there remain approximately as many families today as have become extinct, there are more than twice as many extinct genera known as living ones. Clearly, the information indicates that mammals have been involved in a great expansion, proliferation, and diversification. One product of this evolutionary explosion is the order Primates, the mammalian subdivision to which man belongs.

Order: Primates

The primates are good examples of generalized mammals and are themselves a diversified and evolutionarily successful group. At first sight, most members of the order do not appear to be likely candidates for the dubious honor of being closely related to man: many are small, nocturnal, insectivorous, and almost all live in trees. When they are examined closely, however, they begin to show traits that more clearly indicate an affinity to man. By observing their behavior, we see that they are alert, curious, heavily dependent upon vision, playful, capable of semierect or erect posture, able to use their hands to manipulate objects in their environment, banded together in organized and territorially defined groups, and they appear capable of carrying on some degree of communication with one another. By inspecting their structural traits, we find other similarities: stereoscopic vision, elongated limbs with five digits, complex and large brains, big toes and thumbs that can be placed in opposition to the other digits of the foot or hand, nails instead of claws. No list of traits, however, can be expected to provide anything like a profound appreciation of the many ways in which the primates are distinctive as a group and the ways in which man shares these distinctive features with the rest of the members of the order. One can only list a few of the most important features and emphasize the fact that primates are not highly specialized. They share a large number of traits in common but do not show any particular tendency to specialize in any one, except possibly brain size and intelligence (although this would seem to be more a particular specialization of man and his ancestors rather than a general one for the primates).

Most of the attributes common to the primates stem from either of two factors: 1) the retention of ancient or primitive generalized vertebrate or mammalian characteristics, and 2) the development of an arboreal adaptation. For example, the structural differentiation of the hands and feet into five digits is in fact not a "primate" trait in the sense that it was developed by them or is unique to them, but is rather a "vertebrate" trait much older than the primate order but which has been retained in that group. An emphasis on vision, particularly stereoscopic and color vision, is however a trait that has come about as the primates have evolved and this appears to be directly due to the requirements of an arboreal adaptation, that is, to living in the trees. Presently, the evolution of the primates will be dealt with in more detail, but for the moment simply recognize that the primates have stereoscopic vision, and some, at least, have color vision. The consequences of poor vision in an arboreal form are obvious: falling out of the trees, injury, and death.*

As a group, then, the primates may be broadly described as generalized, arboreal, and clever. They are broadly distributed throughout the tropical regions of both the New and Old World. The primate order may be sub-divided into three suborders (see Table 2–2): Prosimii, Platyrrhinae, and Catarrhinae. The following is a more detailed consideration of the pri-mates and each of these suborders and their subdivisions.

Prosimii. The prosimians were the first primates and thus represent the earliest stage in the evolution of the primates. There are four major kinds of prosimians among the living primates, and these correspond to the superfamily subdivisions commonly known as tree shrews, lemurs, lorises, and tarsiers. It is difficult to point to any specific morphological features shared by all of them that justify their being included together in the prosimian suborder. However, from an evolutionary point of view it makes good sense; these are the living descendants of the earliest primate evolutionary experiment, the arboreal adaptation. If there is anything that provides this group with biological integrity, it is the fact that all members show, in a lesser or greater degree, the consequences of the early ancestors of the primates taking to life in trees. This is, of course, true of all living primates, but the prosimians provide us with some insight into the earliest ways that this arboreal adaptation was translated into morphological characteristics. To be sure, the living prosimians give us a biased view of this early stage in the evolution of the primates, since they include, on the one hand, only the descendants of the successful groups that continue to survive, while, on the other hand, they do not in-clude representatives of the more progressive ancestors that eventually evolved into higher primate forms. It is clear, then, that the prosimians are of interest to physical anthropology not only because they belong to the

* It would seem worthwhile to introduce here a point that is not always emphasized: monkeys and apes do fall out of trees and, what is more, do it all the time. We are inclined to think that man is the only imperfect animal; while it is human to err, we think of other animals as going about their daily lives in more or less perfect adapta-tion to their environments. But of course animals err too, and when they do, the consequences are more likely to be fatal. It is perhaps a measure of just how con-vinced we are of their perfect adaptation to observe the reaction to a monkey or squirrel falling out of a tree. Often the observer will remark that "the little things are human after all."

TABLE 2-2

CLASSIFICATION OF MODERN PRIMATES

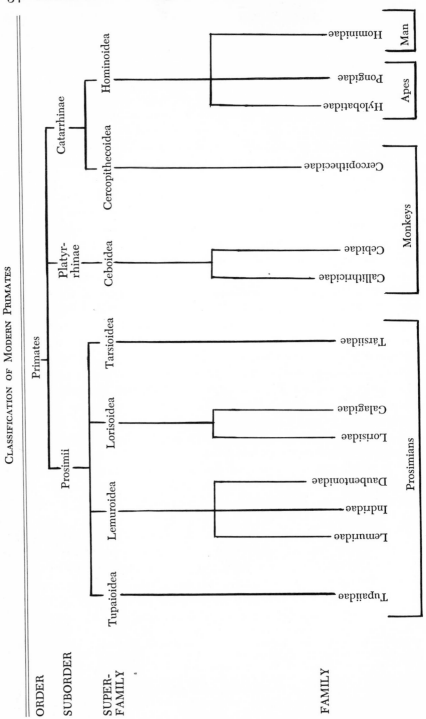

same order as man, but furthermore because of the insights they may provide concerning the origin of the primates. We can take a closer look at the prosimians by considering the four superfamilies: Tupaioidea, Lemuroidea, Lorisoidea, and Tarsioidea.

Morphologically the Tupaioidea (tree shrews) of Southeast Asia stand between more typical primates on the one hand and insectivores on the other. Because of this intermediate appearance, zoological taxonomists have disagreed on the classification of the tree shrews: some put them into the Insectivora, others include them with the primates, and one primatologist has concluded that they belong in a separate order all to themselves.

The tree shrews are generally described by such adjectives as quick, alert, small, and arboreal. On first appearance they look like small squirrels, but on closer inspection one can see many distinctive features. Like the primates and unlike the insectivores, the tree shrews have large eyes, more-fully-developed visual areas of the brain, and less-fully-developed olfactory areas. They have highly mobile fingers and toes that can be used for grasping. And, while their diet is predominantly insectivorous, they will eat fruit, seeds, small mammals, and, if confined together, one another. They differ from other primates in terms of the following characteristics: all their digits have claws; they lack stereoscopic vision; they commonly have multiple births and multiple pairs of mammaries; their lower jaw has three incisors in each quadrant (thus they have a total of six incisors in the lower jaw), whereas the upper jaw has two in each quadrant (total of four).

One subfamily, the Tupainae, are generally diurnal; another, the Ptilocercinae, nocturnal. The Ptilocerinae have bald tails except for a tuft of

Figure 2–2. Tree shrew (*Tupaia*). (Courtesy Zoological Society of San Diego.)

Figure 2–3. Front and side views of a female tree shrew skull (*Tupaia nicobarica surda*). (Courtesy Smithsonian Institution.)

hair at the very tip. Both subfamilies are indeed adapted to life in the trees, but members of all species spend much of their life on or near the ground. They live in pairs or small groups and build nests for sleeping.

In summary, the tupaioids display a most unusual assortment of traits, some of which ally them with the primates, others with the insectivores, and still others are not common to either order. It is, however, for these very reasons that the Tupaioidea are of interest to the primatologist; there are good reasons to believe that the primates evolved from insectivore ancestors, and thus the tree shrew provides some important indirect information about the kinds of animals that bridged the evolutionary gap between the orders.

The Lemuroidea are confined to Madagascar and the Comoro Islands and consist of three families, Lemuridae, Indridae, and Daubentonidae. The Lemuridae are often referred to as the "true lemurs." Like all lemuroids, they are a combination of familiar primate characteristics and specialized adaptations rarely found in other primates. Among the usual primate features are fingernails (except for the second toe on each foot, which has a claw), opposable great toes and thumbs, enormous eyes, and heavy dependence on vision. Further, the females generally bear but one offspring at a time.

The most peculiar specialization found among the Lemuridae is the distinctive habit of one subfamily, the Cheirogaleinae, to estivate, that is, to sleep throughout the hot season, during which time they obtain sufficient nutriment to survive by drawing upon a massive deposit of fat located near the base of the tail. Most species of the Lemuridae are nocturnal, and all are arboreal. They are primarily vegetarian, but will eat insects and small birds. They live in small groups, presumably organized socially, but the structure and functioning of this organization is as yet unclear. They are "territorial" in the sense that groups know the boundaries of their own territories and defend themselves against intrusion. They apparently

Figure 2–4. A brown lemur (*Lemur fulvus*) of the family Lemuridae. (Courtesy Oregon Regional Primate Research Center, photo by F. S. Shininger.)

Figure 2–5. A ring-tailed lemur (*Lemur catta*) of the family Lemuridae. (Courtesy Oregon Regional Primate Research Center, photo by F. S. Shininger.)

mark the limits of their territories by means of scent glands and thus recognize boundaries by olfactory discriminations.

The Indridae display the same generalized primate traits mentioned above in connection with the Lemuridae. Their most distinctive features are: 1) except for the opposable great toe, the other four toes are webbed together, and 2) they have two incisors in each quadrant of the upper jaw and only one in each quadrant of the lower jaw.

The Daubentonidae show a number of specialized traits when compared not only with other families of the Lemuroidea superfamily, but

Figure 2–6. Top and front views of a lemur skull (*Lemur ruffifrons*). (Courtesy Smithsonian Institution.)

with any other primate group as well. They are commonly called Aye-Ayes, and their most distinctive features include: 1) long, curved, chisel-like incisors that look like and function as the incisors of rodents, and 2) except for the great toe all other digits of both the hands and feet have claws. There is only one genus, and all members are nocturnal, arboreal, and often live in pairs.

The Lorisoidea are more broadly distributed than the Lemuroidea. Lorises may be found in South and West Africa and in Southeast Asia and Malaysia. The lorises share essentially the same generalized primate features as the lemurs do. The Lorisidae are small, slow-moving animals with enormous eyes and possess a long claw on the second toe of each foot, which is used to impale and extract grubs embedded in bark.

The Galagidae (known also as "bush babies") vary the general lorisoid adaptive theme by possessing a specialized architectural structure

Figure 2–7. A potto (*Perodicticus potto*) of the family Lorisidae. (Courtesy Oregon Regional Primate Research Center, photo by F. S. Shininger.)

Figure 2–8. Front and side views of a skull from the family Lorisidae (the slow loris or *Nycticebus coucang*). (Courtesy Smithsonian Institution.)

Figure 2–9. A galago or bush baby (*Galago senegalensis*) of the family Galagidae. (Courtesy Oregon Regional Primate Research Center, photo by F. S. Shininger.)

on their feet, involving a lengthening of the heel and ankle bones to provide for a hopping mode of progressing through the trees. In this respect they are like the tarsiers.

The Tarsioidea superfamily is represented among living primates by only one genus. The individuals that belong within this group show several peculiar specializations, most of which are related to the hopping mode of progression they share with the Galagidae. The tarsiers have elongated heel and ankle bones and, in addition, small suction pads on the soles of their feet.

If one can ignore the specializations of the tarsier, however, it begins to become obvious that this suborder of prosimians is somewhat more advanced than the others. They have a more fully developed visual apparatus which includes not merely large eyes, but an enlarged area of the brain that controls vision and a bony orbit which houses and encloses most of the back of the eye (as in higher primates). This more highly developed vision is accompanied by a corresponding reduction in the brain center that controls the sense of smell. These features are so strikingly advanced in the tarsier that one anatomist claimed that these little prosimians were man's closest living relatives. However this is certainly not the majority opinion.

Tarsiers may be found in their natural habitats in the Philippines, Borneo, and the Celebes. All are small, arboreal, and nocturnal, and all have very large eyes and are able to rotate their heads 180 degrees. This ability to completely reverse their vision, coupled with their ability to hop as high as six feet in getting from branch to branch, makes them interesting

Figure 2–10. A Philippine tarsier (*Tarsius syrichta*) of the family Tarsiidae. (Courtesy Oregon Regional Primate Research Center, photo by F. S. Shininger.)

Figure 2–11. Front and side views of a male tarsier skull (*Tarsius bancanna*). (Courtesy Smithsonian Institution.)

and entertaining to watch, but not much is known about their behavior, as they do not survive well in captivity, their habitats are difficult to get to, and tarsiers are most active at night.

Platyrrhinae.   This suborder consists entirely of monkeys found exclusively in Central and South America, and is made up of one superfamily and two families. There is no sharp qualitative distinction between the platyrrhines and the prosimians, but there are several differences in degree that, when taken as a whole, serve to distinguish them clearly. It would seem that the New World monkeys display the morphological consequences of the early arboreal adaptation in a more fully developed way than the prosimians do. As pointed out earlier, the living prosimians do not include representatives of their more progressive ancestors, but such illustrations can be found among the living monkeys. The platyrrhines differ from the prosimians in that the platyrrhines are generally larger, more intelligent, and have more highly developed vision. All New World monkeys are arboreal, and all possess greater dexterity than the prosimians in the use of their hands and feet for grasping and manipulating objects. In short, the platyrrhines are more representative of the "typical" primate pattern than are the prosimians.

The family Cebidae includes animals with a wide range of adaptive features. Some are brachiators, that is, they get from one branch to another by grasping a branch with the hands and swinging their bodies under the branch and leaping to the next one. (The brachiating mode of locomotion is also characteristic of the Hylobatidae and Pongidae, both of which are families of the Catarrhinae.) Some Cebidae have prehensile, or grasping, tails, which they use for grasping, suspending, and balancing.

All but one species of the Cebidae are diurnal, and all have opposable big toes with the thumbs either imperfectly opposable or completely without function.

Included within the family Callithricidae are the marmosets and tamarins, the most aberrant of the platyrrhines. Except for the great toe, all

Figure 2–12. Hooded capuchin (*Cebus capucinus*) of the family Cebidae. (Courtesy Zoological Society of San Diego.)

Figure 2–13. Front and top views of a female capuchin skull (*Cebus albifrons*). (Courtesy Smithsonian Institution.)

Figure 2–14. Howler monkey (*Alouatta seniculus*) of the family Cebidae. (Courtesy Zoological Society of San Diego.)

the digits have claws instead of nails, and females commonly bear two or three offspring at one birth. They are small, diurnal, and subsist principally on insects and fruit. It is impossible to know whether the unusual features found among the Callithricidae are primitive or specialized. Traits are primitive if they represent retentions of old adaptations in more advanced lines. They are specialized when they are recent and represent specific responses to an adaptive problem within one phylogenetic line.

Catarrhinae. The Catarrhinae are subdivided into two superfamilies: the Cercopithecoidea, or Old World monkeys, and the Hominoidea, including the apes and man. It should be clear from this that the Catarrhinae are more varied than the Platyrrhinae. In beginning our discussion of the Old World forms, it will be more convenient to compare the platyrrhines to the Cercopithecoidea rather than to the catarrhines in general. In this way, the comparison is between New and Old World monkeys rather than between New World monkeys on the one hand and Old World monkeys, apes, and man on the other.

The superfamily Cercopithecoidea may be thought of as differing from the prosimians in the same general way that the platyrrhines do. In detail, of course, the platyrrhines differ from the Old World monkeys, the Cercopithecoidea, in many respects. The Platyrrhinae have prehensile, or grasping, tails; the Cercopithecoidea have tails, but they are not prehensile. The New World monkeys have three premolars, whereas the Old World monkeys have two. Some New World forms brachiate; no cercopithecoids do. Old World monkeys use all four limbs in getting about from one place to another. Old World monkeys are able to oppose both their thumbs and their great toes with strength and efficiency; the platyrrhines are much less able to oppose their thumbs to their fingers and palms than they are their great toe to their other toes and plantar surfaces. Finally, the Old World monkeys show distinctive calloused areas on their buttocks known as ischial callosities, which are not found among the platyrrhines. The function of the ischial callosities is still uncertain, but they appear to be related to the fact that the cercopithecoids sleep in a sitting position in the trees. Any particular Old World monkey will differ in many more ways from any

Figure 2–15. Front and side views of skull of a male marmoset (*Mico argentata*) of the family Callithricidae. (Courtesy Smithsonian Institution.)

Figure 2–16. Cotton-topped tamarin (*Leontocebus spixi*) of the family Callithricidae. (Courtesy Zoological Society of San Diego.)

Figure 2–17. Some Old World monkeys. Top: Left, langur; Right, gelada baboon. Bottom: mona guenon. (Courtesy Zoological Society of San Diego, photo by Ron Garrison.)

particular New World monkey. The differences listed here are the most conspicuous.

While the cercopithecoids all fall into the family Cercopithecidae, they are divided into two subfamilies, the Cercopithecinae and the Colobinae. The major distinction between these subfamilies is that the cercopithecines have cheek pouches into which they stuff food to be carried away, chewed, and digested in an area which might be safer than where the food is actually found. The Colobinae subsist primarily on leaves, and, instead of cheek pouches, they have a series of stomachs adapted to the peculiar digestive requirements of this kind of food.

All the cercopithecoids are arboreal except the baboon, which spends most of its day foraging on the ground; but even the baboons sleep in trees and use them for protection when attacked by predators.

Included also within the Catarrhinae are apes and man, grouped together in the superfamily Hominoidea. The apes are classified into two

Figure 2–18. Skulls of three Old World monkeys. Top: guenon (*Cercopithecus mona*). Middle: baboon *(Papio comatus)*. Both are members of the subfamily Ceropithecinae. Bottom: langur (*Presbytis rubicundes*) of the subfamily Colobinae. (Courtesy Smithsonian Institution.)

families: the gibbons and siamangs in the Hylobatidae, and the orangutan, chimpanzee, and gorilla in the Pongidae (see Figure 2–19). As a group, the apes are distinctive primarily because of their adaptation to a brachiating mode of progression in the trees. Like the New World brachiators, they possess longer forelimbs than hind limbs, flattened front to back contours of the chest cavity, and large clavicles (the collarbone which serves in part to keep the shoulder joints to the side). In other respects (those not associated with brachiation) the apes are much more like the Old World cercopithecoids than the platyrrhine brachiators. Indeed, many have maintained that the apes are more closely similar to man than they are to the monkeys, but this is difficult to resolve, since man's physical makeup does not enable us to know with confidence if his

Figure 2–19. Representatives of the Hominoidea. Top: Left, chimpanzee; Right, lowland gorilla. Bottom: Left, agile gibbon; Right, orangutan. (Courtesy Zoological Society of San Diego, photo by Ron Garrison.)

Gorilla

Chimpanzee

Orangutan

Gibbon

0 CM 5

Figure 2–20. Side and front views of modern apes' skulls.

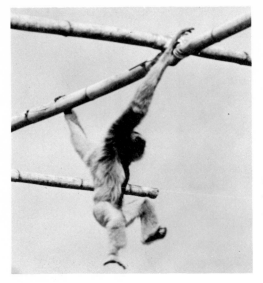

Figure 2–21. White-handed gibbon brachiating. (Courtesy Zoological Society of San Diego, photo by Ron Garrison.)

ancestors shared a brachiating ancestry in common with the apes. Man has, for example, the well-developed clavicle and flattened thorax of an efficient brachiator, but he lacks the long forearms relative to hind-limb length. Since the evidence is ambiguous, there is room for disagreement, and this is indeed reflected in the question of whether or not man's ancestors passed through a brachiating ancestry. Must the argument be resolved before we can conclude if man's closest living relatives are the apes or the Old World monkeys? Something of a compromise may not only bypass this problem, but may, in fact, be nearer to the truth as well. It is certainly within the realm of possibility that efficient brachiation and its associated anatomical specializations are relatively recent things among the ancestors of the modern great apes. If this is indeed true, then man and the apes could have shared an evolutionary phase during which their common ancestors just were not very good brachiators, and thus lacked the controversial specializations. This would, of course, mean that man is more closely related to the great apes and would further help to explain the discordance between the two groups in the attributes associated with brachiation.

In summary, it is now possible to view the variation within the primate order as a consequence of major adaptive shifts (e.g., arboreal way of life, brachiation) followed by proliferation and ramification into the environmental possibilities opened up by these major shifts. Only one major primate group remains for our consideration here, and that is the one we are most interested in knowing about, the one that includes man and his immediate ancestors, all of whom belong to the family Homi-nidae. Man is a distinctive member of the Hominoidea superfamily by virtue of two major adaptive features: erect posture, with its associated bipedal gait, and, of course, culture.

Erect posture had the effect of distinguishing man morphologically quite sharply from the rest of the primates. In fact, most of the anatomical features in which man is unique are a result of erect posture (most of the unique morphological features which distinguish between and among contemporary groups within the human species may be due to cultural factors). Among the most important features that came about as a conse-quence of erect posture and ultimately served to distinguish the hominids as a group are the following: large relative brain size, a pelvis adapted to erect posture, an S-shaped vertebral column (see Figure 2–22), and a large number of features of the skull which appear to be principally a consequence of man's dependence on culture.

Culture enables us to understand why the abrupt changes brought about by erect posture did not result in a rapid expansion and a proliferation of species within the Hominidae. Culture provides the means for man to evolve biologically without splitting into separate species largely because of two features: 1) culture makes it unnecessary for groups of mankind

Man

Figure 2–22. Comparison of pelvis and spinal column in man and quadrupedal pri-mate (stump-tailed macaque).

Stump-tailed Macaque

to adapt to differing environmental requirements by the usually slow process of accumulation of somatic changes which necessarily results in speciation in lower forms. Man could and did adapt by cultural means rather than biological means; and 2) culture offers the basis for communication and cooperation which are unknown and unavailable to other species. As a consequence of these factors, the normally expected proliferation and diversification has not occurred in the Hominidae. Man remains a single species today, and there is good reason to conclude that this has been true ever since he became man; that is, since he became an erect, bipedal, and cultural animal.

Genus: *Homo*

The genus to which we belong is distinctive among the primates in having erect posture and bipedal locomotion. These traits have characterized four groups: 1) the australopithencines, occasionally referred to as *Homo africanus;* 2) *Homo erectus;* 3) *Homo neanderthalensis;* and 4) *Homo sapiens.* Our knowledge of the first three of these is based entirely on paleontological and archaeological evidence. The nature of this evidence is considered in detail in Part II.

Species: *sapiens*

Sapiens is the only living species of the genus *Homo;* it includes all mankind. The distribution of variation within the species *sapiens* is discussed in Part III.

Primate Behavior

Throughout the preceding discussion the emphasis has focused almost exclusively on morphological features; that is, groups have been contrasted with others on the basis of having or lacking one or more physical characteristics. This necessarily introduces some distortion, for, as noted earlier, it emphasizes a static and immutable quality in the discussion of taxonomy. In fact, however, the morphologies of organisms are the products of the dynamic interaction between their genetic potentials and the environments in which they occur. Stated in simplified form:

$$\text{Environment} \times \text{Genetic Potential} \rightarrow \text{Morphology}$$

In this way it is possible to see that morphological variability is the product of a continuous process of dynamic interaction.

Turning attention now to behavior, it is perhaps surprising to find that the comments just made about morphology can also be made about behavior. Behavior too is a product of interaction between genetic and environmental factors. Moreover, behavior and morphology interact together so that the relationships might be expressed more simply as follows:

$$\text{Environment} \times \text{Genetic Potential} \longrightarrow \begin{array}{l} \text{Morphology} \\ \text{Behavior} \end{array}$$

Thus morphology and behavior may be seen as aspects of the same interacting elements, and each may be used to inform us about the ways in which organisms adapt to their environments.

Until recently the way in which animal behavior was investigated was not conducive to improving our understanding of human evolution and human variation. Investigations were commonly carried out on animals only remotely related to man under controlled laboratory conditions. In recent years, there has been a great increase in the number of studies that have examined the behavior of animals in their natural setting, and nowhere has this increased interest been more pronounced than in the area of primate behavior. Up to ten years ago the picture that anthropologists presented of primate behavior was clear and simple, consisting of the following elements: 1) primates live in socially organized groups that, both within and between species, vary in size and structure; 2) typically a group consists of a dominant male, a group of sexually mature females, their immature offspring, and, as outcasts on the periphery, the other adult males; and 3) behavior among the members of the group is a function largely of sexuality. The dominant male was portrayed as a sultan and the females as his harem; he would guard the females against the advances of the outcast males and thereby protect his exclusive sexual rights, and, as a result, the integration of the group could be maintained.

This view can be traced directly to some observations of primate behavior conducted in the early 1930's. Field studies by Bingham (1932) on gorillas and Nissen (1931) on chimpanzees established the fact that these animals live in socially organized groups and that the composition of the group varied widely from one locality to another. Carpenter (1934) conducted what has come to be regarded as the pioneer work in systematic observations of primates living in their natural habitat as he studied howler monkeys in Central America. His observations led him to a view of primate behavior and social organization that contrasted sharply with the "typical" view characterized above. Carpenter observed that the howler monkey displayed very little competition for sexual partners, and in general noted that sexuality seemed to play a relatively minor role in their lives.

Carpenter's observations tended to be regarded simply as evidence of the vast difference between New and Old World primates. The typical view of social organization among Old World primates stems from the earlier work of Solly Zuckerman (1932) on baboons. First it should be emphasized that Zuckerman based his conclusions almost exclusively on observations of animals in captivity. Nevertheless, he and many others regarded this as no serious limitation and generalized his conclusions to apply not merely to baboons in nature, but to all Old World primates. His observations led him to put forth the view of primate society summarized above: groups of animals dominated by sexuality and characterized by jealousy and promiscuity. The dominant male, dominant by physical strength, remained in that position until a stronger rival deposed him. Not only did Zuckerman believe this form of social organization to be common to all the Catarrhinae, but since man evolved in the Old World, he felt as well that it represented a stage of social organization through which man's ancestors passed in their evolution.

Zuckerman's views were widely accepted by anthropologists for the next twenty-five to thirty years. E. A. Hooton (1942) in synthesizing the available data on primates agreed in all essential features with Zuckerman but added, for reasons that are hard to understand, the proposition that the closer one comes to man in the taxonomic classification, the more intelligence and individuality tempered the sexually motivated behavior. As recently as 1959, Sahlins, in surveying much the same material as Hooton did, concluded that sexuality and dominance were the primary bases of primate social organization, but, unlike Hooton, Sahlins failed to see human social organization as a simple outgrowth of the gradual ameliorative effects of increasing intelligence and individuality. Sahlins presented the view that human social organization was a product of cultural factors (particularly economic) that simply do not occur in nonhuman primates.

Field observations on primates were resumed in the 1950's, and by 1960 the first extended reports on these investigations began to appear, and interest in the area has grown dramatically since then. Recently, two new journals and an international professional society have been established to focus the publication of the data and to provide a convenient forum in which interested specialists might exchange their ideas and observations.

The newer studies have made a number of things obvious, and among them the most important are: 1) primate social organization differs markedly from one group to another; 2) sexuality is seasonal and but one of several factors that integrate primate society (Harlow and Harlow, 1965); and 3) dominant structures vary between species and function in more complex ways than was formerly believed. This recent work displaces the older view, but not with a clear picture of its own. With more evidence and thought, one can anticipate exciting advances in the near future.

This completes a brief tour through the animal kingdom, which enabled us to obtain only the barest impressions of the differences that prevail between man and his relatives. But the trip has enabled us to see some important things; all the groups examined here are unique, yet all are similar in some ways too. Man is a primate, a mammal, a chordate, and an animal. He is unique both in morphology and in having culture. Realizing how man is like and how he differs from other animals is at least a beginning to an understanding of man's place in nature.

REFERENCES AND
SUGGESTIONS FOR ADDITIONAL READING

CARPENTER, C. RAY
    1934   A field study of the behavior and social relations of howling mon-keys. *Comparative Psychology Monographs* 10.
    1940   A field study in Siam of the behavior and social relations of the gibbon (*Hylobates lar*). *Comparative Psychology Monographs* 16:1–212.
COON, CARLETON S.
    1962   *The origin of races.* New York: Alfred A. Knopf.
DAY, CLARENCE
    1920   *This simian world.* New York: Alfred A. Knopf.
DEVORE, IRVEN
    1965   *Primate behavior.* New York: Holt, Rinehart & Winston.
EIMERL, SAREL, AND IRVEN DEVORE
    1965   *The primates.* New York: Time, Inc.
FIEDLER, W.
    1956   Übersicht über das System der Primates. In *Primatologia*, ed. H. Hofer, A. H. Schultz, and D. Stark, 1:1–266. Basel: S. Karger.
HARLOW, HARRY F., AND MARGARET K. HARLOW
    1965   The affectational systems. In *Behavior of non-human primates,* ed. Allan M. Schrier, Harry F. Harlow, and Fred Stollnitz, 2:287–334. New York: Academic Press.
HOOTON, EARNEST ALBERT
    1942   *Man's poor relations.* Garden City, N.Y.: Doubleday, Doran.
    1947   *Up from the ape.* Rev. ed. New York: Macmillan.
JAY, PHYLLIS C., ED.
    1968   *Primates: studies in adaptation and variability.* New York: Holt, Rinehart & Winston.
KOFORD, CARL B.
    1963   Group relations in an island colony of rhesus monkeys. In *Primate social behavior,* ed. Charles H. Southwick, pp. 136–152. Princeton, N.J.: Van Nostrand.
    1965   Population dynamics of rhesus monkeys on Cayo Santiago. In *Primate behavior,* ed. Irven DeVore. New York: Holt, Rinehart & Winston.
MAYR, ERNST
    1963   *Animal species and evolution.* Cambridge: Harvard University Press.
MOODY, PAUL A.
    1962   *Introduction to evolution.* 2d ed. New York: Harper & Row.

MORRIS, DESMOND
    1967   *Primate ethology*. Chicago: Aldine.
NAPIER, J. R., AND P. H. NAPIER
    1967   *A handbook of living primates: morphology, ecology, and behavior of non-human primates*. New York: Academic Press.
OXNARD, CHARLES E.
    1968   Primate evolution—a method of investigation. *American Journal of Physical Anthropology* (n.s.) 28:289–301.
    1969   Mathematics, shape and function: a study in primate anatomy. *American Scientist* 57:75–96.
QUIATT, DUANE
    1966   Social dynamics of rhesus monkey groups. Ph.D. dissertation, University of Colorado.
SAHLINS, MARSHALL D.
    1959   The social life of monkeys, apes, and primitive man. *Human Biology* 31:54–73.
SCHALLER, GEORGE B.
    1963   *The mountain gorilla: ecology and behavior*. Chicago: University of Chicago Press.
SIMPSON, GEORGE GAYLORD
    1945   The principles of classification and a classification of mammals. *Bulletin of the American Museum of Natural History* 85:1–350.
    1949   *The meaning of evolution: a study of the history of life and of its significance for man*. New Haven: Yale University Press.
    1950   Some principles of historical biology bearing on human origins. *Cold Spring Harbor Symposia on Quantitative Biology* 15:55–66.
    1961   *Principles of animal taxonomy*. New York: Columbia University Press.
    1963   The meaning of taxonomic statements. In *Classification and human evolution*, ed. S. L. Washburn. Viking Fund Publications in Anthropology, no. 37. Chicago: Aldine.
SNYDER, LAURENCE H.
    1954   The effects of selection and domestication on man. *Journal of the National Cancer Institute* 15:759–769.
VAN LAWICK-GOODALL, JANE
    1967   *My friends the wild chimpanzees*. Washington: National Geographic Society.
WASHBURN, SHERWOOD L., AND IRVEN DEVORE
    1961   The social life of baboons. *Scientific American* 204, June, pp. 62–71.
ZUCKERMAN, SOLLY
    1932   *Social life of monkeys and apes*. London: Kegan Paul.

CHAPTER 3

THE BACKGROUND OF GENETICS

INTRODUCTION

The most outstanding intellectual achievement in biology since Darwin's time is the demonstration that life is controlled by the same physical and chemical laws that regulate other forms and organizations of matter. The basic view is not a new one, but the experimental evidence supporting it has been accumulated largely within the last twenty years. This work has brought about a new and revolutionary approach in biology, but most particularly in genetics.

Therefore, a consideration of genetics and its bearing on physical anthropology is essential. After all, physical anthropology can expect to advance at least in part as biology advances, and at the present time, genetics is biology's most rapidly advancing area. Yet there are other reasons for turning to genetics, and among the most compelling are the following: 1) Physical anthropology attempts to explain human evolution. Genetics provides a basis for investigating similarities and differences between parent and offspring generations. Indeed, evolution may be defined as the accumulation of genetic changes over generations. 2) Physical anthropology attempts to describe and explain man's biological variation. Genetics has made it possible to employ a distinctive set of traits, inherited ones, in describing and analyzing man's variation, and these may be analyzed in ways that other traits cannot (see Chapter 9). 3) In classifying man's variation, physical anthropologists have relied heavily on racial classifications that basically are pre-Darwinian or non-evolutionary in outlook. Genetics, in the development of its theory of population structure, has laid the foundations for classifying human variation into categories with clearer evolutionary unity and thus with clearer biological meaning than traditional racial classifications imply. In short, physical anthropology can be discussed without a knowledge of genetics, but such discussions are destined to be specialized, trivial, or both.

The field of genetics has diversified rapidly since 1900, and any attempt to cover the field in a complete way would have to give attention to at least the following subdivisions: medical, formal, population, experimental, biochemical, cytological, behavioral, quantitative, developmental, molecular, plant, microbial, serological, and immunological genetics. Several books and countless articles have been written on each of these specialties, and, clearly, it is not desirable, in view of the objectives of this book, to deal with each of them. The discussion here is limited to: 1) *formal genetics* since its conclusions are basic to all the others, 2) enough *molecular* and *biochemical genetics* to illustrate some of the important recent advances, and 3) *population genetics* because of its direct relevance to the problems and traditional interests of physical anthropology. These should serve to sharpen one's understanding of the paleontological record even though it is not at present possible to deal with it directly in genetic terms. Likewise, these discussions should help one to see that heterographic variation is a clue to the dynamics of evolutionary processes, and to appreciate more clearly the present status of physical anthropology and its future probabilities.

DEFINITIONS

Before considering formal genetics in some detail, it will be useful to introduce a few basic terms. A *gene* is the physical structure transmitting hereditary potential from one generation to the next. A *chromosome* is a discrete set of genes arranged in linear order. The space a gene occupies on a chromosome is referred to as a *genetic locus*. As the structure of a gene varies, its hereditary potential varies. Changes in the structure of a gene are *mutations*. Mutations give rise to alternative structures of the same gene; these alternative forms of a gene are *alleles*. Under normal conditions, a person obtains one complete set of genetic loci from his mother and another from his father. Thus, he has a pair of alleles for each locus. One complete set is said to contain the *haploid* number of chromosomes; one complete set of pairs, the *diploid* number. If at any locus a child obtains the same allelic form from his mother as from his father, he is *homozygous* for that gene. If he obtains different alleles he is *heterozygous*. The pair of alleles an individual inherits constitutes his *genotype* for that particular locus. The hereditary potential of the genotype may be modified by environmental factors, and the manner in which the genetic material is expressed in an individual is termed the *phenotype*. Thus identical genotypes can, in contrasting environments, result in differing phenotypes. Likewise, different genotypes can, under many circumstances, result in indistinguishable phenotypes.

The term *frequency* is used commonly throughout this and later chapters. The *frequency* of an event is the number of times it occurs out of the total number of occasions it could have occurred. Thus, if you flip a coin 12 times, and if 7 of those flips come up heads, the frequency of the event "heads" is 7 out of 12, a relationship that may be expressed as a fraction (7/12), or a proportion (.58), or a percentage (58 percent).

FORMAL GENETICS

Mendel's Laws

Mendel laid the foundation for the science of genetics. As discussed in Chapter 1, his experiments led to the conclusions that: 1) inheritance is particulate; 2) the particles, i.e., the genes, are present in pairs which separate in the formation of sex cells (first law); and 3) the segregation of one pair of alleles is independent of that of any other pair (second law). Thus Mendel not only discovered what later were called genes, but also two basic laws regulating the manner in which they are passed on from one generation to the next. These remain today as the basic laws of heredity, and a review of their implications may be useful.

Mendel's first and second laws of heredity imply that the components of an organism's genotype, the genetic loci and the alleles that occupy them, are reshuffled and brought together in new combinations in the process of forming sex cells. As an illustration, consider an individual with the following genotype for two genetic loci:

	Allele 1	Allele 2
Locus 1	A	a
Locus 2	B	b

The individual is heterozygous at both loci.

Mendel's second law implies that A is as likely to be combined with B as with b in the formation of sex cells; likewise a is as likely to end up with B as with b. The process is random; the offspring obtains a complete set of genetic loci from each parent. Thus, from the parent in the illustration a child must get either A or a, and either B or b (first law), but whether the offspring gets *AB, Ab, aB,* or *ab* is entirely a matter of chance (second law).

Linkage

There is one major exception to Mendel's second law: loci that are, in fact, linked together on the same chromosome. The genes, as noted earlier, are located on chromosomes, and one chromosome contains many loci. Since chromosomes normally remain intact, genes located together on the same chromosome are transmitted together as a single genetic package. Thus, in the illustration used above, if *A* and *B* were linked together, then *a* and *b,* their alleles, would also be linked together on the homologous chromosome, and the two loci could not assort independently. In this instance a child could receive only *AB* or *ab* from that parent. Thus a geneticist who finds two or more loci that do not assort independently has evidence that the loci are linked together on the same chromosome. These discoveries led ultimately to chromosome maps that show what loci are linked and the order of their appearance on the chromosome. The latter point, the linear order, can be estimated as a function of another exception, in this case an exception to linkage. Linked loci can and do become separated by a process called *crossover,* wherein two homologous chromosomes exchange segments. Again, if *A* and *B* and *a* and *b* are linked, and crossover should occur between them, the result will be to link together *A* and *b* and *a* and *B,* thus:

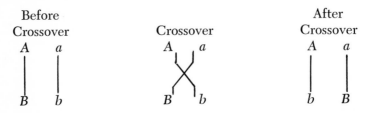

Linear order of the loci may be obtained as an extension of the assumption that *the closer together two linked loci are situated, the less likely they will be separated by crossover;* or, conversely, the farther apart two loci, the more frequent their separation by crossover. Thus the two loci most frequently separated are those at the extreme ends of the chromosome, and having discovered these, it is possible to determine by crossover frequencies the map of the chromosome. Although detailed maps are available on a few organisms, not enough is known about linkage groups and crossover frequencies to be able to construct such a map for man.

Table 3–1 compares the effects of linkage with nonlinkage and shows that independent assortment assures a wide range of variation in the distribution of genotypes.

TABLE 3–1

COMPARISON OF THE EFFECTS OF LINKAGE AND INDEPENDENT ASSORTMENT.
LINKAGE RESTRICTS THE NUMBER OF DIFFERENT GENOTYPES.

Linkage
Mother

		AB	ab
Father	AB	AABB	AaBb
	ab	AaBb	aabb

Number of different genotypes = 3

AABB
AaBb
aabb

Independent Assortment
Mother

		AB	Ab	aB	ab
	AB	AABB	AABb	AaBB	AaBb
Father	Ab	AABb	AAbb	AaBb	Aabb
	aB	AaBB	AaBb	aaBB	aaBb
	ab	AaBb	Aabb	aaBb	aabb

Number of different genotypes = 9

AABB
AABb
AaBB
AaBb
AAbb
Aabb
aaBB
aaBb
aabb

Further Implications of Mendel's Laws

The validity of Mendel's laws also makes it possible to apply probability theory and combinatorial mathematics to genetic problems and to the formulation of genetic theory. This has contributed greatly to the rapid development of the field. To go into this point in detail would involve a long digression. Basically what is meant here is that advances in biological and behavioral sciences are restricted for the most part to inductive methods employing the technology of statistics. One advantage to the inductive approach is that any scientific investigation may begin with a hypothesis that two or more conditions or events are related in specific ways; for example, that the widths of tree rings are directly related to mean annual rainfall. This is a relationship that can be tested by appropriate experimental and analytical procedures which, in turn, should make it possible to draw either the conclusion that tree-ring width and mean annual rainfall are unrelated, or that they might be related. Inductive methods are, of course, essential in all sectors of science.

However, some relationships simply cannot be tested, some because of deficiencies in the instruments of science, some because the available statistical procedures are inadequate, and, more to the point when studying man, still others because we are unable to apply the appropriate experimental procedures. On occasion, however, it happens that the broad implications and general applicability of a discovery make it possible to advance directly on many investigative fronts at once with great speed. In these instances what is involved is the discovery of a basic or fundamental principle of nature. This is a comparatively rare event in science, but when it occurs, it makes possible the employment of more efficient methods of deduction in predicting the outcomes of specific experiments and in generating new theories to serve as guides for the formulation of new hypotheses. Mendel made this kind of discovery and thereby made possible the rapid formulation of genetic theory that has served to direct much of the work in experimental genetics which, in turn, produces a confirmation or modification of the theory. (An example of this can be seen in Table 3–2.)

TABLE 3–2

IMPLICATIONS OF MENDEL'S LAWS IN THE DISTRIBUTION OF GENOTYPES
AMONG OFFSPRING FROM ALL MATING TYPES

Parents Mating Types			Expected Percentages of Offspring Genotypes		
♂		♀	AA	Aa	aa
AA	×	AA	100		
AA	×	Aa	50	50	
AA	×	aa		100	
Aa	×	AA	50	50	
Aa	×	Aa	25	50	25
Aa	×	aa		50	50
aa	×	AA		100	
aa	×	Aa		50	50
aa	×	aa			100

From Mendel's laws alone if one is able to identify the genotypes of the parents, then one can predict the genotypes and their expected frequencies in the offspring. Moreover, the same relationships that hold within a family between parents and their children hold between one generation and the next in a population. That is, it is possible by a comparatively simple extension of the logic implied in Table 3–2 to construct a more generalized table summarizing the expected proportion of offspring genotypes that arise from a parental population of any determinable genetic structure. To extend the logic in this manner requires making some assumptions, but having made them allows the logical foundation for the branch of genetics known as population genetics (see page 85). At this juncture, the important point is that Table 3–2 can be constructed solely on the basis of Mendel's laws.

Meiosis and Mitosis

The physiological mechanism underlying Mendel's laws is *meiosis*, the process that produces sex cells. As far as genetics is concerned, the most important consequence of meiosis is that it results in cells that contain only one complete set of alleles. Since genes are located on chromosomes, this means that cells produced by meiosis contain only half the chromosome number that other cells have, the haploid number as compared with the diploid number. *Mitosis* is the cellular process that results in two cells identical to one another and to the parent cell that divided to produce them. All have the diploid number of chromosomes. The two processes are simplified in Figure 3–1. In human beings, meiosis produces cells with 23 chromosomes in the nucleus, and mitosis produces cells with 46.

Figure 3–1. Comparison of mitosis and meiosis of male germ cells. Meiosis of female cells differs in detail but not in principle.

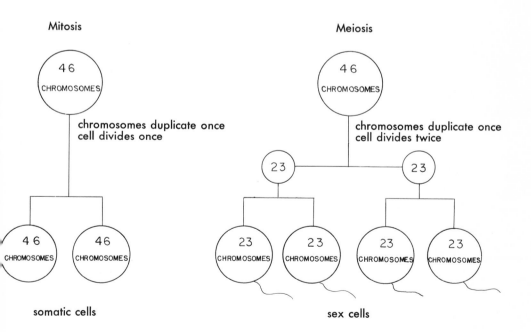

Karyotyping

In recent years, largely because of the rapid improvement in laboratory techniques and equipment, it has become possible to study chromosomes in great detail. Figure 3–2 is a photograph of the chromosomes of two human beings. Man's chromosomes have been classified into the conventional groups on the basis of their size and the position of the centromere. The photograph is an indication of how refined the cytological techniques have become, and it should not be mistaken as a rare one-of-a-kind picture. Such procedures, called karyotyping, are employed more and more frequently as aids in the diagnosis of certain kinds of disease. For example, mongolism, more properly called Down's syndrome, is associated with an extra chromosome in the G group.

In classifying human chromosomes, one encounters a clear and consistent difference between males and females. Figures 3–3 and 3–4 are karyotypes of a normal female and a normal male. The normal male has 15 chromosomes in the C group; the female has 16. The normal male has three chromosomes in the G group; the female has two. Thus both sexes have 23 pairs; 22 pairs are called autosomal chromosomes, and the pair differentiating males and females, sex chromosomes. The larger sex chromosome is called the X chromosome; females, of course, have two. Males

Figure 3–2. Metaphase plate showing the chromosome complement. Left: a normal human male. Right: a normal human female. (Courtesy David T. Arakaki, University of Hawaii.)

Figure 3–3. Karyotype of a normal human female. (Courtesy David T. Arakaki, University of Hawaii.)

have only one X chromosome and another, in the G group, called the Y chromosome. Thus it is the male that determines the sex of the offspring in man. Females contribute X and only X chromosomes; males contribute X or Y chromosomes.

Sex Chromosomes

Because of the way in which sex is determined in man, the traits controlled by genes located on the X and Y chromosomes are more readily

Figure 3–4. Karyotype of a normal human male. (Courtesy David T. Arakaki, University of Hawaii.)

recognized than traits inherited on the autosomes. Genes located on the Y chromosome, for example, may be found only in males. In fact, there are no well-documented Y-loci traits in man, and it may be that the entire chromosome functions only in producing the enzymes necessary for the production of male hormone, which, in turn, regulates the development of male sex characteristics.

The X chromosome bears genes that influence a number of characteristics in human beings that have nothing to do with sex. Genes inherited on the X chromosome are, however, called sex-linked genes and include such things as one form of color blindness, hemophilia, an enzyme deficiency in glucose-6-phosphate dehydrogenase, and a blood group gene, the Xg group. Because of their location on the X chromosome, these traits have a distribution that differs between males and females. Homozygous conditions on the sex chromosomes require two alleles in females, one in males (*hemizygous*). Heterozygous conditions cannot occur in males for sex-linked traits. Thus hemophilia, a homozygous condition determined by a rare allele, is much more common in males than females. Normal females who are heterozygous for hemophilia transmit the condition to half of their sons on a statistical basis.

Examination of human chromosomal material during interphase, the so-called resting period of mitosis, reveals another difference between males and females: females have a mass of chromatin material that may be observed to be balled up on the edge of the nucleus (see Figure 3–5). Males do not show this phenomenon. Although the significance of this difference is still a controversial subject, the most widely accepted theory is one proposed by Dr. Mary Lyon (1962) which specifies that in any cell, one and only one X chromosome is active and functional. Some support for this view comes from an investigation of nuclei with abnormal numbers of sex chromosomes. The number of X chromosomes identifiable

Barr body

Figure 3–5. Sex chromatin mass in a normal human female cell. (Courtesy David T. Arakaki, University of Hawaii.)

at metaphase is always one more than the number of sex chromatin bodies identifiable at interphase. Thus an XXY (Klinefelter's syndrome) individual is a male, a sterile one to be sure, and one whose cells show a sex chromatin body during interphase. Likewise XXX females have been identified, and they show two sex chromatin bodies.

Dominant and Recessive

Dominant and *recessive* are two terms with long histories of respectable use in genetics. The meanings of the two words are clear enough: dominant alleles are those expressed in both homozygous and heterozygous combinations, and recessive alleles are expressed only when paired together in a homozygote. In recent years, however, the need to use the terms has decreased as improved techniques have made it possible to distinguish heterozygotes from homozygotes in many cases where it was formerly impossible to do so. If the genotypes are distinguishable, then it would seem to be unnecessary to continue the dominant-recessive dichotomy. This is not to say that classic examples of dominants and recessives no longer exist; indeed they do, and it may never be possible to detect differences between heterozygotes and homozygotes for these loci. But if recent trends are indicative, we might hope that such distinctions will eventually be made.

Summary of Formal Genetics

The area of formal genetics was established first for the obvious reason that its principles underlie investigations in all other subdivisions. Essentially it specifies the ground rules of gene and chromosome behavior: 1) inheritance is by means of genes, 2) genes are situated on chromosomes, 3) chromosomes are paired in the nuclei of cells, a condition maintained by mitosis, 4) chromosome pairs segregate and assort independently in meiosis. Two such cells, one from a male and one from a female, when joined together re-pair the chromosomes and thereby initiate the development of a new individual.

In this manner formal genetics has established clearly a relationship between genes and traits in the phenotype, thus:

$$\text{ENVIRONMENT}$$
$$\text{Gene} \longrightarrow \text{Trait}$$

But a clearly established relationship is not the same as a clearly understood one. More questions have been generated by formal genetics than have been answered. Among the most penetrating of these are the following: What is the nature of the gene? How does a gene act to produce a trait in the phenotype? The search initiated by these problems has produced the most exciting and most consequential genetic discoveries of this century. These are the discoveries that have joined genetics, and thereby all of biology, to the well-established laws and highly developed theories of modern physics and chemistry. These developments are new, and their full impact is only now beginning to be felt.

MOLECULAR AND BIOCHEMICAL GENETICS

The Nature of the Gene

If one asks simply the question, What is a gene? there are several acceptable answers. The question of interest here, however, is more particular. It asks: What are the material elements that make up a gene, and how do they fit together? An obvious place to begin to investigate the molecular properties of the gene is within the nucleus of the cell—for two good reasons: 1) this is where the chromosomes are located, and 2) males and females contribute equally to the hereditary composition of their offspring, and equally in nuclear material but unequally in the non-nuclear components of the cell.

In the nucleus, one may find in abundance three kinds of molecules: water, protein, and nucleic acids. Water, as the element of heredity, is, of course, out of the question; its simple structure could not begin to account for the wide variety of gene effects. Nuclear proteins are large and complex molecules consisting of long sequences of amino acids capable of being varied in almost endless ways and were, for this reason, considered for a time as the hereditary material. However, experimental evidence eventually eliminated nuclear proteins from consideration, and, in the process, focused attention on the nucleic acids.

Genetic Transformation

The foundation for the conclusion that the nucleic acid material is the genetic material was laid down in 1928 as the outcome of an experiment demonstrating genetic transformation. The classic transformation experiment involves two strains of *Pneumococcus*, the bacterium that can cause pneumonia. These strains differ in appearance and effect. One, the smooth strain, is encapsulated in a shell composed of sugar molecules joined together to form a polysaccharide. This is the virulent strain. The other, the rough strain, lacks both the polysaccharide capsule and the virulence. The experiment performed by F. Griffith (1928) involved the inoculation of mice with a mixture of living rough and dead smooth *Pneumococcus* bacteria. One might expect little effect on the mice, since the rough strain is not virulent and the smooth strain injected consisted only of dead cells. Surprisingly, however, many of the mice died of pneumonia, and, in addition, examination of the blood of the mice revealed the presence of living smooth as well as living rough bacteria. Some of the rough bacteria had apparently become *transformed* into smooth *Pneumococci*. Moreover, the transformed smooth strain, when allowed to divide and proliferate, produced smooth type daughter cells, indicating clearly that the transformation was a genetic one.

Refinements in techniques eventually made it possible to demonstrate transformation in the test tube, and this, in turn, meant that greater precision and control could be introduced into the experiment. The components could be tried one at a time or in all possible combinations, and, by this means, it was discovered that only a part of the smooth bacteria was required to bring about the transformation. The part required was identified as the nucleic acid, deoxyribonucleic acid, or DNA (see Hershey and Chase, 1952).

At this point it is possible to answer the question, What is a gene? in a more satisfactory way. A gene is presumably some part of DNA. This raises another obvious question: What is DNA?

DNA

DNA is made up of carbon, hydrogen, nitrogen, oxygen, and phosphorus. These elements are joined together in various ways to form purine, pyrimidine, deoxyribose, and phosphate molecules. Two kinds of purines, adenine and guanine, and two kinds of pyrimidines, cytosine and thymine, are found in DNA. Phosphorus occurs only in the composition of a phosphate ion that is invariable in its structure and always found to be a part of the DNA substance. Likewise, deoxyribose is always a part of DNA and is the five-carbon sugar that gives the substance its name. The chemical structure of all of these components is illustrated in Figure 3–6. The basic unit that these components join together to form is called a *nucleotide*, which consists of one phosphate group joined to one molecule of deoxyribose, which, in turn, is joined with either one purine or one pyrimidine. Since there are two purines and two pyrimidines, there are then four possible nucleotides, and these are illustrated in Figure 3–7. Nucleotides are themselves joined together in pairs by weak bonds known as hydrogen bonds. In DNA, nucleotide pairs always join together one purine and one pyrimidine; more precisely, the pairs always consist of adenine joined together with thymine, or guanine joined to cytosine. These pairs are illustrated in Figure 3–8. The DNA molecule consists of a long chain of these nucleotide pairs joined together on both sides at the phosphate group. A section of the DNA molecule is illustrated in Figure 3–9.

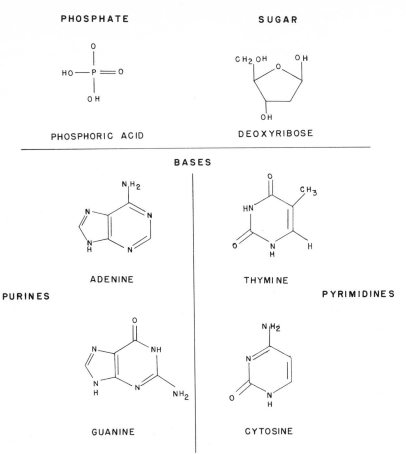

Figure 3–6. The chemical structure of the components of a DNA molecule.

Figure 3–7. The four nucleotides in DNA.

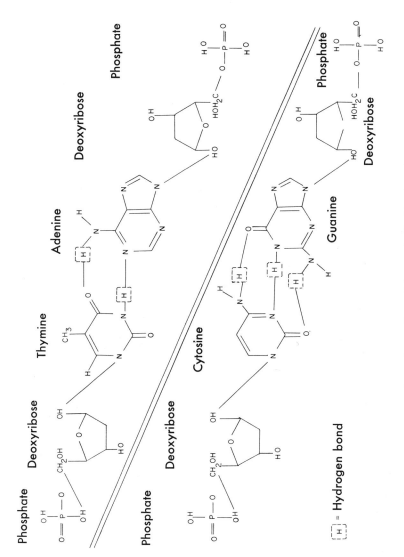

Figure 3–8. Comparison of the two kinds of nucleotide pairs.

Figure 3–9. Sequence of two nucleotide pairs.

Most of these advances are recent and have been the result of X-ray diffraction studies and chemical analyses of the composition of DNA which were initiated by the transformation experiments. These different lines of investigation were brought together by J. D. Watson, F. H. C. Crick, and M. H. F. Wilkins, who were awarded a Nobel Prize for their work. In their view, which is the generally accepted view, the DNA molecule is not simply a flat chain of polynucleotide pairs, but rather a doubly-coiled helix (see Figure 3–13 on page 78).

This helps to improve our understanding of the composition of DNA, but it does not further an understanding of the nature of the gene. If asked the question, What is a gene? at this point, we would still have to answer that it is some part of DNA. We would indeed be able to say something about DNA, but nothing more about the gene. Is a gene a nucleotide? This is unlikely on logical grounds alone, since there are only four different nucleotides, and genes can reasonably be expected to have considerably greater variation than this provides. For the same reason, a gene is not likely to be equivalent to a nucleotide pair since, even with reciprocals, there are only four different pairs:

Adenine - Thymine
Thymine - Adenine
Guanine - Cytosine
Cytosine - Guanine

Moreover, the DNA (or some part of it) must be able to duplicate, to allow for the implicit requirements of mitosis, and, in addition, to segregate in meiosis and assort independently in hereditary transmission. Our understanding of the details of these processes has been greatly improved by research into the question of what a gene does, or, more broadly, how a gene functions. We know that a gene can influence the phenotype, but how does it manage to exert its influence?

The Function of a Gene

Some of the earliest information about gene function was obtained from studies on human beings. Two hereditary conditions pointing to the same general conclusion about the function of a gene are alcaptonuria and phenylketonuria. These are both rare inherited diseases. The striking symptom of alcaptonuria is that the urine of a person with the disease turns black on exposure to air. This is a consequence of the fact that alcaptonurics have in their urine an unusual substance, homogentisic acid, which normal persons lack. The presence of homogentisic acid in the urine indicates a simple metabolic defect in which affected persons lack the enzyme needed to convert homogentisic acid to acetoacetic acid, the latter a compound commonly found in the urine of normal persons.

Thus it would appear that the genetic difference between normal persons and those with alcaptonuria is nothing more than the presence of an enzyme in the former that is absent in the latter.

The condition known as phenylketonuria (PKU) has been given much attention recently and points to a similar flaw. In this case, normal persons possess an enzyme that converts phenylalanine to tyrosine. Persons lacking the enzyme build up excessive amounts of phenylalanine in their bloodstream and excrete in their urine a by-product of phenylalanine known as phenylpyruvic acid. Normal persons do not excrete this substance. In the case of PKU, the associated symptoms are more severe than in that of alcaptonuria. Phenylketonurics are always mentally deficient, and they tend to have light skin color and blond hair. The condition, if detected sufficiently early, can be ameliorated by feeding the affected person a diet low in phenylalanine.

The significant observation in regard to phenylketonuria for the present discussion is that, like alcaptonuria, the inherited condition again corresponds with the absence of a specific enzyme. This is the same conclusion reached in the more completely controlled investigations of one of the organisms responsible for bread mold, *Neurospora*. This organism has several characteristics which make it a particularly useful one for genetic studies, but without going into them we may simply observe that several strains of *Neurospora* have been produced by means of radiation-induced mutations, and many of the strains are unable to complete their normal metabolic activities due to the lack of specific and identifiable enzymes. The work on *Neurospora* indicated too that a one-to-one relationship exists between a gene and an enzyme; or, more broadly, that the life process may be thought of as an orderly steplike sequence of physical-chemical events with each step controlled by a specific enzyme which, in turn, is produced by a particular gene (see Beadle and Tatum, 1941). These indications have subsequently been confirmed on several other organisms, and the conclusion is now widely accepted that genes apparently function by controlling the reactions carried out by living organisms in converting their food resources to the substances required to carry out the life processes. Although it has had to be revised slightly, the accumulation of evidence led to the one-gene-one-enzyme hypothesis, or, in other words, that for every enzyme there is one gene controlling its synthesis.

These experiments provide an empirical basis for answering the question, What is a gene? in a more detailed way than we have been able to do up to now. It is reasonable at this point to say that a gene is some part of DNA that controls the manufacture of a particular enzyme. As before, the definition raises additional questions, and among them the very pertinent one: How does this occur? To understand the answer that is now generally accepted concerning the way that genes make enzymes requires a consideration of an even more basic question: What is an enzyme?

Enzymes and Other Proteins.   First of all, an enzyme is a protein. Enzymes function by regulating the sequence and rate of chemical reactions. They are basic to the occurrence of any biological reaction. Enzymes are, however, only one of two kinds of protein. The other kind is called structural protein, which may be found in the structure of cell walls, connective tissue, muscle, hemoglobin, collagen, etc. The differences between enzymes and structural proteins are essentially functional. Structurally they are made up of the same kinds of molecules organized in the same general ways. These structural similarities suggest the broader possibility that genes function to make proteins, and, as the evidence has accumulated, this view has replaced the narrower one-gene-one-enzyme hypothesis. Thus, the broader question of what a protein is should be discussed before returning to the problem of how genes manufacture them.

Hemoglobin.   Figure 3–10 is an illustration of a model of the structure of hemoglobin, a structural protein. As the illustration clearly shows, proteins are too complex to be described directly. It is necessary to take them apart and put them back together again before one can have a detailed understanding of their structure. The first impression that one is likely to get on looking at Figure 3–10 is that the surface contour of the molecule is highly twisted and folded back on itself. This particular corrugated form is characteristic of all hemoglobin molecules. Proteins have their own distinctive shapes, which are presumed to be responsible, to a large extent, for the specific properties of the protein. That is to say that in the case of hemoglobin, all normal hemoglobin molecules are believed to have the same surface configurations and thus the same amount and kind of elec-

Figure 3–10. Model of a molecule of horse hemoglobin. (From V. M. Ingram, *The Hemoglobins in Genetics and Evolution*, copyright 1963, by permission of Columbia University Press.)

trical charges on the exposed surfaces, which, in turn, are responsible for the particular physical-chemical properties of hemoglobin.

The pattern of electrical charges present on the surface of the molecule is controlled, however, by more than simply the gross configuration of the structure. Clearly the components that make up the macro-molecule are also involved. On opening up the hemoglobin molecule, it would be possible to note that the surface structure is fixed by molecular linkages that join together the long chains that make up most of the hemoglobin material. On breaking these linkages (and ignoring their composition), however, the hemoglobin molecule may be seen to be made up of four chains—not just one long one as might be expected. Spectacular refinements which have been made in laboratory procedures in the last few years make it possible to examine the composition of these chains. Applying these procedures and thus looking even more deeply into the structure of hemoglobin, one can see that the four chains are, in fact, two pairs of twin chains, a pair of alpha and a pair of beta chains. Examination of these chains, one at a time, would reveal that each chain is itself twisted helically and that the molecules that make up a chain are amino acids. All

Figure 3–11. Common core to amino acid structure and the distinctive side chain for each amino acid.

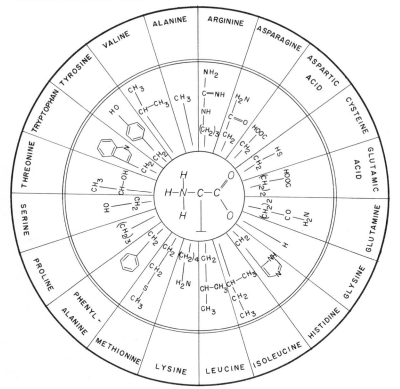

amino acids share a common molecular core. There are twenty different kinds of amino acids, and each one adds a distinctive molecular configuration to the common core (see Figure 3–11). Amino acids are joined together by strong bonds known as peptide bonds, and because of this, chains of amino acids are referred to as *polypeptide chains*.

Thus, hemoglobin is made up of two pairs of polypeptide chains. An alpha chain consists of 141 amino acids; a beta chain of 146. Moreover, the sequence is identical in all normal human hemoglobin; it is always as it is shown in Figure 3–12. Hemoglobin is, of course, but one of many kinds of proteins; not all are made up of four polypeptide chains—some have only one chain, others more than four. All proteins, however, are basically constructed of amino acids joined together by peptide bonds. Each chain is itself twisted helically and, finally, folded into a distinctive surface configuration.

It has become clear, in recent years, that genes function directly to regulate the construction of polypeptide chains. How the chains get together to form the larger macro-molecule remains unclear. It is, however, certain that the earlier one-gene-one-enzyme hypothesis must be generalized not simply to one-gene-one-protein, but even more broadly to one-gene-one-polypeptide chain. This implies a modification of our answer to the question of what a gene is: at this point it is obviously more correct to answer that a gene is some part of DNA that controls the manufacture of a particular polypeptide chain. Thus the relationship established earlier should be modified to:

ENVIRONMENT
Gene ———⟶— Polypeptide Chain ———⟶— Trait

This draws our attention to the next problem: How is it that genes make polypeptide chains?

Replication.   Genes have two functions: 1) they duplicate themselves, and 2) they regulate the construction of polypeptide chains. As noted earlier, Watson and Crick (1953) proposed the generally accepted theory of the structure of DNA. They also put forth an explanation for the way in which DNA copies itself as required in the normal processes of mitosis and meiosis. They proposed that the complementary strands of a molecule of DNA come apart at their hydrogen bond joints, and each strand then acts as an assembly line for the construction of two DNA molecules identical to one another and to the original sequence of nucleotide pairs. Thus any pair of nucleotides, for example adenine-thymine, separate at the hydrogen bond sites that normally join them together in the intact DNA molecule. On the one strand, adenine will "accept" thymine and

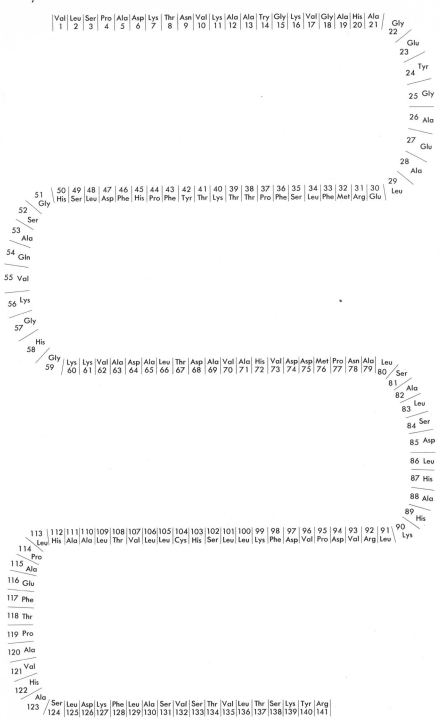

Figure 3–12 (A). Sequence of amino acids in the alpha chain of normal hemoglobin.

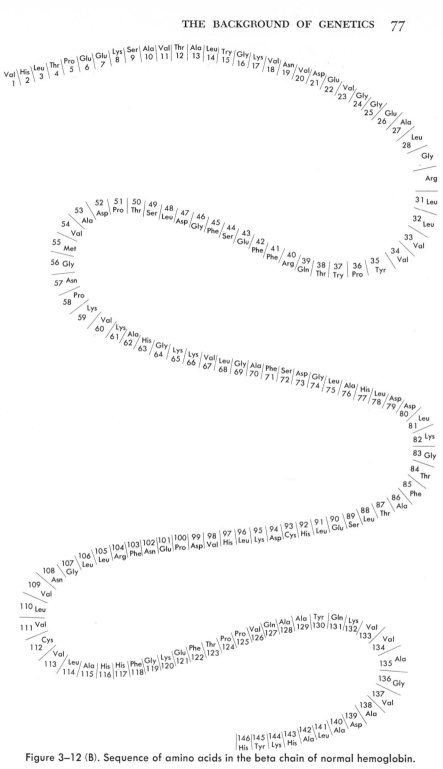

Figure 3–12 (B). Sequence of amino acids in the beta chain of normal hemoglobin.

only thymine from among the free nucleotides available as metabolic by-products in the nuclear environment; whereas, on the other, the thymine-bearing nucleotide will "accept" only adenine. This highly selective process, continuing the entire length of both sides of a DNA chain, results in two identical DNA chains, as illustrated in Figure 3–13. A number of experiments conducted since the original proposal have tested the validity of this theory, and all have reached conclusions that support this view of DNA replication.

Figure 3–13. DNA replication.

DNA coiled helix   a. paired nucleotides

DNA undergoing replication   b. nucleotides separate and additional bases are positioned

Identical DNA sections   c. replication complete

In explaining how DNA controls the construction of a polypeptide chain, the first obstacle is essentially a spatial one; protein synthesis has long been known to occur in the cytoplasm in particles known as ribosomes, whereas DNA is located in the cell nucleus and is walled off from the cytoplasm by the nuclear membrane. The obvious question then is: How is it that the DNA in the nucleus can influence the manufacture of proteins in the cytoplasm?

RNA

Some insight has been obtained into the structure of DNA and the manner in which it replicates itself, but until now no attention has been given in this chapter to the multitude of reactions known to occur outside the nucleus. Since it is known that ribosomes are the sites of protein synthesis, and this is the process under investigation, they would seem to be reasonable places to begin. Ribosomes themselves are made up of two major molecular components: 1) protein, and 2) a polynucleotide chain remarkably similar, but not identical, to DNA. The protein part can be ignored, since it is the synthesis of protein that is the interesting question. The nucleotides of the ribosomal chain consist of components like those in a chain of DNA: a phosphoric acid molecule, a distinctive sugar known as ribose, and one purine or pyrimidine. The purines are identical to those found in DNA: adenine and guanine. The pyrimidines include cytosine, but, instead of thymine, the ribosomal polynucleotide chains contain the pyrimidine uracil. These and other attributes to be considered presently clearly distinguish this polynucleotide chain from DNA, and, drawing largely on the sugar molecule again for its name, this kind of chain is called ribonucleic acid, or RNA. Figure 3–14 compares a thymine nucleotide of DNA with a uracil nucleotide of RNA; note the differences between deoxyribose and ribose, and between thymine and uracil.

RNA may be found elsewhere in the cytoplasm. This soluble or transfer RNA (sRNA or tRNA) is identical to ribosomal RNA in its basic components. The soluble RNA consists of short polynucleotide chains with specific functions to be discussed presently. The important observation at this point, however, is the clue provided by yet a third form of RNA that may be found in *both* the nucleus and the cytoplasm. This particular kind of RNA is distinctive in that it is able to pass freely through the nuclear membrane and thus to act as the vehicle by which the genetic information is taken into the cytoplasm. This third kind of RNA is thus referred to as *messenger RNA.*

Together DNA and the three forms of RNA constitute the basic tools the cell employs in making a protein. The entire process is not as yet

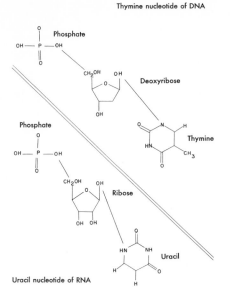

Figure 3–14. Comparison of a thymine nucleotide of DNA with a uracil nucleotide of RNA.

entirely clear, but the major sequence seems well established. DNA makes messenger RNA in a manner strikingly similar to that it employs in replicating itself. The messenger RNA breaks off in short strands, and each of these may well correspond to a gene, but in any event it should be emphasized that a strand of messenger RNA is the exact complement of the DNA template on which it is formed, just as in DNA replication. The two processes are distinguished by the substitution of ribose for deoxyribose and of uracil for thymine in the synthesis of messenger RNA. Also, unlike DNA, messenger RNA is a single chain of nucleotides. It is not a sequence of paired nucleotides.

These small strands of messenger RNA enter the cytoplasm, where they become the sites of attachment for one or more ribosomes. Ribosomes are generalized in a sense; any ribosome is able to attach to any strand of messenger RNA and carry out its function. Ribosomes act rather like the magnetic head of a tape recorder. They "sense" the nucleotide sequence "pulses" of the messenger RNA and provide the location for their translation into a polypeptide chain. The process of building up a sequence of amino acids requires the resolution of both a selection problem and an activation problem. That is, at the ribosome, the appropriate particular amino acid must be called into position and must be joined to the segment already formed. The selection of appropriate amino acid is made on the basis of the ribosome's "sensing" of the messenger RNA polynucleotide chain, itself a transcription of DNA. The positioning and joining together of the amino acid is taken care of by soluble RNA. There are twenty different kinds of soluble RNA, each constructed so that it is able to attach to one and only one kind of amino acid. Amino acids get into the cytoplasm as the by-products of an organism's food. They enter the cell simply as free amino acids. Any particular kind of soluble RNA attaches to its specific amino acid, and in doing so, the amino acid becomes activated for its role in the biosynthesis of a polypeptide chain and is provided with the energy needed to play this role. The activation process is known in some detail, but will not be considered here.

Thus it is that DNA makes messenger RNA, which enters the cytoplasm. Ribosomes interpret the genetic instructions of the messenger RNA and call for a particular sequence of amino acids attached to activated transfer RNA molecules. The amino acids are set into place and joined together at the ribosome, which moves the entire length of the messenger RNA strand, thereby producing a complete polypeptide chain. The entire process is illustrated in Figure 3–15.

Genetic Code

Reference was made previously to ribosomal RNA acting in a manner similar to that of a tape recorder head sensing the impulses provided by the messenger RNA as transcribed directly from the DNA in the nucleus. In this analogy, it is clear that DNA may be thought of as a set of instructions coded in the sequence of purines and pyrimidines and specifying thereby the sequence of amino acids to be joined together to form a polypeptide chain. Looking at it in this way, it then becomes a logical step to inquire into the nature of the code; that is to say, how does DNA code for a particular amino acid? Some progress in solving this problem can be made on logical grounds alone. A coding unit of DNA, that is a codon, necessarily consists of more than one nucleotide, since there are only four nucleotides, and, obviously, four different things taken one at a time cannot code for twenty different amino acids. Likewise nucleotide pairs are insufficient, since four different things can make only sixteen different pairs. Thus, on logical grounds alone, the minimum number of nucleotides has to be three. However, four different nucleotides can be arranged into sixty-four triplet sequences, and, as noted, there are only twenty amino acids. At this point logic alone cannot advance our understanding much further. We need more information. For example, are some triplet sequences redundant? That is, does more than one triplet code specify the same amino acid? Are some triplets meaningless? Or does DNA contain codes for other kinds of information? These are questions that can be answered only by experimentation.

The genetic code has been cracked, and the extraordinary work that broke it was made possible largely because of refinements in the techniques of analyzing the contents of living cells outside of the cells.

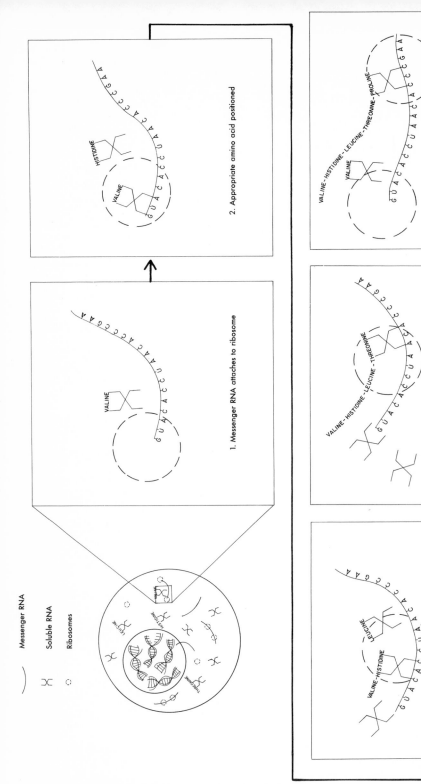

Figure 3–15. Steps involved in the synthesis of a polypeptide chain. The illustration shows the positioning of the first five amino acids in the beta chain of human hemoglobin.

The basic ingredients of these cell-free studies of the genetic code are messenger RNA, transfer RNA, ribosomes, amino acids, and enzymes. These may be obtained by using gentle techniques that destroy cell walls without damaging cellular contents. In a cell-free environment, the normal process of protein synthesis stops very quickly because messenger RNA is rapidly used up and there is no DNA to produce new strands of it. It is, however, possible to synthesize messenger RNA artificially with known purine-pyrimidine sequences, and this synthetic RNA can be introduced into the cell-free medium to act as messenger RNA. The earliest experiment of this kind introduced synthetic messenger RNA consisting entirely of uracil nucleotides; it was found to stimulate the production of a polyphenylalanine chain. Presuming that the genetic code consists of triplet sequences, then, by implication, the messenger RNA codon for phenylalanine is U — U — U, and, extending the implications even further, the DNA codon for phenylalanine is A — A — A. Subsequently, it has been determined that adding synthetic messenger RNA consisting of adenine nucleotides made only polylysine; that with only guanine produced polyglycine; and, finally, strands of only cytosine nucleotides of RNA, when added to the cell-free medium, resulted in the amino acid polyproline chains.

Eventually messenger RNA was synthesized in various triplet combinations, and today the genetic code is known in detail, as shown in Table 3–3. An examination of the table reveals that the code is redundant; that is, more than one triplet may code for the same amino acid. Likewise it may be seen that two triplets (U — A — A and U — A — G) code for no amino acid. These "nonsense" triplets appear to be the genetic equivalent of a period in punctuation. They terminate the synthesis of messenger RNA on the DNA template. At this point, if one were so inclined, he could turn to Table 3–3 and, with a knowledge of the genetic code, infer the precise sequence of purines and pyrimidines in the messenger RNA that makes the beta chain of human hemoglobin.

Summary of Molecular and Biochemical Genetics

This section began with the broad question of the nature of the gene and subsequently considered the more specific questions of what the physical components of the genetic material are. How do they fit together? How do they work? In reviewing the evidence that has accumulated and the conclusions that have been drawn in regard to these questions, molecular biology and biochemistry have yielded answers in such detail that to even hope for such things twenty-five years ago would have been presumptuous. We have touched here only on the highlights and indeed not all of them, but a summary of these would now seem to be in order. 1) DNA is the genetic material. 2) DNA consists of a long, helically

TABLE 3–3

THE GENETIC CODE

Amino Acid	MRNA Triplet Code*			Amino Acid	MRNA Triplet Code*		
	1st	2nd	3rd		1st	2nd	3rd
1. Alanine (Ala)				12. Lysine (Lys)			
	G	C	C		A	A	A
	G	C	U		A	A	G
	G	C	A	13. Methionine (Met)			
	G	C	G		A	U	A
2. Argenine (Arg)					A	U	G
	C	G	C	14. Phenylalanine (Phe)			
	C	G	U		U	U	U
	C	G	A		U	U	C
	C	G	G	15. Proline (Pro)			
	A	G	A		C	C	C
	A	G	G		C	C	U
3. Asparagine (Asp-NH₂)					C	C	A
	A	A	U		C	C	G
	A	A	C	16. Serine (Ser)			
4. Aspartic Acid (Asp)					U	C	C
	G	A	U		U	C	U
	G	A	C		U	C	A
5. Cysteine (Cys)					U	C	G
	U	G	U		A	G	U
	U	G	C		A	G	C
6. Glutamic Acid (Glu)				17. Threonine (Thr)			
	G	A	A		A	C	C
	G	A	G		A	C	U
7. Glutamine (Glu-NH₂)					A	C	A
	C	A	A		A	C	G
	C	A	G	18. Tryptophan (Try)			
8. Glycine (Gly)					U	G	A
	G	G	C		U	G	G
	G	G	U	19. Tyrosine (Tyr)			
	G	G	A		U	A	C
	G	G	G		U	A	U
9. Histidine (His)				20. Valine (Val)			
	C	A	C		G	U	C
	C	A	U		G	U	U
10. Isoleucine (Ileu)					G	U	A
	A	U	C		G	U	G
	A	U	U	no amino acid			
11. Leucine (Leu)					U	A	A
	U	U	A		U	A	G
	U	U	G				
	C	U	U				
	C	U	C				
	C	U	A				
	C	U	G				

* G = Guanine, C = Cytosine, U = Uracil, and A = Adenine.

coiled chain of paired nucleotides. 3) The paired nucleotides separate in the process of DNA replication, and the two surfaces thus exposed serve as templates for the construction of two identical chains, thereby fulfilling the implicit structural requirements of mitosis. 4) DNA specifies the sequence of amino acids in the biosynthesis of polypeptide chains, which, in turn, constitute the primary components of proteins. To accomplish this function, DNA makes messenger RNA, which, when it passes into the cytoplasm, directs the activity of soluble RNA at the cellular sites of protein synthesis, the ribosomes. 5) The specifications of DNA are coded in triplet sequences of nucleotides. The messenger RNA triplet sequences that specify particular amino acids form the genetic code.

A consideration of the elements of formal genetics led to the realization that the laws of heredity apply to all living things. In a like manner, at the molecular and biochemical levels of organization, the life process for all organisms consists of a complicated series of chemical reactions driven and replenished by the available food resources and controlled and directed by enzymes. Not all organisms have been studied, of course, but from those that have, it is becoming increasingly clear that this is true for all, from the simplest to the most complex.

This brief survey of advances in molecular and biochemical genetics should make it clear that whenever a limit is reached in our ability to extend our knowledge further by means of logic, then it becomes essential to obtain new information. In these areas and in formal genetics, the acquisition of new information usually implies experimentation. But physical anthropology has its primary interest in man, and clearly man is not amenable to experimentation. How can the science of genetics be applied to improving our understanding of human evolution and human variation? This is the question of particular interest to physical anthropologists. Or, conversely, how may human beings be studied to inform us further about genetics? This is the question of greatest interest to human geneticists. Population genetics has been the most informative area in both of these problems and thus serves as a common ground of interest for both human genetics and physical anthropology.

POPULATION GENETICS

Experimental and Natural Populations

Populations in nature differ from experimental populations in two fundamental ways as far as the study of genetics is concerned. In natural populations: 1) the distribution of genes and genotypes, the genetic structure, is not known, and 2) the system of mating is not controlled. Population genetics is concerned with the determination of the genetic structure of natural populations and the factors that maintain or alter their genetic structure.

Hardy–Weinberg Law of Equilibrium

Fundamental to the genetic investigation of natural populations is the realization that, given certain assumptions, the proportions of genotypes will remain constant from generation to generation. Shortly after the rediscovery of Mendel's work in 1900, a notion began to formulate which carried with it the implication that dominant genes must, over time, become more and more abundant and eventually swamp out of existence their respective recessive alleles. This notion, known as *genophagy,* was erroneous, and was shown to be incorrect in 1908 by two persons working independently, Hardy,* a British mathematician, and Weinberg, a German physician. Their discovery resulted from applying probability rules to aspects of Mendel's laws, and in the process, they formulated what has come to be known as the Hardy–Weinberg law of genetic equilibrium. The law specifies that, contrary to the notion of genophagy, the frequencies of the genes and proportion of genotypes will reach and remain at a stable equilibrium level after one generation of random mating in a population. This may be illustrated by returning to Table 3–2 on page 60. Consider the table to represent an idealized population that just happens to marry in the nine different ways shown in the table. First, it may be seen that among the parents, the alleles *A* and *a* occur with equal frequency, and, since there are only two alleles, their frequencies must total unity. Thus, in this case, if p equals the frequency of *A*, and q equals the frequency of *a*, then $p = .50$ and $q = .50$ and $p + q = 1$. Or, more generally, to cover all cases, $p = $ the total number of *AA* persons plus one-half the *Aa* persons and this total divided by the total number in the sample. Thus:

$$p = \frac{AA + Aa/2}{AA + Aa + aa} \quad \text{and} \quad q = \frac{aa + Aa/2}{AA + Aa + aa}$$

Now according to the implications of genophagy, one would anticipate an increase of dominants (in this case A-bearing genotypes) among their offspring. If, however, each marriage produces four children, then, by Mendel's laws, we would expect the offspring to be distributed as shown in Table 3–4. If one compares the distribution of alleles among the parents with that found among the children, it is apparent that the frequencies have not changed; thus for both generations:

$$p = .50$$
$$q = .50$$
$$p + q = 1$$

But what about the genotypes? Among the parents one-third are *AA*, one-third are *Aa*, and one-third are *aa;* whereas among the children, one-

---

* For an informative exchange on this see the comments of Mr. Udny Yule (1908) and the reply by G. H. Hardy (1908).

quarter are *AA*, one-half are *Aa,* and one-quarter are *aa*. What happens in subsequent generations? Hardy and Weinberg were able to demonstrate that no matter what the original values of p and q, the genotypes in a randomly-mating population will remain in the ratio of p^2 (*AA*) to $2pq$ (*Aa*) to q^2 (*aa*). Thus, in this instance, if the assumptions required by the Hardy–Weinberg law are applicable, the next generation of genotypes and all subsequent generations can be expected to remain in the proportion of 25 percent *AA*, 50 percent *Aa,* and 25 percent *aa*. For this genetic locus under these conditions the population is said to be in genetic equilibrium.

TABLE 3–4

DISTRIBUTION OF OFFSPRING GENOTYPES ASSUMING
FOUR OFFSPRING PER MATING TYPE

Mating Type			Offspring Genotypes		
♂		♀	*AA*	*Aa*	*aa*
AA	×	*AA*	4		
AA	×	*Aa*	2	2	
AA	×	*aa*		4	
Aa	×	*AA*	2	2	
Aa	×	*Aa*	1	2	1
Aa	×	*aa*		2	2
aa	×	*AA*		4	
aa	×	*Aa*		2	2
aa	×	*aa*			4
	Total		9	18	9

Random and Nonrandom Mating

The requirement of random mating has been mentioned as a condition necessary for the equilibrium specified by the Hardy–Weinberg law. This is but one of several factors that are needed to fulfill completely the logical and mathematical requirements of the law. Before presenting a definition of random mating, it might be helpful to provide a few illustrations of nonrandom mating and the consequences on the proportions of genotypes. Consider, for example, a population that permitted only marriages between persons who are alike in some biological respects. Although less rigidly defined, such a mating system exists in our own society wherein people of the same race tend to marry. Moreover, even within a race, people tend to marry others like themselves with respect to stature, intelligence, and certain personality characteristics. To illustrate the effect of this kind of nonrandom mating, it will be useful if we remain with the more clearly stated case where alikes and only alikes are allowed to marry, and, furthermore, where "alike" is defined in terms of genotypes. Then we may return to the situation considered in Table 3–4. In a population such

as this, mating under the nonrandom system, wherein only persons genotypically alike for this locus are allowed to marry, there could be only
three kinds of marriage. Presuming that each type yields four offspring,
the expected genotype proportions are shown in Table 3–5.

TABLE 3–5

EXPECTED DISTRIBUTION OF OFFSPRING GENOTYPES UNDER
COMPLETE POSITIVE ASSORTATIVE MATING

| Mating Type | | Offspring Genotypes | | |
♂	♀	*AA*	*Aa*	*aa*
AA × *AA*		4		
Aa × *Aa*		1	2	1
aa × *aa*				4
Total		5	2	5

This form of nonrandom mating is referred to as positive assortative
mating, and it may be seen from the table that its effect on the distribution
of genotypes in the offspring generation is to increase the proportion of
homozygous genotypes, and thus, correspondingly, to decrease the proportion of heterozygotes. Making analogous assumptions, the reverse system
of mating, negative assortative mating, wherein persons genotypically
alike are forbidden to marry, is illustrated in Table 3–6. Negative assorta-

TABLE 3–6

EXPECTED DISTRIBUTION OF OFFSPRING GENOTYPES UNDER
COMPLETE NEGATIVE ASSORTATIVE MATING

| Mating Type | | Offspring Genotypes | | |
♂	♀	*AA*	*Aa*	*aa*
AA × *Aa*		2	2	
AA × *aa*			4	
Aa × *AA*		2	2	
Aa × *aa*			2	2
aa × *AA*			4	
aa × *Aa*			2	2
Total		4	16	4

tive mating results in a higher proportion of heterozygotes and thus a
lower proportion of homozygotes than expected under genetic equilibrium.

The illustrations are extreme as far as human populations are concerned.
To the extent that assortative mating occurs in man, it is in the form of a
tendency for likes to marry or a *tendency* for likes to avoid one another.
If, however, these tendencies involve inherited traits, the effect is the
same: positive assortative mating distorts equilibrium expectations by

increasing the proportion of homozygotes, negative assortative mating by increasing the proportion of heterozygotes.

Another form of nonrandom mating of particular interest to physical anthropologists is inbreeding, wherein biological relatives are more likely to marry one another. In many human societies, the preferred marriage is between cousins, and for this reason there is a substantially higher frequency of marriages between related persons than expected by chance. Since related persons share a much closer common ancestry than unrelated or distantly related persons, they are more frequently alike in genetic characteristics; thus the effect of inbreeding is the same as positive assortative mating: homozygosity increases. Outbreeding, where relatives are forbidden to marry, is similar in effect to negative assortative mating.

Perhaps the phenomenon of random mating is clearer now. It is the lack of any systematic tendency in the mate selection process within a population. A population is mating at random with respect to any particular trait if individuals select mates independently of their having or not having that trait. Any departure from random mating upsets the equilibrium distribution of genotypes specified by the Hardy–Weinberg law; a single generation of random mating will, however, restore the equilibrium. In effect what Hardy and Weinberg showed was that the genetic structure of populations will not change unless some force causes them to change. Thus, in an evolutionary sense, a population at rest will remain at rest. In this way, the natural population may be seen as a unit with evolutionary integration, as a unit with biological significance. This might well have been demonstrable by other means, but the Hardy–Weinberg law yields the logical basis for joining these properties to the laws of formal genetics and thereby enables the further investigation of the genetics of natural groups. From the point of view of physical anthropology, this raises the interesting question of identifying the forces, other than nonrandom mating, that can cause changes in the genetic structures of populations and the exciting prospect of answering such a question by means of the study of human groups. As noted earlier, the entire evolutionary process may be regarded as the accumulation of changes in the genetic structure of populations, and with this as a definition, it is reasonable to refer to the forces that cause these changes as mechanisms of evolution. They occupy a position of central importance in population genetics.

Mechanisms of Evolution

Understanding the process of evolution as it affects natural populations requires an appreciation of the following: 1) the genetic structure of natural populations consists of alleles in varying frequencies joined together in genotypic pairs, in short, of genes and genotypes; 2) the composition of the genetic structure remains constant until something causes it to change; 3) such changes are the very essence of evolution; and 4) any agency able to bring about such changes is thereby a mechanism of evolution. In addition to nonrandom mating as a source of change, evolutionary mechanisms that have been identified include: natural selection, mutation, genetic drift, gene flow, and meiotic drive.

Natural Selection. In Chapter 1, natural selection was identified as the first known mechanism of evolution, described and detailed by Darwin over one hundred years ago. It will be recalled that the view of selection presented by Darwin may be thought of as a continuously fluctuating environmental template, the form of which at any given time determines the outline of variation in living species. Within any species, individuals with attributes that do not fit the contours of the template leave fewer offspring than those that do. The product of this process is a gradual streamlining of the species' variation to conform to the requirements of selection. Thus from the standpoint of selection, the only measure of fitness within a species is the number of offspring produced which, in turn, go on to reproduce subsequent generations.

This is a view that can be understood directly on a population level. It provides an explanation for the origin of species by means of natural selection. It is, however, a view that focuses on broad generational changes, and, as our knowledge of genetics has grown, our understanding of selection has become more refined. The specific question of interest at this point is: How does natural selection affect the genetic structure of populations? Darwin provided a general answer; modern population genetics offers more detail.

Consider again A and a as an illustration. If the following assumptions are made: a) that the population is mating at random for this locus, and b) that at the outset each allele is equally frequent, then we see that:

$$p = .50 \qquad q = .50$$
$$AA(p^2) = .25 \qquad Aa(2pq) = .50 \qquad aa(q^2) = .25$$

In this way the genetic structure of the population is known. Moreover, the frequency of each type of marriage may be determined by a simple application of the probability rule: the rate of occurrence of a compound event is the product of the frequencies of its component events. Since the frequency of AA genotypes is p^2, then in a randomly-mating population the frequency of $AA \times AA$ marriages is $p^2 \times p^2 = p^4$. The frequencies of all possible marriages are shown in Table 3–7.

With this background we can see that, with respect to the distribution of genotypes, natural selection is able to exert its influence in any of four ways, selection against: 1) either homozygote, 2) either homozygote and the heterozygote, 3) both homozygotes, and 4) the heterozygote.

TABLE 3–7

FREQUENCIES OF MATING TYPES UNDER RANDOM MATING

Mating Type δ $\male$ $\female$		Frequency Under Random Mating	
		Genotype Frequencies	Mating Type Frequencies
AA	$\times$	AA	$p^2 \times p^2 = p^4$
AA	$\times$	Aa	$p^2 \times 2pq = 2p^3q$
AA	$\times$	aa	$p^2 \times q^2 = p^2q^2$
Aa	$\times$	AA	$2pq \times p^2 = 2p^3q$
Aa	$\times$	Aa	$2pq \times 2pq = 4p^2q^2$
Aa	$\times$	aa	$2pq \times q^2 = 2pq^3$
aa	$\times$	AA	$q^2 \times p^2 = p^2q^2$
aa	$\times$	Aa	$q^2 \times 2pq = 2pq^3$
aa	$\times$	aa	$q^2 \times q^2 = q^4$

Selection Against One Homozygote. Consider now a simple case wherein persons of one homozygous genotype, say *aa*, are sterile; that is to say, so severely selected against that they leave no progeny. Then of the nine possible types of marriages only four produce offspring, or, stated in another way, out of every 100 marriages only 56.25 percent yield offspring (see Table 3–8).

TABLE 3–8

MATING TYPES PRODUCING OFFSPRING
WITH COMPLETE SELECTION AGAINST ONE HOMOZYGOTE (*aa*)

Mating Type δ $\female$			Frequency	Frequency Assuming $p = q = .50$
AA	$\times$	AA	p^4	.0625
AA	$\times$	Aa	$2p^3q$	.1250
Aa	$\times$	AA	$2p^3q$	.1250
Aa	$\times$	Aa	$4p^2q^2$	.2500
	Total			.5625

If each of the mating types is presumed to be equally productive, then Table 3–9 shows the expected number of offspring by genotypes per 100 matings. The effect is clear: not only is the proportion of *aa* genotypes reduced, but the frequency of the *a* allele is likewise reduced. The value for

$$p = \frac{100(AA) + 50(Aa)}{225} = .67 \text{ and for } q = \frac{25(aa) + 50(Aa)}{225} = .33.$$

Beginning with these changed frequencies and continuing under the same conditions, subsequent generations will continue the trend. The four mating types producing offspring account now for 79.40 percent of all possible matings in the population (see Table 3–10).

TABLE 3–9

Expected Distribution of Offspring Genotypes per 100 Marriages
Under Complete Selection Against aa Genotype

Mating Type		Frequency	Offspring by Genotype (assuming 4 children per marriage)		
♂	♀		AA	Aa	aa
AA × AA		.0625	25		
AA × Aa		.1250	25	25	
Aa × AA		.1250	25	25	
Aa × Aa		.2500	25	50	25
Total			100	100	25

TABLE 3–10

Expected Distribution of Mating Types and Offspring Genotypes
With $p = .67$, $q = .33$, and Complete Selection Against aa Genotype

Mating Type		Frequency		Offspring by Genotypes (assuming 4 children per marriage)		
♂	♀			AA	Aa	aa
AA × AA		p^4	.2015	80		
AA × Aa		$2p^3q$	.1985	40	40	
Aa × AA		$2p^3q$	.1985	40	40	
Aa × Aa		$4p^2q^2$	.1955	20	40	20
Total			.7940	180	120	20

Thus, the number of offspring produced is increased, the proportion of
both aa and Aa individuals reduced, and the gene frequency of a is reduced from .33 to .25. Changes in the frequencies of p and q over the
three generations are summarized in Table 3–11.

TABLE 3–11

Three Generations of Gene Frequencies
Under Complete Selection Against aa Genotype

		Generation		
		1 ⟶ 2 ⟶ 3		
p	=	.50	.67	.75
q	=	.50	.33	.25

The trend that will continue for as long as the conditions prevail is established. The genetic structure of the population moves each generation

systematically toward: a) a greater proportion of A alleles, and b) increasing AA homozygosity. It should be noted, however, that even with this intensity of selection, the rate at which these events proceed declines with each generation, and, for this reason, it takes many generations of intense selective pressure to eliminate an allele completely. Although it is indeed true that in man some homozygous conditions are eliminated each generation in a manner similar to the illustration, for the vast majority of genetic loci the pressure of selection is apparently more gentle and reflected only through slight differences in the contributions of particular genotypes to the next generation. The effects are at times so subtle that they cannot readily be detected. Under these more common circumstances, the rate of change per generation per genetic locus (i.e., evolution) is slower, and it takes many generations to eliminate an allele.

Selection Against One Homozygote and the Heterozygote. Only one form of selection produces faster results in altering the genetic structure of a population: selection against an allele in both homozygous and heterozygous genotypes. Under these conditions if selection is complete, then the allele will be eliminated in one generation. In between complete selection against the homozygote and complete selection against both the heterozygote and one homozygote there exists an intermediate selection: complete selection against one genotype and partial selection against the other. For example, complete selection against a homozygote and partial selection against the heterozygote. If selection is complete against, say, *aa* and partial against *Aa*, then the heterozygotes produce fewer offspring than the AA homozygotes. Again this would, of course, result in a trend toward increasing the frequencies of the A allele and the AA genotypes. The rate at which this would occur would fall between that brought about by complete selection against only the homozygote on the one hand, and complete selection against the heterozygote and one homozygote on the other.

Selection Against Both Homozygotes. Complete selection against *both* homozygotes, or, in other words, selection favoring only heterozygous organisms, has only one significant mating type: *Aa* × *Aa*. These conditions produce an equilibrium; no matter what the initial values of p and q in the parental population, once these conditions prevail the gene frequencies for p and q adjust to .50 in one generation and stay at that level for as long as the conditions continue. Moreover, the genotype frequencies stay at the p^2 (AA), $2pq$ (Aa), and q^2 (aa) levels. There are several interesting implications to this situation, but the point deserving emphasis is that selection can act to maintain the genetic variability of a population. Selection need not always act by eliminating alleles and the genotypes they combine to form; it need not always act, that is, by reducing the genetic variation of a population.

Selection Against the Heterozygote.   Under complete selection against the heterozygote, four mating types are productive:

$$\begin{array}{ccc} \male & & \female \\ AA & \times & AA \\ AA & \times & aa \\ aa & \times & AA \\ aa & \times & aa \end{array}$$

In this instance the effect of selection depends on the values for p and q at the time that selective conditions begin. If p and q are equal, i.e., $p = .50$ and $q = .50$, then the genetic structure of the population remains constant and will continue to remain in this equilibrium as long as the conditions remain the same. If, however, p and q are not equal, then complete selection against the heterozygote brings about a steady increase in the allele which is more frequent at the outset and in its homozygous genotype. The rate at which this occurs depends on the initial values of p and q; in general the closer the initial frequencies, the slower the increase in the more frequent allele.

From these last two illustrations it may be seen that selection is able to bring about effects that may at first glance seem impossible. On the one hand, selection against both homozygotes results in an equilibrium with constant and high frequencies of sterile genotypes every generation. On the other hand, selection against the heterozygote genotype will, if the initial frequencies are unequal, result in the elimination of an allele which otherwise is selectively equivalent to its alternate.

This discussion of selection involves simplification and the omission of many things. Its purpose, however, is to show how selection may operate on the genetic structure of natural populations. As we have seen, natural selection acts by favoring elements and combinations of elements of genetic variability that improve or at least maintain adaptation and by rejecting other elements and combinations. In this activity, it is limited to the available supply of variability. If the supply is not adequate, the population becomes extinct. But where does genetic variability come from? Or, in other words, what source provides natural selection with its raw materials? The answer is genetic mutation, another mechanism of evolution.

Mutation.*   As noted earlier, the mechanisms of evolution act in ways that upset the equilibrium conditions specified by the Hardy–Weinberg law. At this point, the major interest in mutations is in understanding how they are able to bring about changes to the genetic structure of a

---

* This discussion deals solely with the effects of genetic mutation as the source of variability and ignores the variety of chromosome changes (e.g., polyploidy, inversions, translocations, etc.) that produce evolutionary novelty. They are omitted so that the discussion may be simplified. Interested readers will find clear discussions of these topics in Crow (1963) and Srb, Owen, and Edgar (1965).

population. In considering this effect, it will be useful to make assumptions similar to those made in the discussion of natural selection: the population is very large, mating occurs at random, and mutation is the only evolutionary mechanism at work.

From one standpoint, the effect of mutation on the genetic structure of a population is simple and obvious. If A mutates to a, this is in and of itself a change in the genetic composition of the population. To be sure, if this happens only once in a very large population, the effect is very slight indeed. Yet this slight change, repeated over generations, will, given enough time, lead to the complete replacement of A by a. In this process, mutation is irreversible, that is:

$$A\longrightarrow a$$

One can see that the effect here is simply a product of the rate at which A mutates to a and the number of generations this process has been at work. But what of the condition in which A mutates to a and a mutates to A? That is:

$$A\rightleftharpoons a$$

Clearly, if the rates are equal, that is, if the proportion of A's changing to a's is equal to the proportion of a's changing to A's, the two alleles will tend toward equal frequencies no matter what their original frequencies. For example, if 1 in 10 A's changes to a, and 1 in 10 a's changes to A, the frequency of A and a will eventually be the same, i.e., $p = q = .50$. Some alleles are, however, more stable than others, and it is far more common to find that A mutates to a at a rate different from the one at which a mutates to A. At first it might appear that the allele that mutates more rapidly will eventually disappear, but a little reflection will make it clear why this is not the case. Consider, for example, the situation wherein 1 in every 10 A's mutates to a, and 1 in every 5 a's mutates to A. No matter what their original frequencies, the alleles will in time reach a stable equilibrium where $p =$ gene frequency of $A = .66$ and $q =$ gene frequency of $a = .33$. Under these conditions 6.6 of every 66 A alleles mutate to a (1 in 10), and 6.6 of every 33 a alleles mutate to A (1 in 5). Thus a stable situation is achieved with the proportion of A alleles mutating to a exactly matching the proportion of a alleles mutating to A. The equilibrium depends solely on the rates at which A and a mutate; no matter what the beginning values of p and q, the equilibrium values of $p = .66$ and $q = .33$ will be reached if the rates of mutation are as illustrated, 1 in 10 and 1 in 5.

In sharp contrast to the rates of 1 in 10 and 1 in 5 that are employed here to illustrate the effect of mutations on the genetic structure of populations, mutations in nature are very rare events. Most mutation rates in man, for example, fall between 1 in 10,000 and 1 in 100,000. Or, in other words, from 1 in 10,000 to 1 in 100,000 sex cells will contain a mutant allele for any particular genetic locus. Thus, when considered in the context of a particular genetic locus, mutations are indeed rare. There are, however, thousands of genetic loci in every human sex cell; so many in fact that the occurrence of mutations per sex cell is undoubtedly a commonplace event with most, if not all, carrying several loci with mutant alleles.

Distinguishing between the rate per genetic locus and the rate per sex cell emphasizes the two most important ways that mutations may influence evolution. One we have discussed already, that is, the production of totally new allelic varieties of a gene. Mutation is ultimately the source of all genetic variation, a role that is impossible to overemphasize in any discussion of evolution. If, however, one takes a broader look, the effect of mutation may be seen in a different way. To see it in this perspective, it will be necessary to consider the following propositions: 1) included in the genetic structure of all natural populations is a regular supply of mutations; 2) the adaptation of a population to its environmental requirements is a fine and delicate balance that may take millions of years to bring about; and 3) mutations are changes, and, under these conditions, it may be seen that any change in this situation is much more likely to disrupt the intricate and delicate adaptation of the population than it is likely to improve it. From this point of view, the mutation process may be seen as a continuous source of pressure against the formation of a "perfect" adaptation in any natural population. This feature of the mutation process has been recognized for over thirty years, and was first identified by Sewall Wright as *mutation pressure*. Recently it has been renamed and given separate status as an independent mechanism of evolution. C. Loring Brace (1963) calls the process the "probable mutation effect" and sees it as the mechanical means of explaining the occurrence of comparatively common events observed in paleontology known as structural reductions. In brief, the argument Brace presents is simple, involving simultaneously a consideration of selection and the mutation process. Brace suggests that a trait is developed under positive selection, and, as this process continues, there is an accompanying loss of variation in the expression of the trait. When selection is relaxed, however, the pressure of mutation, that is, the "probable mutation effect," provides for new variations, and as these increase over time, the effect is a reduction in the structure of the trait. Mutation may well provide the pressure that causes structural reduction in some instances. In any case, it is the same process that is responsible for new genetic variations, and for this reason it does not deserve designation as a separate and distinct evolutionary mechanism.

Earlier in this chapter, a mutation was defined as a heritable alteration in the composition of the genetic material. This definition by implication emphasizes the molecular basis of the mutation process, yet up to now the discussion has focused on it as the process relates to the Hardy–Weinberg equilibrium law and operates as an evolutionary mechanism.* Basically it appears that mutations may be brought about when an error is made in the normal replication of DNA. The way this can happen may be shown by returning to the structure of hemoglobin. Figure 3–12 shows the sequence of amino acids in the alpha and beta chains of normal hemoglobin. Many abnormal hemoglobins are known. One of them, Hemoglobin S (Hb S), differs from normal hemoglobin in one and only one respect: valine replaces glutamic acid in the sixth position of the beta chain. Consulting the genetic code (Table 3–3), it may be seen that this change can occur by substituting only one nucleotide. Glutamic acid is specified by either G — A — A or G — A — G, whereas two codes for valine are G — U — A and G — U — G. This seemingly slight difference, however, can produce drastic results in the phenotype. Persons unable to make any normal beta chains, i.e., homozygotes for Hb S, suffer a severe disease called sickle-cell anemia which usually results in the death of the individual during childhood. This is a condition which we will return to again in Chapter 8.

Mutation and Selection. To illustrate their respective properties, it is helpful to isolate mutation and natural selection and deal with each separately. In any natural population, however, the two factors are commonly in operation at the same time, but acting in different directions. Mutations continually replenish and add to the background of variability. Most are detrimental or offer no adaptive value and for this reason are eliminated or kept at very low frequencies as the mutation rates and selection intensities approach equilibrium. Thus in any natural population, selection brings about *adaptation;* mutation provides for *adaptability.* This is the impression one is left with by considering them separately, and it is essentially correct. But when mutation and selection are examined simultaneously, it is possible to obtain an added insight into the evolutionary process of far-reaching significance. For with this background in the two evolutionary mechanisms, it may be seen that any particular inherited locus may be identified as *monomorphic, idiomorphic,* or *polymorphic* (see Morton, 1967).

A monomorphic locus shows a distribution that includes one and only one allele. Thus the entire population is, for that trait, homozygous, and the genetic structure homogeneous. Since no heterogeneity exists, the monomorphic trait is of no interest to the geneticist, for without some variation, the inheritance of a trait cannot be determined. Idiomorphs are rare alleles, and in homozygous form are usually responsible for inherited diseases. Polymorphs are common alleles.

---

* For a detailed and readable account of the molecular basis of mutation see the September, 1959, issue of *Scientific American,* or, more recently, in the May, 1967, issue of the same journal, the article by Charles Yanofsky.

Polymorphisms are of special interest to the population geneticist since they are, in a sense, unexpected and, probably for this reason, have yielded more understanding of the dynamics of evolutionary change. They are unexpected simply because a separate consideration of mutation and of selection usually leads to the expectation that what really exists in natural populations are monomorphs, idiomorphs, and perhaps polymorphisms on their way to becoming idiomorphisms and monomorphisms. But stable polymorphisms are known to be a common phenomenon (see Chapter 10 for a discussion of some well-known polymorphisms in human populations), and the interesting question this raises for the population geneticist is how they can be maintained. On reflection it will be recalled that two factors already considered can maintain a polymorphism: 1) selection for the heterozygote, and 2) nonrandom mating. There are others, but to date the best-documented cause is heterozygote advantage.

Selection and mutation together provide an almost complete picture of the mechanics of evolutionary change. However, other factors which have been identified can change the genetic structure of a population and thereby qualify as mechanisms of evolution.

Genetic Drift.   In small populations, special circumstances exist and can produce rapid changes in the genetic structure, changes that may be completely independent of selection and mutation. In the foregoing discussions of selection and mutation, the effect of population size is ignored, and populations are presumed to be large. In general, however, it may be said that the larger the population, the more resistant its genetic structure to changes from accidental or chance causes. Conversely, the smaller the population, the more susceptible it is to change due to chance. Thus in a small population, chance may act as an evolutionary mechanism, and as such it has been identified variously as: 1) Sewall Wright effect (after the man who first drew attention to the mechanism); 2) small-population-size effect (for obvious reasons); and 3) genetic drift, which will be used here.

As an illustration, return again to the A and a alleles, their genotypes, and the mating types formed by them. In earlier discussion, these mating types have been assumed to be equally productive and, moreover, to produce offspring genotypes in exactly the proportions specified by Mendel's laws; thus an $Aa \times Aa$ mating produced one-quarter AA children, one-half Aa, and one-quarter aa. In very large populations, this is not an unreasonable view, since genetic segregation and fertility accidents in one direction are likely to be balanced by others of equal magnitude in the opposite direction. For example, by chance alone one would expect about four $Aa \times Aa$ matings in a thousand to produce four aa genotypic offspring, but within that same thousand mating types, four others may on chance alone be expected to produce four AA genotypes in their offspring.

Moreover, within a mating type, if fertility is not affected by other factors, the mean number of offspring will be the resultant of many individual marriages above and below the mean. The essential point is that in small populations this stability due to size is absent, and the genetic structures of such populations are thus more volatile.

As a specific example consider Table 3–12. In a very large population

TABLE 3–12

CHANGE IN GENETIC STRUCTURE DUE TO GENETIC DRIFT

| Mating Type | | Offspring Produced | | |
$\male$	$\female$	AA	Aa	aa
AA × AA		4		
AA × Aa		3	1	
AA × aa			4	
Aa × AA		2	2	
Aa × Aa		1	2	1
Aa × aa			2	2
aa × AA			4	
aa × Aa			2	2
aa × aa				4
Total		10	17	9

each of the mating types may occur thousands of times, but we can consider a very small population wherein each occurs only once. This implies that at the outset A and a are equal, or:

$$p = .50$$
$$q = .50$$

To make the illustration as clear as possible, we will assume further that each mating type is equally productive (four children) and that no other evolutionary mechanism is affecting the distribution of the gene in the genetic structure of the population. Now to illustrate genetic drift consider the second mating type, $AA \times Aa$. Normally this mating is one that produces half homozygous and half heterozygous offspring. However, it will by chance produce different proportions on occasion. The proportions shown here (Table 3–12) of 3 to 1 can be expected to occur by chance alone in a family of four children in 25 percent of such marriages, so the event is not an exceptionally rare one, but in a small population its effect is reflected in the resulting gene frequencies:

$$p = \frac{10 + 17/2}{36} = .51 \qquad\qquad q = \frac{9 + 17/2}{36} = .49$$

Chance alone is the factor responsible for the changes in genetic structure; the population has "drifted" in its genetic composition, and the drift bears no systematic relationship to the adaptive requirements of the organism. The change is random and controlled entirely by chance.

Genetic drift is a potential panacea for the solution of problems in physical anthropology. When, for example, two or more populations which are believed to be distantly related are found to be similar in gene frequencies, the *similarity* can be explained as due to genetic drift, or, in other words, to chance. The American Indians and Polynesians provide a case in point. These two groups are believed on other grounds to be derived by very different historical routes from common but ancient Asiatic ancestors. Their ancestry would imply that the Polynesians are more closely related to, say, the Micronesians than they are to the American Indian. Yet in terms of the frequencies of the ABO blood groups, the Polynesians and American Indians are more alike than are the Polynesians and Micronesians. These similar gene frequencies are usually rejected as indicators of close relationship and considered as due to chance, that is, genetic drift.

Conversely, genetic drift may be used to explain *differences* between populations believed on other grounds to be closely related. Thus, the differences between the Micronesians and Polynesians may be explained by genetic drift. Or two communities separated by only a mile or two in the same valley in New Guinea having very different genetic structures may be "explained" by genetic drift.

These may be correct explanations since the effect of genetic drift is random, but to accept drift as the explanation for discordancies in situations where it cannot be demonstrated with some conclusiveness leads to a complacent acceptance and conformity with "traditional" explanations. Under these conditions, the demonstration of genetic differences or similarities is considered unimportant and uninformative unless it supports a more standard view. Yet, it is certainly possible that these discordant similarities and differences between populations may be the source of exciting new discoveries, either about the populations or about the processes of evolution or both. For this reason, genetic drift might well be considered the least acceptable explanation in doubtful cases.

Since genetic drift is effective only in small populations, it follows that it must have played a more significant role in man's early stages of evolution than it does today. The magnitude of the role is impossible to measure directly, but it is certainly clear that at one time all of man's ancestors lived in exactly the conditions that permit chance factors to operate effectively in bringing about change, i.e., in small isolated groups. Moreover, these are the conditions that prevailed throughout the vast majority of time that man has been in existence. With the introduction of agriculture, and particularly irrigation agriculture, into the stream of cultural evolution, population size and density increased with sedentary communities emerging as the first step in a trend that today culminates in huge sprawling urban centers.

In summary, genetic drift makes explicit the fact that chance can bring about changes in gene and genotype frequencies. It is effective in small populations, and for this reason must have been a more important mechanism of evolutionary change in man's early history than it is today.

Gene Flow, Migration, and Population Structure. From one point of view, the effect of migration as an evolutionary mechanism is obvious. If a population, characterized by a particular genetic structure, is the recipient of a group of migrants with a different distribution of gene and genotype frequencies, then clearly if they intermarry the resulting generation will have a genetic structure that is different from either parental population. This is a simple model and rarely approximates real situations in human populations. It has, however, been elaborated and developed to the point where it is possible, given the genetic structures of both the original population and the migrants, and the rate of intermarriage, to calculate the genetic effects of the migration on the offspring generation (see Glass and Li, 1954).

A common situation in natural populations is the presence of subpopulations within them. The analysis of this condition requires a different view of population structure. Up to this point, a population has been considered as a homogeneous and undifferentiated unit consisting of individuals that intermarry at random. This latter condition, however, implies that the structure of a population may be internally heterogeneous and highly diversified. That is, a population may consist of many subunits that tend to mate more often within themselves but are nonetheless linked together by regular outmating, the rate of which may vary from one subunit to another. Under these circumstances, no actual migration need take place for the same kind of phenomenon described above to occur and, for this reason, the phenomenon is now generally identified as gene flow instead of migration. Gene flow identifies the source of changes in the genetic structure of populations that arise through the differentiation of a population into integrated subunits.

Some of the more interesting advances in population genetics today center around the problem of population structure. Indeed, the area serves as an intellectual battleground for one of the exciting controversies presently emerging among both human geneticists and physical anthropologists. An example will illustrate the fundamental differences in outlook. Are the several communities existing together in one valley best thought of as so many separate populations (isolates) differentiated by genetic drift, or might it be more appropriate to represent such a situation as a single population consisting of subunits which may vary in genetic structure, thereby contributing to the total variance in the population, and which are linked together by continuous outbreeding? In this situation, the solution depends, obviously, on the empirical circumstances. Anthropologists are accustomed to the isolate model—so accustomed, indeed, that it has determined both the kind of information they have sought and the choice of groups they have studied (see Morton, 1968).

The main point to be emphasized here is that gene flow can and does alter the genetic structures of natural populations, but the magnitude of its effects is difficult to measure without an adequate model of population structure. This point, in turn, serves to demonstrate the related observation that an understanding of gene flow in any population requires a knowledge of population structure, inbreeding, the movements in and out of the population, mating practices, and the effect of other evolutionary mechanisms on the population and its subunits. It is an interesting but complex area in the study of natural populations.

Meiotic Drive. Mendel's laws imply that heterozygotes produce sex cells with equal proportions of each allele. As noted earlier, the physiological process that accommodates this segregation process is meiosis. Although not clearly demonstrated in human populations, exceptions to this have been noted in corn, mice, and fruit fly populations. That is, heterozygotes have been observed to produce sex cells containing the chromosome bearing one of the alleles significantly more frequently than the other chromosome. The production of unequal proportions of sister chromosomes in heterozygotes is called *meiotic drive.* The phenomenon is perhaps not correctly identified as a distinctive evolutionary mechanism, since the difference between one chromosome and the other may be regarded as a difference in fitness. Thus it is that meiotic drive calls attention to the fact that selection can operate even before the formation of a zygote, by favoring one of the two possible kinds of sex cells in fertilization. It might, then, be more logical to regard meiotic drive as one form of selection. Indeed, in recognition of this relationship to selection, some investigators prefer to call the phenomenon *prezygotic selection.*

Population Genetics and Physical Anthropology

These constitute the known factors that can operate to alter the genetic structures of natural populations. It is certainly possible that many more will be identified, but for the time being, these are the only means known to be capable of changing gene or genotype frequencies. Nevertheless, one might well wish to know at this point how population genetics is relevant to the problems of physical anthropology. To some, the relevance may be obvious, but to the beginner, it may be useful to consider some illustrations. You will recall that the broad areas of interest to physical anthropology are: 1) the investigation and interpretation of human evolution, and 2) the examination of the causes and significance of the range of man's heterographic variation. How can population genetics be of use in the solution of these problems? Consider first the area of human evolution. In all candor, population genetics has contributed little to the resolution of conflicting interpretations of the fossil record of primate and human evolution, and perhaps it never will. However, in detecting changes in the genetic structure of populations in the present, population genetics provides a most powerful background of theory and technique. Suppose, for example, that we wish to know whether a population is undergoing evolutionary change with respect to the Aa locus. Assuming an appropriate model of population structure, an investigator able to obtain a large unbiased sample of nuclear families (both parents and all their natural offspring) near or beyond the completion of their reproductive period can determine whether, in fact, the distribution of offspring genotypes is that expected under Mendel's laws, or whether there are consistent distortions in the expected distribution of genotypes from particular mating types. The existence of such distortions is direct evidence of evolution. The cause of the distortion remains to be determined, but the activity of one or more evolutionary mechanisms is implied. It should be emphasized also that the lack of segregation distortions does not necessarily imply the absence of evolutionary mechanisms. The genetic structure of the population may be undergoing change at the locus at a rate too slow to be detected by a two-generational segregation analysis.

A simple adaptation of this approach can also be used to illustrate a way in which population genetics can be applied to a problem in human heterography, namely, the effects of outcrossing. Outcrossing is often referred to as race mixture, and estimating the effects of such marriages on the resulting offspring has been a problem of long-standing interest in human biology. There are two contradictory views on the subject. There are those who argue that race mixing may lead to harmful effects in the offspring. Others maintain that race mixture may result in more vigorous, more healthy, and more fertile offspring. The evidence is not conclusive for either viewpoint. The one classic study by Davenport and Steggerda (1929) concluded that race mixture is harmful; however, the research was badly designed, vague, and illogical. Those studies supporting heterosis (hybrid vigor) in man (Shapiro, 1929, 1936; Hulse, 1958, etc.) are hampered by an inability to distinguish between heterosis and selective migration. That is, the offspring can on many grounds be demonstrated to be more "vigorous" in outcrosses, but it is not clear whether this is due to some heterotic effect or to the fact that the parents are a hardier group than the average members of their respective source populations. Likewise, some apparent heterosis could be due to environmental factors, since the children are often reared under conditions very different from those of either parent group. Morton, Chung, and Mi (1967) applied principles of population genetics to this traditional problem in physical anthropology and concluded that among the many crosses between distinctive groups in Hawaii there is no apparent effect in either direction.

These may serve to illustrate ways in which population genetics may be of use in solving traditional physical anthropological problems, but, in fact, the most common way of relating the two areas is in the presumed potential of population genetics in the solution of the hoary physical anthropological problems of tracing past migrations and establishing degree of biological relationship among contemporary populations. Population genetics provides a means of characterizing human groups in terms of gene frequencies. As noted earlier, the frequencies of A and a can be determined directly and simply when all three genotypes are recognizable. Thus:

$$\text{Frequency of } A = p = \frac{\text{No. of } AA \text{ persons} + \frac{1}{2} \text{ No. of } Aa \text{ persons}}{\text{Total } AA, Aa, aa \text{ persons}}$$

$$\text{Frequency of } a = q = \frac{\text{No. of } aa \text{ persons} + \frac{1}{2} \text{ No. of } Aa \text{ persons}}{\text{Total } AA, Aa, aa \text{ persons}}$$

The calculation is slightly more complicated when the locus in question involves more than two alleles, and also when it is not possible to distinguish all the genotypes. Many physical anthropologists and human geneticists have believed that these gene-frequency estimates can be used to disclose migrations that took place in the past and to detect the degree of biological relationship between two or more populations. The assumption underlying both applications is simply that the more similar the frequencies, the closer the relationship. Some aspects of this problem will be taken up again in Chapter 9, but from the earlier discussion it now should be clear that gene-frequency estimates drawn from natural populations are affected by sampling procedures, intensity of inbreeding, population structure, and, of course, by any one or more of the mechanisms of evolution. Contrary to the view that similarity in gene frequencies implies close relationship, the potential influence of these factors makes it impossible to know with any confidence just what any particular gene frequency may imply. Leaving aside this limitation, however, population genetics more than any other subdivision of genetics serves to draw the attention of physical anthropologists to the processes and dynamics of evolutionary change in human populations.

REFERENCES AND
SUGGESTIONS FOR ADDITIONAL READING

BEADLE, G. W., AND E. L. TATUM
    1941   Genetic control of biochemical reactions in *Neurospora*. *Proceedings of the National Academy of Science* 27:499–506.

BRACE, C. LORING
1963   Structural reduction in evolution. *American Naturalist* 97:39–49.
CROW, JAMES F.
1963   *Genetics notes.* Minneapolis: Burgess.
DAVENPORT, C. B., AND M. STEGGERDA
1929   Race crossing in Jamaica. *Carnegie Institution of Washington* 395:454–477.
DOBZHANSKY, THEODOSIUS
1959   Evolution of genes and genes in evolution. *Cold Spring Harbor Symposia on Quantitative Biology* 24:15–30.
DUNN, L. C.
1959   *Heredity and evolution in human populations.* Cambridge: Harvard University Press.
1963   Cross currents in the history of human genetics. In *Papers on human genetics,* ed. Samuel H. Boyer, IV. Englewood Cliffs, N.J.: Prentice-Hall.
GLASS, B., AND C. C. LI
1954   The dynamics of racial intermixture—an analysis based on the American Negro. *American Journal of Human Genetics* 5:1–20.
GRIFFITH, F.
1928   The significance of pneumococcal types. *Journal of Hygiene* 27: 113–159.
HARDY, G. H.
1908   Mendelian proportions in a mixed population. *Science* 28:49–50.
HERSHEY, A. D., AND M. CHASE
1952   Independent functions of viral protein and nucleic acid in growth of bacteriophage. *Journal of Genetic Physiology* 36:39–56.
HULSE, FREDERICK S.
1957   Exogamie et hétérosis [Exogamy and heterosis]. *Archives Suisses d'Anthropologie Générale* 22:103–125. English translation by the author in *Yearbook of Physical Anthropology* 9:240–257.
LERNER, I. MICHAEL
1968   *Heredity, evolution, and society.* San Francisco: W. H. Freeman.
LYON, MARY F.
1962   Sex chromatin and gene action in the mammalian X-chromosome. *American Journal of Human Genetics* 14:135–148.
MAYR, ERNST
1959   Where are we? *Cold Spring Harbor Symposia on Quantitative Biology* 24:1–14.
MENDEL, GREGOR
1866   Experiments in plant hybridization. *Proceedings of the Natural History Society of Brünn.* English translation—Cambridge: Harvard University Press, 1948.
MORTON, NEWTON E.
1967   Genetic studies of northeastern Brazil: summary and conclusions. *Ciencia e Cultura* 19:14–30.
1968   Problems and methods in the genetics of primitive groups. *American Journal of Physical Anthropology* (n.s.) 28:191–202.

MORTON, N. E., C. S. CHUNG, AND M. P. MI
    1967   *Genetics of interracial crosses in Hawaii.* Basel: S. Karger.
MORTON, N. E., AND N. YASUDA
    1962   The genetical structure of human populations. In *Les déplacements humains,* ed. J. Sutter. Paris: Hachette.
SHAPIRO, H. L.
    1929   Descendants of the mutineers of the bounty. *Memoirs of the B. P. Bishop Museum.* Honolulu.
    1936   *Heritage of the bounty.* New York: Simon & Schuster.
SNYDER, LAURENCE H., AND PAUL R. DAVID
    1957   *The principles of heredity.* 5th ed. Boston: D. C. Heath.
SRB, ADRIAN M., R. D. OWEN, AND R. S. EDGAR
    1965   *General genetics.* 2d ed. San Francisco: W. H. Freeman.
STANSFIELD, WILLIAM D.
    1969   *Schaum's outline of theory and problems of genetics.* New York: McGraw-Hill.
STERN, CURT
    1960   *Principles of human genetics.* San Francisco: W. H. Freeman.
SUTTON, H. ELDON
    1965   *An introduction to human genetics.* New York: Holt, Rinehart & Winston.
WATSON, JAMES D.
    1965   *Molecular biology of the gene.* New York: W. A. Benjamin.
    1968   *The double helix.* New York: Atheneum.
WATSON, J. D., AND F. H. C. CRICK
    1953   Molecular structure of nucleic acids. *Nature* 171:737–738.
WORKMAN, P. L.
    1969   The analysis of simple genetic polymorphisms. *Human Biology* 41:97–114.
YULE, U.
    1908   Comments on Mendelism in relation to disease. *Proceedings of the Royal Society of Medicine* 1:164–166.

PART II

Human Paleontology

PRELIMINARY CONSIDERATIONS

T HE CONCERN OF THIS BOOK IS WITH MAN, and the focus of this section on human paleontology is on the fossil evidence of human evolution. But that evidence is contained within a thin outer layer of the earth's crust. The earth is estimated to be six billion years old, but human evolution has taken place within the last two million years. Most of the material in this section deals with these last few million years, but an effort is made to put the human period into proper perspective by first presenting brief discussions of the earlier parts of the geological record.

Life began over three billion years ago. During this vast period, the earth has undergone enormous changes, some abrupt, some gradual. Land forms changed; ocean levels shifted; mountains were formed, eroded, and formed again; volcanoes erupted; and time and again glaciers swept out from the poles and down from the mountains scarring the earth's crust, depositing and redepositing its surface in unlikely places. All the while, the less dramatic forces of wind and water erosion were constantly changing the earth's surface. These and many other forces placed continual pressure on living species to adapt to the changing environmental circumstances or face the only alternative—to become extinct. Those that survived did so because they were able to adapt, or, put in a different way, had a sufficiently wide range of variability upon which to draw during these changing conditions to survive them. Since the better-adapted members of the species contribute more offspring to the next generation, the effect over time is not simply change, but systematic improvements in the species' adaptation. This is, of course, evolution, and its effects are seen in the staggering array of variation that may be found within the nearly two million species of animals alive today.

It would be both useful and comforting to know the details of the changes that life has undergone over this long time period, but this is impossible, since no record exists on which we might reconstruct the details. There is some direct evidence, however, that enables us to learn something about the general outlines of the record: the evidence of fossils, the artifacts of life. Discovering, describing, and interpreting the significance of the fossil evidence is the province of the science of *paleontology*.

There is a widespread view that fossils are simply bones that have become mineralized or turned to stone. This is often, but not always, true. A fossil is anything that provides us with direct information about organisms that lived in the past. Thus, in reconstructing the distant past, a fossil may be an imprint, a soil discontinuity caused by a burrowing animal, a seed, a completely preserved form, as well as many other kinds of things. In addition, the human paleontologist has another fossil record to be concerned with over and above that usually confronting a paleontologist—the fossil record of cultural change, or, as it is more commonly called, the archaeological record. An attempt is made in Chapter 6 to integrate the details of these two fossil records, but at this point the discussion will focus on some of the problems associated with the analysis of bones and teeth, the more common paleontological fossils, and with the archaeological record.

Far too often we assume that the facts speak for themselves. For example, it might be held that all the human paleontologist needs to do is to discover relevant fossil material and describe it, and eventually the answers to all significant questions would then be found. This view demonstrates a lack of awareness of some fundamental principles of scientific procedure. How, for example, do we decide that a particular fossil is relevant whereas another is not? Since any bone, or fragment of a bone, can be thought of as possessing an infinity of attributes, how do we develop our description? What observations do we note? What measurements do we record? These sound like impractical objections, but much valuable information has been lost, destroyed, or simply not obtained because of an investigator's naïve presumptions that he could recognize and describe all relevant attributes. Unfortunately, no amount of information or training can provide us with certainty in our judgments about relevance. No one knows what information may be called for in future investigations and analyses. However, some simple general principles can be recognized. In the description of fossil materials, features should be observed and measured: 1) on the basis of their utility for comparative purposes, and 2) on the basis of their integrity as functional units themselves. The first of these criteria is the less justifiable; in effect what it says is that measurements should be taken because others have taken such measurements. This alone is not a good principle, but following it does make comparing one fossil with another not merely easier, but possible. Employing the second criterion in the choice of measurements and attributes for description is usually more desirable but more difficult to apply, for it involves serious thought and careful judgment. Consider, for example, facial height (see Figure II–1). What is the functional integrity or significance of this measurement? Is this a measurement of some element of the face that has some physiological, anatomical, genetic, or evolutionary integrity? No. In fact it crosses two major functionally integrated parts of the face: the mouth and the nose. This is not to say that there are no important functional relationships between eating and breathing, but rather from the standpoint of unit integrity it is useful to separate them—just as breathing is functionally related to running, yet it is useful to consider them as separate activities. The evolutionary forces responsible for the size and form of the mouth (food, techniques for preparing and storing food, the use of the mouth as an implement, sources of tooth wear, etc.) are most certainly different from the evolutionary forces responsible for the form and size of the nose (temperature, humidity, altitude, degree of cultural development, etc.). Indeed, it is likely that the factors responsible for the length of the nose may be different from those that determined its width.

So what sense does it make to take facial height as a measurement? Only the sense that follows from tradition—anthropologists have been doing it for many, many years. This is a reason, but not a very good one.

Deciding what units constitute biologically meaningful and function-

Figure II–1. Facial height measurement.

facial height

Haversian canals

lacunae

lamellae

canaliculli

Figure II–2. Microscopic view of a cross section of a long bone.

ally integrated features is a task for trained professional specialists. There are ways of arriving at correct decisions, but at least one element appears to be fundamental not only to the solution of this particular problem, but to the problems of interpreting paleontological data in general: a knowledge of the properties of bone and at least a minimal understanding of the processes of fossilization.

We are inclined to think of bone as an essentially solid and fixed material that serves as a firm base to hold the other body parts together and provide some structure. We think of bone as stable and as playing an important but passive role in its relationships to the rest of the body, like that of a coat hanger to a coat. Bone is, of course, strong, but it is by no means inactive; the elements that make it up are continually undergoing changes accommodating the requirements of growth and development, responding to regular fluctuations in diet, restoring damaged tissue, and carrying out regular physiological functions, such as the production of red blood cells. These are only a few of the factors known to cause alterations in the structure of bony tissue.

Some of the activity of bone is implicit in its structure, particularly as we view it under the microscope. Figure II–2 is a microscopic view of a very small area of a thin cross section of one of the larger bones in the body, the femur. You will notice patterns of concentric rings, each surrounding a hole in the center. The concentric rings are called lamellae, and the holes are known as Haversian canals. With the exception of the Haversian canals, the light areas are deposits of minerals, particularly calcium and phosphate, which provide bone with much of its solid structure. The little black areas with extensions are lacunae, in which the bone cells or osteocytes lived in life. The thin branches of the osteocytes come into contact with adjacent osteocytes, and all are ultimately connected with one or more Haversian canals. In this way the bone cells remain in contact with the circulatory system, taking on food and eliminating waste materials, for running through the Haversian canals are blood vessels and nerves. Looking through a longitudinal section (Figure II–3), it is possible to verify that the Haversian canals run longitudinally through the bone and form complicated network connections with one another. Already bone can be seen to be structurally more complicated than might be concluded by casual inspection. However, one should realize that these osteocytes, lamellae, and Haversian canals are continually undergoing change and replacement. Viewing it thus, one can begin to appreciate the structure of bone and the activity continually going on within it. When one adds to this the function of bone as a reservoir for the storage of minerals and as a center for the manufacture of blood cells, he has taken an important first step in realizing the plastic quality of bone. This is really the point to be emphasized: there is nothing fixed or immutable about the form of bone. Within broad limitations set by genetic factors, bone responds to the mechanical and physiological forces that operate on it, and these are largely responsible for both its gross and microscopic form. Thus when one looks at a bone, he is examining the product of forces imposed by the environment on the genetic potential of the individual. This view is fundamental to the appropriate interpretation of fossil bones.

What happens to a bone when it becomes fossilized? Almost everyone has a general appreciation for the process made explicit in the common

Figure II–3. Microscopic view of a longitudinal section of a long bone.

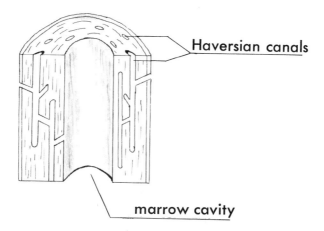

Haversian canals

marrow cavity

statement "it becomes petrified," that is, turns to stone. But how does this happen? First it should be emphasized that it does not happen often. Bones must be deposited in just the right circumstances to become fossilized, and not only are the conditions rare, but the likelihood that bones will be discovered is even more rare. Far more often the agencies of decay and erosion cause bones to decompose and disintegrate, leaving no detectable trace. However, rare events do occur; some bones are preserved and discovered, and these constitute the major part of the known fossil record.

The process of fossilization occurs in any of three ways: 1) the replacement of the organic components with minerals, 2) chemical changes in the inorganic components of the original bone, and 3) a combination of these two processes.

Once a bone is deposited and exposed to soil, its original components begin a series of gradual chemical reactions with the materials around it. The organic components such as the osteocytes, nerves, and vascular tissue decompose and disappear rapidly, most often from action by soil bacteria. From time to time water is likely to seep through the soil, and, as it does, there is a slow but regular depositing of the minerals contained in the water in the gaps formerly occupied by the organic substances. This process was at one time thought to be the only way in which bones became fossilized, but there are a number of fossil bones now known in which the major changes can be seen in the composition of the inorganic components and in which, for instance, a sizable proportion of the lacunae formerly occupied by osteocytes remain empty. Thus, it is clear that simple substitution of inorganic for organic is by no means the entire explanation. The changes undergone by the inorganic matrix of bone are irregular, varying largely as a function of the elements that are present in the soil. It may be said that these elements enter into a complex of reactions with the bony matrix and with themselves, with the eventual result of changing the entire structure of the original bone. In short, fossilization usually involves the filling up with inorganic materials of all the holes, including the large marrow cavities, the Haversian canals, and the lacunae and canaliculi, and, in addition, involves a series of unspecifiable changes in the structure of the original organic matrix, such changes depending upon the local conditions in which the bone is deposited.

Fossilization of bone can be seen, then, as a long-term process, as indeed it is. It is not a process, however, with a common or constant rate. Thus when one finds a fossil bone, he can conclude only that it is old—not how old it is. Variations in the rates at which the process occurs depend upon such factors as soil composition, bacterial concentrations, and humidity.

One of the striking consequences of the way in which some bones become fossilized is the retention in the fossil of an exact copy of the structure of the original bone right down to the preservation of the microscopic features mentioned earlier. One is often able to see the original Haversian canals and lacunae, as well as the more obvious and expectable features of the bone's gross morphology. This is of more value than simply appealing to one's antiquarian instincts. As mentioned before, the arrangement of the Haversian canals within the shaft of the bone is determined by the mechanical requirements the bone accommodates in the living animal. Thus they provide an unexpected direct clue, not only about the way the bone functioned, but ultimately how the animal behaved. Clearly there is more to be learned from the fossil record than simply the structure of the bones.

Knowing about the structure of bone, the forces responsible for its form, and the factors that cause it to fossilize are all important to the human paleontologist but preliminary to the main business of the field, the description and analysis of the fossil evidence bearing on man's ancestry. Adequate description and analysis in human paleontology depends upon the recovering of correct information for all fossil material in the following dimensions: time, space, and form. The human paleontologist must know for any fossil how old it is (time), where it was discovered (space), what its properties are (form), and how it functioned (inferred from form) before he can obtain an adequate appreciation of its significance. Recovering information in the dimensions of time, space, and form is the essence of paleontological work, and requires the application of methods and specific techniques.

The need to recover temporal information underscores a basic difficulty confronted by paleontologists when compared with other zoological taxonomists. Recall from Chapter 2 how the zoological taxonomist attempts to classify animals by assessing degrees of similarity. Paleontology has the same objective, but by the nature of the subject matter, deals with forms of life that lived at some time in the past. Thus, using fragmentary information, paleontologists must assess degree of relationship between and among animals that may have lived millions of years ago and, in addition, assess the degree of relationship between these ancient forms of life and contemporary species. This is obviously a formidable task, and it should be clear from this that the recovery of information about the time during which fossils were living is a dimension basic to paleontology.

How do paleontologists estimate the age of a fossil? There are two general ways: 1) by evaluating the properties of the fossil itself, or 2) by inference from the location in which the fossil is discovered. The former method may be illustrated by either the fluorine or the C^{14} dating technique. Consider for a moment the fluorine test. Buried bones are from time to time exposed to the percolation of ground water. The water often contains fluorine picked up from the soil. The bone takes on some of the fluorine from the ground water and incorporates it into its structure as part of the fossilization process. The amount of fluorine a particular fossil has, then, will vary according to the following factors: 1) the amount of fluorine in the soil, 2) the degree of exposure to ground water, and 3) the length of time the bone has been in the ground. For fossils found together in the same location, it is reasonable to assume that the first two factors might be constant. Thus any variation in fluorine content should reflect differences in age. It was this technique that led to the disclosure that Piltdown man was a hoax (see page 175). The jaw and skull fragments had different fluorine contents, and both differed from the fossil remains of other animals found in the same location.

Likewise, the well-known carbon 14 dating technique is based on the observation that C^{14}, which is present in all living materials, begins to disintegrate at a known rate at the time an organism dies, and thus a measure of the amount remaining is an indication of the amount of time that has lapsed since the organism died. The method has too short a range (from 20,000 to 40,000 years) to be of much use to paleontology, but it is well enough known to be a familiar illustration.

The location of a fossil discovery may provide a basis for estimating its age. For example, lava flows can be dated with a high degree of precision by means of the potassium-argon method. Like C^{14}, the K-A technique is based on the knowledge that quantitative changes occur at a known rate. K^{40} disintegrates at a known rate to A^{40}, and in volcanic rock the product is trapped and therefore measurable today. Fossils found near or between volcanic layers can thus be dated by the K-A technique. This has been the most important technique used in dating the fossils discovered in recent years by L. S. B. Leakey in East Africa.

From the foregoing it should be clear that the question of the age of a fossil can be answered in either of two different ways. One answer is obvious: the animal lived x many years ago. The techniques available to answer the question in this way are called *absolute* dating techniques; they yield age estimates in terms of years. A second way is to answer: I do not know exactly, but I know that it lived before this fossil and after that one. This is more vague and establishes simply a sequence. The techniques that yield such information are called *relative* dating techniques.

A second dimension of fundamental importance to the paleontologist is that of space—the location of the fossil material. If the paleontologist were interested solely in describing and naming the material he discovered, then the location of a fossil in terms of altitude, longitude, and latitude would simply constitute additional data of use in deciding where the material should be placed in the taxonomic system. The location of the fossil becomes more important as the magnitude of the taxonomic category gets smaller. But the paleontologist, like the modern taxonomist, wishes to know more; he wants to know the significance of differences and similarities and wishes to identify the factors responsible for them. To do this, the paleontologist must confront several unique problems. Explanations for differences and similarities invariably require a knowledge of the ecological setting, and the paleontologist is unable to observe this. Therefore, he depends on reconstruction and inference.

The ecological setting is particularly important to the human paleontologist for, in understanding the course of human evolution, it is important to know about the opportunities for intermixture or, as indicated earlier, gene flow. This involves knowing what factors may have acted as barriers, or alternatively, what connections may have been open in the past that are closed today. Did man's ancestors, for example, have access to routes between equatorial Africa and Asia that are no longer open? Apparently so. The Sahara was not always the severe barrier to migration that it is today.

In recovering information on location and ecological setting, paleontologists may employ any of a number of excavation techniques. Good field paleontologists pride themselves on "clean excavations." This usually means a carefully worked out plan of excavation, one of several possible choices of systems of locating the site and fossils within it in terms of latitude, longitude, and altitude, and an adequate set of records for preserving as much information as possible. A "clean excavation" also means straight lines and vertical trenches. This may sometimes reflect no more than a compulsive neurosis on the part of the investigator-in-charge, but, more often than not, it implies that attention is being given to details, and in the process of obtaining information about location and setting, much attention must be given to details. Flexibility is also a desirable attribute in any excavation.

Thus it is that the paleontologist finds himself continually concerned with the information provided by a knowledge of where fossils come from. Should you make a discovery and ask a paleontologist to identify it, this will become clearer, for the first question he is likely to ask is: "Where did you find it?"

So far, we have been talking about bones—how they become fossilized, how they are discovered, and, once discovered, what is done with them. Clearly two items of fundamental importance to know about them are their age and location. We now know something minimal about the procedures available for obtaining information on these matters. These constitute two of the three fundamental dimensions of human paleontology, time and space. The third is form. In paleontology, form refers to all the properties of a fossil. The formal properties of a fossil may be viewed in two ways: 1) from the point of view of *structure*, that is, all of the physical features such as length, width, ridges, joint surfaces, tubercles, etc.; and 2) from the point of view of *function*, that is, the way in which the structural components are interrelated, and how they relate to the way of life of the complete organism. In more familiar terms, form is the appearance of the fossil and what its appearance offers in evidence for the way the animal lived. Form is the basic dimension of paleontology, the one to which paleontologists pay the most attention, for it is primarily on the basis of formal properties that judgments are reached on the degrees of relationship among fossils, and between them and living organisms. Such judgments can be reached entirely on the basis of form. For example, it is possible to conclude that a particular fossil is a member of the genus *Homo* and species *sapiens* completely on the basis of structural features and without knowing where the fossil came from or when it lived. The reverse is obviously not possible; without a knowledge of its formal properties it is of little value simply to know where a fossil came from and how old it is.

Measurements and observations are the means we use to translate the form of a fossil into a useful description of the fossil. Paleontologists, in dealing with temporal and spatial factors, confront unusual problems in description because of the nature of the fossil record. These limitations have made it necessary for paleontologists to emphasize the details of structure in their descriptions, since these can be seen directly. In dealing with fossil material, the functional aspect of form can be known only indirectly through inference. For this reason, paleontologists commonly base their interpretations on the one thing they can readily measure and observe: the structure of fossils. This approach is, of course, necessary and indeed has yielded virtually everything known about the evolutionary histories of modern plants and animals, but it has its dangers, particularly when conclusions are reached on very little evidence. An example will make this clearer. In 1922 a fossil tooth from Nebraska was identified as that of an ape. This was amazing, since no fossil apes had ever been found in the New World, but the tooth was later identified as that of a fossil pig. The lesson to be learned from this is simple: the amount of fossil evidence available influences the reliability of interpretations.

Paleontologists are becoming more and more interested in the functional aspect of form. How do they obtain information on function? There are two general ways: 1) from the functional properties of the structure of the fossil, and 2) from the context in which it lived. In drawing inferences about the functional significance of bone structure, we draw heavily upon the field of comparative anatomy, and particularly its subspecialty, comparative osteology. As we have seen already, the shape of a bone is determined by genetic and environmental factors. The genetic factors appear to establish initial functional relationships, and environmental factors, such as strain and load, determine much of both the microscopic and gross morphological structure of bone. Thus, it is clear that studies of the microscopic and gross structure of bone should provide us with direct information on the strain and load factors the bone was subjected to in life. Such information provides us with a basis for drawing conclusions about how the particular bone functioned. Again, such studies as these depend on analogies with structures found in living animals. Advances in experimental functional anatomy can be expected to provide broader insight and better understanding of the functional significance of skeletal structure.

Statements and conclusions about function can also be based on observations of the context in which a particular fossil lived. With particular reference to fossil material, the study of functional processes implied by attributes in the context is known as *paleoecology*. Ecological data can provide evidence on such factors as climate, population structure and density, diet, predators, disease, and many other items that bear upon the functional or processual relationships between the species represented by the fossil and the many elements of its environment. Inferences drawn concerning the functional properties of fossil forms, on the basis of ecological data, are probably more subject to error simply because they require assumptions about relationships for which there often is little empirical evidence.

Having located our fossils in time and space, and having extracted all the relevant structural and functional details of their formal properties, what comes next? Fossils are of value as they improve our understanding of evolution. Thus, we use the data provided by human paleontology as a background of empirical information on which are tested hypotheses and theories about the course of man's evolution. We turn now to a consideration of those data and some of the theories and insights they have generated.

**REFERENCES AND
SUGGESTIONS FOR ADDITIONAL READING**

DE BEER, GAVIN
    1964   *Atlas of evolution.* London: Thomas Nelson & Sons.
EISELEY, LOREN
    1946   *The immense journey.* New York: Random House.
JEPSEN, GLENN L., ERNST MAYR, AND GEORGE GAYLORD SIMPSON
    1949   *Genetics, paleontology, and evolution.* Princeton: Princeton University Press.
MOODY, PAUL A.
    1962   *Introduction to evolution.* 2d ed. New York: Harper & Row.

MURRAY, P. D. F.
    1936   *Bones.* London: Cambridge University Press.
SIMPSON, GEORGE GAYLORD
    1949   *The meaning of evolution: a study of the history of life and of its significance for man.* New Haven: Yale University Press.
ZEUNER, F. E.
    1952   *Dating the past: an introduction to geochronology.* 3d rev. ed. London: Methuen.

CHAPTER 4

ORIGIN AND EVOLUTION OF LIFE

THEORIES OF THE ORIGIN OF LIFE

A problem of long-standing interest to man is the question of how life originated. This is but one of several possible convenient places to begin; one could begin, for example, with other questions, such as the origin of matter, of the universe, of our galaxy, our solar system, or our planet, but the answers to these questions are either completely unknown or dependent upon theories based on scant evidence. Apart from being of greater immediate importance, the evidence now available on the subject of the origin of life is enough to be scientifically respectable, and, put together in a logical way, makes a fascinating story.

Almost everyone has an answer to the question of how life came into being. This is true not only for members of our own society, but for primitive cultures as well. The question is apparently one that has been of interest to man for a very long time, and, further, one which all groups of men have felt compelled to answer in one way or another. The condition of not knowing the answer appears to be intolerable to man. So there are some feelings of uneasiness that generally accompany the subject, particularly in a scientific context. Apart from this difficulty, the question seems hopeless, since the event, the origin of life, took place so long ago that trying to find any evidence of its occurrence can only be regarded as futile. This is, of course, true; there is no fossil evidence to bring to bear on the problem. There does exist, however, a reasonable scientific argument and enough experimental evidence to support it to make it plausible. That argument and some of the evidence supporting it are presented in what follows.

In general, there are only three possible ways to answer the question of how life originated: 1) life was created from nothing, that is, simply willed into existence by a supernatural force; 2) life arose from preexisting life— say, for example, that life on earth arose from life that reached here from some other planet; or 3) life is a product of nonliving matter.

Creation

The belief that life was made from nothing, that it arose as a product of the will of a supernatural being, is by far the most commonly accepted view of the origin of life. It has a peculiarly comfortable appeal to human beings. Men make things all the time, so when they are confronted with the problem of explaining the existence of something they did not and could not make, it is an easy psychological step to conclude that some power that has *super*natural abilities did the making.

In any event, Creation, as such, is an unacceptable explanation in science, for it requires the invoking of a force *outside* of nature to account for natural events, and this violates the fundamental ground rules of science. Man uses science to explain and better understand his experience by establishing relationships between and among naturalistic phenomena. That is, science attempts to explain nature, or the materialistic world, in terms of itself. When Creation is invoked, it implies something outside of nature, a supreme being, as the cause of the origin of life, and thus is not a scientific explanation. This does not make it good or bad, right or wrong —just outside of science.

We cannot, then, in this context consider the Creation explanation further, except to point out that it is not necessarily incompatible with acceptable scientific views on the origin of life and matter. Life could very well have come from inorganic substances by means of naturalistic and knowable processes and still be regarded as an event in the unfolding of a Creator's plan.

Biogenesis

The view that life arose from preexisting life is, of course, no explanation whatever for the origin of life. It merely postpones the problem. It is perhaps some comfort to say that life on earth arose from life that already existed somewhere else in the cosmos, but to explain it in this way is to provide only an answer to the problem of the origin of life *here on earth*. It does not even attempt to answer the general question of how the first life came into being. At best it is endless. It is like asking how life came about, and being told that it arose from preexisting life, and then asking where the preexisting life came from, and being told that it too came from preexisting life, and on and on.

Apart from the logical difficulties, the notion of life originating elsewhere in the universe is weakened further by the fact that it lacks any solid empirical evidence. To be sure, there is the realm of possibility; that is, life on earth could *possibly* have come from life elsewhere, and it could *possibly* have come to earth by way of a meteor or some celestial vehicle, or it could *possibly* have begun here as the organic garbage left behind by some interplanetary or intergalactic visitors billions of years ago. But there is no evidence for any of these things, and the question of how life originated would still be left unanswered.

Spontaneous Generation

Having rejected Creation as unknowable and biogenesis as irrelevant, it seems that science has no alternative but to conclude that life must have sprung from inorganic matter. But when we begin to look into the situation, we find that this question has come up time and again in the history of science under the name of spontaneous generation. In fact, people believed in spontaneous generation for many hundreds of years, and they had apparently good reasons for believing in it. Anyone could see that flies arose spontaneously from decaying food, or that rats could be made by putting the right things in a damp dark room for a long enough time. There have been, in fact, published books which contained "recipes" for creating various kinds of animals. By following one recipe you could bring about flies, by following another, rats, snakes, etc. This is spontaneous generation: given the right materials and the appropriate environment, life emerged from the nonliving ingredients.

However much common sense supported this view, experimental evidence did not. Redi, in the seventeenth century, demonstrated that flies did not emerge from putrefying meat if it was placed in a jar covered with gauze, thereby preventing flies from laying their eggs in it. Spallanzoni, in the eighteenth century, showed that boiled broth sealed from the air kept indefinitely and did not develop microorganisms. And Pasteur, in the nineteenth century, refined the experiment of Spallanzoni by designing a special container for the broth which, by means of a curved tube, allowed air to get to the nutrient but trapped the bacteria outside.

All these experiments pointed to exactly the same conclusion: life does not originate from nonliving matter.

It would appear that the problem is perhaps one that science simply cannot handle—one that should be left entirely in the hands of theologians. Creation and biogenesis were rejected, and spontaneous generation was clearly demonstrated as false over one hundred years ago. There is one loophole that can provide a basis for retaining the view of spontaneous generation: all that Pasteur's work, and that of his predecessors, showed was that life does not arise from nonlife *at the present time.* Thus one could still argue that life could have originated some time ago when conditions were different from what they presently are. This is fundamental to the modern scientific interpretation of the origin of life, which views it as the product of a very long series of accumulating events that eventually resulted in life, in a compound able to draw upon substances in its environment and, from them, duplicate itself.

For anyone who knows anything about the chemical makeup of living organisms, this steplike process of gradually accumulating the necessary parts sounds like nonsense, for it is clear that the crucial parts of living organisms are fats, proteins, and carbohydrates. Granted, these are made largely from elements that were known to have been plentiful in one form or another in the early atmosphere of the earth—carbon, oxygen, nitrogen, and hydrogen—but they are extraordinarily large and complicated molecules, and to imagine even the simplest of them arising spontaneously would appear to be out of the question. It would appear to be out of the question, that is, if it were something which had to happen within a relatively restricted time period, or if it had to happen again and again. In fact, we are considering an event which could well have taken over a billion years to happen, an event that needed to occur only once as far as our central problem, the origin of life, is concerned. Furthermore, the taking of each step may well have increased the likelihood that the next step would be taken, so we might well be talking about a chainlike sequence, the outcome of which becomes more and more likely as each new link is added.*

Cannot one argue, however, that this is only in the realm of possibility, as in the case of biogenesis? Is it not true that all that is being offered here is simply something that could *possibly* have occurred? In one sense, yes, but in the very same sense we would have to argue that all we have ever learned from scientific exploration was nothing more than simply possible. Science cannot prove anything; it strives to solve problems by establishing relationships between and among things and events. Appropriate scientific procedures and availability of empirical information enable investigators to determine probabilities between things and events. This science can do, and it is what has been done here. The evidence for the view that life originated gradually and sequentially, as proposed here, is by no means conclusive. No one has proved that this is the way it

* For a detailed and readable account of this view see Wald, 1955.

happened, and no one ever will. But the conclusions are supported by empirical evidence of processes that are known to occur in inorganic substances today, and thus by the orderly formulation of hypotheses, testing them against the data, and the correct application of the rules of logic, we have put probability on the side of this view. Someone who wishes to challenge the view will have to do so by showing: 1) the reasoning is invalid, 2) there is empirical evidence that contradicts it, or 3) another explanation has a higher probability of being correct.

Without arguing the issue further, one thing can be agreed upon: life did occur. Once it came into existence, natural selection and mutation must have begun to operate immediately, bringing about a very slow process of adaptation and differentiation and eventually readaptation and redifferentiation, and on and on.

At first, this process must have occurred wholly within the sea, and the first living organisms must have been very simple. Perhaps, were it possible to observe the circumstances, even now it might be impossible to distinguish between living and nonliving substances. It is likely that these simple life substances subsisted on the simpler organic molecules, themselves the end products of a very long accumulative process. The natural breakdown of organic materials by organisms is a process known as fermentation and, at first, it must have been a very slow process indeed, taking up perhaps one-half of the total amount of time that has lapsed since life began and leaving virtually no clear evidence of its existence. It was, however, a process that had to end, for even though it progressed slowly, it went on more rapidly than the rate at which organic molecules accumulated. Thus the food supply, upon which the fermentation process depended, decreased inversely as life expanded. It was one of the waste products of fermentation—carbon dioxide—that, together with water and chlorophyll, provided a new way for living systems to obtain energy—the process of photosynthesis. Photosynthesis enables plants to obtain the energy necessary for carrying out the life process directly from the sun and to convert this energy into a form usable in the manufacture of their own cells. Part of the process involves extracting hydrogen from water and thereby liberating free oxygen as an unused waste product. Thus as plants evolved, at first in the sea and later on land, an increasing amount of free oxygen entered the earth's atmosphere and ultimately permitted animals to live on land.

THE FOSSIL RECORD OF THE EVOLUTION OF LIFE

The Precambrian

The origin of life, photosynthesis, and oxygen respiration are clearly events of enormous importance to understanding the evolution of life. Yet none of these momentous events left any detectable trace in the paleontological record. Our understanding of how they originated is inferential and indirect, based on recent experimental evidence. By the time organisms began to leave a clear and reasonably continuous record of their existence, they had already differentiated into plants and animals, many with complex and specialized parts, implying a long but largely unknown evolutionary past. The fossil record of approximately one-half billion years is simply the relatively small visible part of a process that began over three billion years ago. Paleontologists refer to the "submerged" part of the record as the Proterozoic and Archaeozoic eras, or the Precambrian (see Table 4–1). Some of the best evidence of what hap-

TABLE 4–1

SEQUENCE OF GEOLOGICAL ERAS, PERIODS, EPOCHS

Era	Period	Epoch	Time (approximate beginning in millions of years ago)*
CENOZOIC	Quaternary	Pleistocene	2
	Tertiary	Pliocene	12
		Miocene	28
		Oligocene	40
		Eocene	60
		Paleocene	75
MESOZOIC	Cretaceous		145
	Jurassic		170
	Triassic		200
PALEOZOIC	Permian		225
	Carboniferous		280
	Devonian		335
	Silurian		375
	Ordovician		435
	Cambrian		520
Proterozoic			990
Archaeozoic			2600

* Except for the Pleistocene, these dates are from Stirton (1959).

pened during the Precambrian comes from the vast expanses of exposed rock that make up the Canadian and Baltic shields. These have been exposed through normal erosion by wind and water, and through the more abrupt effects of repeated glaciations that have swept out from the north, scarring the earth's surface, jarring loose the top layers, and redepositing them farther south. From geological evidence, it appears that the features of the earth were much the same during the Precambrian times as they are now. There were mountains, rivers, lakes, and oceans and regular fluctuations in temperature, including glaciations on all continents. The important difference between then and now is the extreme rarity of evidence of life throughout this vast expanse of time. Clearly, life originated during the Precambrian, developed slowly, and, by the close of the era, began to leave occasional lasting signs of its existence.

Until recently there was very little fossil evidence from the Precambrian. The first discoveries came from the Canadian shield in rocks estimated to be over two billion years old. The fossil remains in these deposits consisted of algae and fungi. More recently, discoveries in the Ediacara Hills of South Australia have yielded an astounding variety of Precambrian fossils, including several varieties of jellyfish, corals, worms, and two other forms that do not resemble any other organisms (Glaessner, 1961).

As these and other investigations have continued in recent years, the Precambrian has become less and less a mystery. There are now good indications of not only the algae and fungi, but of other plants and, more important for present purposes, of animals as well. By the close of the Precambrian, there is evidence of coelenterates (today including the corals and jellyfish), crustaceans (lobsters, crabs, shrimp), porifera (sponges), and trilobites (no living representatives).

So much for the dark ages of the origin and early evolution of life. There is a fossil record that becomes more abundant as it approaches the present, and it continues in the Cambrian, the first period of the Paleozoic era.

The Paleozoic

In dividing the geological record into epochs, periods, and eras, it should be stated that these are largely arbitrary divisions in a long and continuous sequence.

However, there are good geological reasons for distinguishing between the close of the Precambrian and the beginning of the Paleozoic. Events occurred which can be said to have divided one from the other. These geological events are known as revolutions, even though they were drawn out over millions of years, and their general features have been divided into three stages, as follows: 1) a period of intense volcanic activity, usually along the edges of large continental land masses; 2) a period of mountain-building and extreme fluctuations in temperature variation; and 3) the long, slow processes of erosion, weathering down the uplifted surfaces, and the consequent effects on sea levels and coastlines. The causes of these revolutions are not well known, and the problem is not one that needs to be examined here. What is important is that the Paleozoic began during one of these revolutions. The eras, periods, and epochs that followed were also initiated by geological changes, generally of less magnitude than revolutions, but of sufficient consequence to bring about the relatively clear stratigraphic discontinuities of the paleontological record.

At the outset of the Paleozoic, the contours of the continents as we know them were very different. Nevertheless, the major continental land masses were recognizable. The actual boundaries during this stage are not well known for any part of the world, but are better known around Europe and North America than anywhere else. As indicated in Figure 4–1, the continents were covered in part by inland waterways. These were

Figure 4–1. Inland waterways (shaded areas) in North America during late Cambrian times. (After R. A. Stirton.)

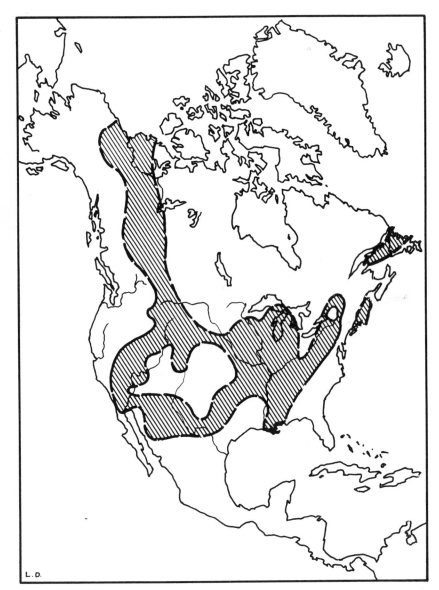

a product of the Charnian revolution and are of greatest importance in appreciating the first significant event in the evolution of life that occurred during the Paleozoic: the filling up of these seaways with a vast array of marine plants and animals and the eventual rise to dominance of many forms of invertebrates. The variation of life forms was so great that, even from the earlier phases of the Paleozoic, it appears that there is fossil evidence of organisms representing all plant and animal phyla. The distinctive feature about these life forms to keep in mind is the fact that during the earlier stages of the Paleozoic all forms were marine.

Beginning in the Cambrian and indeed throughout most of the Paleozoic, the invertebrates remained dominant. By the time the Paleozoic drew to a close, however, some important advances had taken place in the evolution of life. Plants had invaded the earth's land surfaces, and true fishes, amphibians, reptiles, and ancestral mammals had become established. These terrestrial plants and animals appeared as the inland seaways gradually disappeared and as the troughs they occupied began to fill up. Some of the plants and animals whose ancestors were exclusively aquatic adapted first to a transitional and eventually to a completely terrestrial way of life.

All of these changes took place in a span of about 300 million years, which is small when compared with the vast period of time in the Precambrian. Eventually the Paleozoic was brought to a close by another geological event of great magnitude, often referred to as the Permian-Triassic crisis, which occurred about 200 million years ago and which marked the beginning of the next major geological era, the Mesozoic. Before proceeding to the major outlines of the Mesozoic, however, we should first consider in brief detail the periods of the Paleozoic era.

Cambrian. When one is not directly involved with the problems, it is difficult to realize how concerned professional specialists can become over the controversies that exist in their areas of competence. There has been bitter controversy among a handful of paleontologists over the fossil record of the Cambrian (see Simpson, 1960), and more particularly, over how it came into existence. There was an apparent explosive increase in the number of fossils in the Cambrian when compared with the Precambrian. How could this sudden increase be explained? There were three major points of view on the question: 1) There were, in fact, many organisms that lived prior to the Cambrian, but they lacked the attributes which could become fossilized and thus left no record to be discovered. It is to be noted that this is in many ways a restatement of the original problem, since, if one accepts this view, one is then obliged to explain why it is that the necessary attributes "suddenly" appear in so many different phyla during the Cambrian. 2) The ancestral forms of the Cambrian fossils are simply undiscovered, and thus what appears as an abrupt change is, in reality, merely a result of the incompleteness of the evidence. This is hard to think of as a *solution,* since it implies that no problem exists. Given enough time and effort, and presuming that the evidence can be obtained, the entire situation will be clarified. This is one illustration of an amazingly conservative view among scientists, and the Australian discoveries in the Ediacara Hills support this view. 3) The Cambrian fossils are what they appear to be: the varied results of violent changes opening up adaptive possibilities occurring at a time in the evolution of life when the organisms were able to occupy these newly created niches. This explanation is unsatisfactory because it is vague in the sense that very little in the way of specific evidence exists to support it. As time passes, it becomes clear that elements of each explanation are correct.

In any event, the seas and inland waterways probably were teeming with living things during the Cambrian. In addition to different varieties of algae and fungi, there was an abundance of invertebrate forms. Indeed, one can hardly speak of the Cambrian without mentioning the forms known as trilobites (Figure 4–2), a group of invertebrates in the same phylum as insects. The trilobites evolved rapidly during the Cambrian, abounded during much of the Paleozoic, and eventually became extinct before the Mesozoic began.

Very little is known about the conditions that existed on land during the Cambrian, but it is generally agreed that no significant invasion of the land by living organisms had occurred. The Cambrian was probably a time when life existed exclusively in aquatic environments.

Ordovician. The close of the Cambrian was marked by a slight uplifting, particularly in the North American continental land mass. This uplift is reflected in the changed courses of the inland seaways, and in the appearance of new organisms in the next period, the Ordovician.

Figure 4–2. Trilobite. (Courtesy The American Museum of Natural History.)

The Cambrian lasted about 85 million years, or roughly forty times longer than man has been in existence. The Ordovician lasted approximately 60 million years, during which time the invertebrates continued to proliferate and diversify. In their aquatic habitats, some of them reached considerable size. One form, structurally like the modern chambered nautilus, for example, attained lengths up to fifteen feet. The most important occurrence during the Ordovician, however, from the standpoint of human-primate-mammalian evolution, was the appearance of the first vertebrates, fossils of which have been found in deposits exposed by the Colorado River. These were, of course, aquatic forms, fishlike in appearance but lacking jaws. They are called ostracoderms. The evidence from the Ordovician is not too abundant, but apparently the ostracoderms had hard protective covers. There are no Cambrian remains that are clearly chordates, although there have been claims for near-chordates from this period; so the origin of these interesting Ordovician forms remains a puzzle.

Silurian. The Ordovician is followed by the Silurian deposits which provide evidence for the existence of vertebrates in the remains of jawless fishes, the ostracoderms, and, in all likelihood, of the first true fishes, the placoderms, as well. Apart from these, and a variety of evolutionary episodes in the invertebrate lines, the Silurian is of importance in that its deposits provide the first reasonable evidence of completely land-dwelling animals and plants. The animals belonged to a class that became extinct before the end of the Paleozoic. They resembled scorpions more closely than any other modern form. If these animals lived an exclusively terrestrial way of life, and the evidence is not entirely conclusive, then clearly there must also have been plant life, for animals depend ultimately on plants for their subsistence. While direct evidence is lacking, in all likelihood the plants existing during the Silurian were ferns. Perhaps the best indirect evidence of the existence of land-dwelling plants and animals during Silurian times is that both are abundant during the next period, the Devonian. In any case, one should not conclude that the alleged ground-dwelling animals of the Silurian are the ancestors of all later terrestrial forms. These Silurian animals were invertebrates. Vertebrates were already rapidly evolving in the seas, and some of their descendants eventually became adapted to life exclusively on land. We are among those descendants.

Devonian. The Devonian is a most interesting period in the Paleozoic because it provides us with the first evidence of vertebrates emerging from their aquatic environments to spend at least a part of their lives on land as amphibians. It is tempting to think of this occurrence as either the consequence of a kind of "opportunism," as the result somehow of aquatic forms either perceiving the advantages of living on land, or the result of some less perspicacious, more desultory group that was thrown upon the land and had to make their adjustment or become extinct. In all likelihood, changing natural conditions made semiaquatic life impossible for some amphibians. They were faced with adapting to terrestrial life or perishing. The Devonian provides evidence to support this view. The Silurian drew to a close as a result of upheavals that occurred somewhat gradually in a geological sense, but which, in their total effect, had a substantial impact on changing the earth's surface. Former ocean bottoms were raised to become mountaintops, and vice versa. This resulted in not merely a lot more land surface, but changed climatic conditions as well. It appears that the climate throughout the Devonian provided relatively little rainfall, and what there was became concentrated in particular seasonal patterns of alternating moderately moist to very dry seasons.

Many plant and animal phyla were affected by these topographic and climatic changes. Most lines continued to evolve exclusively in aquatic environments. To adjust to life on land, all animals that succeeded were confronted with fundamentally similar problems, particularly those associated with respiration and reproduction. The solutions to these problems were very different, for the obvious reason that each group of animals brought to bear on them very different physiological and anatomical structures.

One immediate difficulty had to be solved if vertebrates were to be able to get along out of water, and that was, of course, getting oxygen. Fish gills provide for the extraction of the oxygen dissolved in water. This is a function they cannot perform in air. A fish taken from water or living in water without sufficient oxygen simply dies of suffocation, as we would if we were put into an airtight bag, or if our heads were held under water. Physiologically, we cannot get oxygen from water any better than fishes can from air.

Understanding the background and conditions of the Devonian makes somewhat clearer the reasons for the appearance in this period of two groups important in the evolution of terrestrial vertebrates—the lunged fishes and the amphibians. Lunged fishes are able to obtain oxygen by means of gills from water and by means of primitive lungs from air. Such an adaptation must have provided a distinct advantage for animals living in ponds that were subjected to alternating wet and dry periods. Among the early descendants of the lunged fishes, the ability to move themselves over land, even very small distances—from a pool that was drying up or becoming stagnant (low in oxygen) to a more favorable location—must have meant the difference between survival and extinction. Refinements in this ability provided by the selective force of evolution resulted in the appearance of amphibians by the close of the Devonian. Amphibians are able to breathe by means of lungs and to cover substantial distances over the ground. Their chief limitation with regard to their ability to live a completely terrestrial way of life is in their reproductive capabilities. Amphibian females lay their eggs in or near water, and in most species these are fertilized externally by the male. Water is an essential medium for the reproductive cycle of all but a few amphibia; lacking a hard shell, the eggs of amphibia, when exposed to the air, dry up rapidly. These were important limitations that eventually were overcome in part by the reptiles, and later more completely by the mammals.

Mississippian and Pennsylvanian (Carboniferous). As far as vertebrates are concerned, the next period of the Paleozoic, the Mississippian, provides very little to hold our attention, simply because very few vertebrate fossils have been discovered in its deposits. The few relevant discoveries simply confirm the existence of a variety of amphibians, and we may conclude our consideration of the Mississippian with a cautious speculation; this was probably the beginning of an evolutionary heydey for the amphibians, for by the next period, the Pennsylvanian, they were both abundant and highly diversified, much more so in fact than they are today. We should also mention that while there is little of importance to the student interested in the forms that included man's ancestors, there is a prodigious amount of fossil material from the Mississippian bearing on the evolution of invertebrates.

The Pennsylvanian is at once more interesting and more puzzling. It is more interesting because the earliest fossil remains of reptiles have been found in its deposits. It is puzzling because the appearance of the reptiles is a difficult evolutionary event to explain.

When European paleontologists discuss the Paleozoic, they include the Mississippian and the Pennsylvanian together in one period they call the Carboniferous. The European name is somewhat more useful, simply because it implies more directly something about the major importance of these periods to modern man, for it is in deposits of these periods that coal was formed. The characteristic habitat for terrestrial plants and animals was widespread marshes and swamps. While the actual composition of the vegetation of these swamps was very different from that of modern times (lacking flowering plants, true conifers, and deciduous trees), there are many superficial resemblances between modern vegetation and that of the Carboniferous period. Covered with a thick overgrowth of a variety of ferns, some of which grew to over fifty feet in height, and scale trees that were twice as tall, ground-level growth was sparse, only patched with sunlight during the day, and inhabited by insects, amphibians, and a wide range of fully aquatic plants and animals.

These conditions continued for many millions of years, during which time the remains of these living forms accumulated to thicknesses of several feet, and, eventually, as the Pennsylvanian came to a close, were gradually compressed by layer upon layer of additional soil. The result of this process was the formation of coal, containing trapped energy in the form of large concentrations of the remains of living organisms laid down millions of years ago, fortuitously preserved, and turned into solid form by extreme pressure.

Some time before the conditions changed and the Pennsylvanian came to an end, true reptiles emerged as a new form from amphibian ancestors. Reptiles differ from amphibians in several ways, but most important, from the standpoint of evolutionary potential, are differences in their reproductive systems. Fossil evidences of changes in the reproductive system are rare indeed. In fact, the differences in the record between the reptiles and amphibians are so minimal that paleontologists occasionally argue over whether particular fossils should be thought of as representing amphibians on their way to becoming reptiles, or early reptiles that retained many amphibian characteristics. The argument is unimportant here, but it serves to emphasize that reptiles emerged from amphibians, and that during the Pennsylvanian the fossil evidences of differences between them are very slight.

Between modern amphibia and reptiles, however, the differences are both numerous and more sharply defined. Probably the most fundamental difference, in terms of evolutionary significance, consists in the fact that amphibians generally lay their eggs in water, to be fertilized externally, whereas reptiles lay hard-shelled eggs, which have been fertilized internally. An important evolutionary implication of this fundamental difference is clear: freed of the requirement of carrying out part of the reproductive cycle in water, the reptiles could become completely terrestrial animals. A hard-shelled egg could be laid on land without dehydrating, and internal fertilization provided a physiological means whereby conception could occur before the shell developed. The fact that a particular adaptation is advantageous, however, is not sufficient to explain how or why it took place, and in the case of the reptiles and amphibians it is not possible to provide reasons from fossil evidence alone. Quite possibly these early ancestors of the reptiles were essentially aquatic animals that laid their eggs on land to protect them from aquatic predators. In this way they may have become better adapted to life on the land and unwittingly provided themselves with a strategic survival advantage as the Pennsylvanian drew to a close, its marshes and swamps drying up, giving way to the Permian, the final period of the Paleozoic.

Permian.   The Permian climate was similar to that of the Devonian, marked by alternating periods of wet and dry, hot and cold, and even glaciations in the Southern Hemisphere. Such abrupt and alternating conditions could be expected to have significant consequences on living forms, and this expectation is supported by the fossil evidence. Amphibians became more restricted as their adaptive zones became reduced in size and number. Many aquatic forms, both vertebrate and invertebrate, died out. The reptiles expanded into completely terrestrial adaptations, setting the stage for the truly remarkable forms that were to appear during the

Mesozoic, the age of reptiles. One event of considerable importance in our concern with the evolution of man and the primates occurred during the Permian: the appearance of a group known as therapsids. Therapsids were basically reptiles with some mammalian characteristics. They were in all probability representative of the evolutionary transition between the reptiles and the mammals. It is not certain that true mammals existed by the close of the Paleozoic. If so, they were small and relatively unimportant, destined to remain relatively inconspicuous throughout the Mesozoic.

Summary of the Paleozoic

The Paleozoic lasted over 300 million years. Mountain-building, volcanic eruptions, glaciations, earthquakes, wind and water erosion, and the activity of living organisms all acted to bring about alterations in the earth's environment. Changing environmental conditions provided continual and often ruthless challenge to living forms to adapt or die out. The possible responses to these stimuli at any one time were limited by the range of life's variations. However, as adaptation followed adaptation, the range of variation increased, providing for new adaptive possibilities. The record of these changes is preserved, in part, in the fossil record, testifying clearly to the succession of events beginning with the Cambrian plants and invertebrates, followed by the appearance of simple vertebrates, true fishes, amphibians, reptiles, and mammallike reptiles, or perhaps true mammals, as the era draws to a close.

The Paleozoic came to a close with a period of geological upheaval. The reptiles emerged as the dominant forms and proliferated extraordinarily during the Mesozoic, producing an amazing array of descendants, mostly terrestrial, some aquatic, and some that could fly. Mesozoic strata record this evolution of the reptiles.

The Mesozoic

The Mesozoic is divided into three periods, Triassic, Jurassic, and Cretaceous. The entire era lasted for about 125 million years—less than one-half the duration of the Paleozoic. It is notable for the occurrence of three events: 1) the origin, development, diversification, proliferation, and extinction of the dinosaurs; 2) the appearance and development of flowering plants; and 3) the early evolutionary record of the true mammals.

Triassic. In the evolutionary record of the reptiles, the Mesozoic is an era of extremes. This is best noted in the appearance of the dinosaurs. Their origin may be found in the curious, small, terrestrial reptiles of Triassic times, some of which had developed a new way of getting around—bipedal locomotion—walking on the two hind limbs. This group of reptiles is known as thecodonts. This modification, so important in man's evolution, liberated the forelimbs from locomotion. How these were put to use provides the basis for most of the fundamental differences between and among the thecodont descendants. Some retained a bipedal gait and reached enormous size, as in *Tyrannosaurus,* probably the most fearsome carnivore ever to walk on land. Others, like *Brontosaurus,* grew to lengths of eighty feet and developed bulks weighing over forty tons, supporting their bulk on all four limbs in swampy areas and shallow lakes. Unlike *Tyrannosaurus, Brontosaurus* was a herbivore (see Figures 4–3 and 4–4). Although often pictured together, they were separated by about 50 million years.

Still other descendants of the thecodonts developed wings which allowed them to glide from heights, but probably not to fly as we usually think of flight. The Mesozoic was indeed the age of reptiles, and as far as most of them were concerned, including the dinosaurs, it spanned their beginning and their ending. There was an abrupt extinction of many groups before the Cenozoic began. One factor that undoubtedly contributed to extinction of the dinosaurs was the selective pressure and competition they faced with the emergence of the mammals. To be sure, the mammals of the Mesozoic were no match for brutish dinosaurs, but they might well have had a taste for reptile eggs, and, under the right circumstances, this could be a most effective selective pressure. In addition, the mammals began to develop an attribute that the reptiles lacked conspicuously—intelligence. Many of the large dinosaurs had brains smaller than the human fist. However, before concluding that this made them inferior, recall that dinosaurs, as a group, lived hundreds of times longer than man seems likely to live.

The mammals, though small and unobtrusive, were clearly present in Mesozoic times. In the fossil record, the evidence for their existence

Figure 4–3. *Brontosaurus,* a giant amphibious dinosaur. (Courtesy The American Museum of Natural History.)

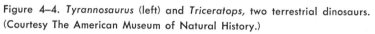

Figure 4–4. *Tyrannosaurus* (left) and *Triceratops*, two terrestrial dinosaurs. (Courtesy The American Museum of Natural History.)

consists of skeletal and dental remains that possess many mammalian features, but these are of secondary adaptive importance when compared with such characteristics as warm-bloodedness, internal development of the young in the mother's uterus, and the feeding of offspring by means of mammary glands. The fossil record fails to provide much direct evidence bearing on the acquisition of these features. An interesting suggestion has been offered that the enlarged "fin" on the backs of some Mesozoic reptiles was a device providing for internal temperature regulation. On skeletal evidence the modern monotremes are very much like reptiles. Perhaps they represent the kind of adaptation that characterizes the earliest mammals. If so, then perhaps, like the modern monotremes, the earliest mammals may have hatched their young from eggs and then fed them from mammary glands. Apart from these considerations, however, what we know about the Mesozoic mammals is based on skeletal evidence.

Jurassic and Cretaceous. Evidence of mammals during the Jurassic is not abundant. As far as the skeletal evidence is concerned, the Jurassic forms are undoubtedly mammals that retained a variety of reptilian traits. These Jurassic reptilelike mammals are known as Pantotheria. By the close of the Mesozoic, pantotherians had given rise to the marsupials and the placental mammals.

While some of the Jurassic pantotherian ancestors were carnivorous or herbivorous, the earliest placental mammals were probably insectivores. They were small (in the size range of modern mice and squirrels) and, as the name implies, insect-eaters. Their diet is implicit in the structure and arrangement of their teeth, snouts, and the development of the areas of their brains which controlled their sense of smell. These insectivores diversified throughout the Cretaceous, occupying several adaptive niches. In doing so, they gave rise to most of the living orders of mammals, including the primates, whose evolutionary picture is drawn in more detail in the next chapter.

Another event during the Mesozoic had far-reaching consequences in modifying the earth's environments: the origin of flowering plants, the angiosperms. Plants had been adapted to living on land since Silurian times. The appearance of flowering plants is of more than passing importance to one interested in the origin of the primates. The angiosperms produce seeds, flowers, and fruits. Thus, while plants abounded on land prior to the Mesozoic, their variety was limited to mosses, ferns, horsetails, conifers, etc. The spread of the angiosperms beginning in the Jurassic provided new adaptive possibilities in the evolution of animals. Insects, for example, were clearly affected. Likewise, mammalian evolution was affected by these changes. Some mammals adapted to grasslands and to forests while retaining a terrestrial way of life. Others adapted to living in the many new kinds of trees, that is, to an arboreal way of life. It was this arboreal adaptation in the evolution of the early mammalian insectivores that eventually led to the origin of the primates.

The appearance of flowering plants also played an important role in the evolution of another group of vertebrates that made its first appearance during the Mesozoic, the birds. Like the mammals, birds arose from reptile ancestors. They are probably descendants of the early Jurassic bipedal reptiles, the thecodonts, the group that gave rise to many of the dinosaurs as well.

While it is common to suppose that the distinctive feature of birds is their ability to fly, this is not the case. Some birds, like the penguins, cannot fly at all, while some animals that are not birds, such as bats and most insects, are able to fly. Flight, then, fails to distinguish birds as a group, but the presence of feathers does. Flight is one of the many locomotive variations that arose from the bipedal thecodonts. As a form of locomotion, it apparently arose twice in descendants of thecodonts, once in the flying reptiles which eventually became extinct, and once in the origin of true birds.

In most fundamental features, the birds closely resemble the reptiles. They differ in two important and related ways: 1) they are warm-blooded, a feature they share with mammals, and 2) they have feathers. Accounting for the origin of feathers is a guessing game at best. Embryologically, feathers develop in much the same way as scales in reptiles, but it is not known what selective factors operated to differentiate the birds, as a group, from their reptile ancestors. In any case, it appears that feathers functioned as heat insulation, reducing heat loss due to continuous and rapid activity, thereby providing the birds with a means of regulating their internal body temperatures. Only secondarily, it would appear from the fossil evidence, and only after modifications occurred in the structure of forelimbs, did the ancestors of the modern birds become successful and eventually graceful flyers.

Summary of the Mesozoic

The events of the Mesozoic were of great importance in the eventual appearance of true primates. If all the events were known—their time, place, and duration—it would be possible to thread them together into clearly outlined deterministic relationships. But only a few of the events are known, and these in a general way. There are enough, however, to provide us with important clues. In summary, the most important features of the Mesozoic times were: 1) *Reptiles were dominant.* They were highly varied and reached extremes in size, and most became extinct by the close of the Mesozoic. 2) *Flowering plants appeared,* bringing about decided and far-reaching changes in the composition of many of the earth's environments. Many new adaptive possibilities were thereby made available. 3) *Birds appeared* and proliferated rapidly with their descendants diversifying and occupying several different adaptive niches. 4) *Mammals appeared for the first time.* Among the earliest placentals were the small insectivores, some descendants of which took to living in the trees. It is the evolution of these that we will continue to follow.

The Mesozoic ended in another great geological upheaval, of which the Rocky Mountains are a magnificent remnant. At the beginning of the Cenozoic, the flora and fauna of the earth appeared much like those of today, with one conspicuous exception: there were no mammals that looked much like today's. Horses, camels, hippopotami, lions, squirrels, mice, dogs, sheep, goats, monkeys, apes, and men had not yet evolved. But they were evolving, and the way in which they evolved is recorded in the fossil record of the Cenozoic. Since our interest is with man, we will proceed to consider the earliest members of man's order, the primates.

REFERENCES AND
SUGGESTIONS FOR ADDITIONAL READING

COLBERT, EDWIN H.
1955 *Evolution of the vertebrates.* New York: John Wiley & Sons.
DE BEER, GAVIN
1964 *Atlas of evolution.* London: Thomas Nelson & Sons.
GAFFRON, HANS
1960 The origin of life. In *The evolution of life: its origin, history, and future.* Vol. 1 of *Evolution after Darwin,* ed. Sol Tax, pp. 39–84. Chicago: University of Chicago Press.
GLAESSNER, MARTIN F.
1961 Pre-Cambrian animals. *Scientific American* 204, March, pp. 72–78.
GREGORY, W. K.
1951 *Evolution emerging.* 2 vols. New York: Macmillan.
MOODY, PAUL A.
1962 *Introduction to evolution.* 2d ed. New York: Harper & Row.

OPARIN, A. I.
    1957   *Origin of life on the earth.* 3d ed. New York: Academic Press.
ROMER, ALFRED S.
    1941   *Man and the vertebrates.* 3d ed. Chicago: University of Chicago Press.
    1966   *Vertebrate paleontology.* 3d ed. Chicago: University of Chicago Press.
SIMONS, ELWYN L.
    1967   Unraveling the age of earth and man. *Natural History,* February, pp. 53–59.
SIMPSON, GEORGE GAYLORD
    1960   The history of life. In *The evolution of life: its origin, history, and future.* Vol. 1 of *Evolution after Darwin,* ed. Sol Tax, pp. 117–180. Chicago: University of Chicago Press.
STIRTON, R. A.
    1959   *Time, life, and man: the fossil record.* New York: John Wiley & Sons.
TAX, SOL, ED.
    1960   *The evolution of life: its origin, history, and future.* Vol. 1 of *Evolution after Darwin.* Chicago: University of Chicago Press.
WALD, GEORGE
    1955   The origin of life. In *The physics and chemistry of life,* pp. 3–26. A Scientific American Book. New York: Simon & Schuster.

CHAPTER 5

ORIGIN AND EVOLUTION
OF THE PRIMATES

The Modern Primates

Until now, the direction taken in our presentation of the origin and evolution of life has been to move from the past toward the present. However, now that our attention is to be focused on the primates, it will be of use to recall the information presented in Chapter 2 on contemporary members of the order, and to point out some of the factors peculiar to the problem of interpreting the evidence of primate paleontology.

First of all, it should be emphasized that there is a great deal of evidence that bears directly on primate evolution. Very little of the evidence, however, is fossil evidence. Most of it comes from living primates, for included among them are representatives of every major evolutionary stage through which the order has passed. The primates are unique among mammals in this respect, having, as they do, living representatives of the insectivore-to-primate transition (tree shrews), of the early arboreal adaptation (prosimians), of the later, more successful, arboreal offshoots of prosimian radiation (the New and Old World monkeys), of the brachiation adaptation (the apes), and finally of the erect-bipedal-cultural stage and its phases. In its most general outline, this is the story of primate evolution, but it is the very existence of this chainlike ordering of living forms that serves to confound interpretations of the fossil record. In popular discussions it causes confusion, for it leads to the impression that man is descended from the apes, which, in turn, are descended from the monkeys, etc. This is, of course, plain nonsense. That the modern species of primates were not ancestral to man is supported best by the fact that they are living species. They are current products of evolutionary pathways that did *not* lead to man but rather to their present adaptive niches. That this confusion continues to be common is probably due to the simple way in which the "evolutionary controversy" is often presented as a choice between special creation and believing that man is descended from monkeys. Claiming that man's ancestors passed through a prosimian or a monkey stage in their evolutionary history is not at all the same as saying that tarsiers, baboons, or gorillas are in our ancestral line. In the same way, saying that the Australian aborigines present a stage in the evolution of culture is not the same as saying that their culture is ancestral to modern culture.

In general, the paleontological evidence supports the prosimian-monkey-ape-man sequence. The fossils are not abundant in any line, since primates have generally lived in tropical regions where conditions allowing fossilization are rare, and, further, because they are more intelligent, they may have avoided getting into circumstances in which duller animals became trapped and fossilized. And wherever there are gaps in the evidence, there is ambiguity and room for disagreement; concordance is rare among primate paleontologists. The following discussion is a continuation of the evolutionary events leading up to modern man, focusing now on the patterns of primate evolution and the available evidence.

INSECTIVORE ORIGINS OF THE PRIMATES

That the primates evolved from insectivore ancestors has already been discussed. The order Insectivora may have been the earliest group of placental mammals to persist. The order has a long and reasonably complete fossil record going back approximately 130 million years. The only other living mammalian order with comparable antiquity is the order Carnivora, and there is no clear record of which of the two was the earlier.

In any case, the Insectivora evolved very rapidly as the Mesozoic was drawing to a close. In addition to providing the ancestral basis for the primates, they also gave rise to the rodents, the lagomorphs (rabbits and hares), and an order that has since become extinct known as the Multituberculata. The insectivores and their early descendants were all small animals with small brains. For example, many had skulls that took up less volume than man's little finger. All were insectivorous, as implied by the name of the order. Beyond these simple features shared in common, most of the known information concerning their differences is drawn from evidence of their dentition, since teeth are by far the most common fossils.

The dentition of the insectivores is often highly specialized, evolving as it has in response to the unusual selective requirements of obtaining and eating insects as the major, or possibly sole, source of food. The degree of specialization is reflected in the arrangement of the teeth, their differentiation into types such as molars and incisors, and particularly in the form of the incisors themselves. Some lines developed incisors for chiseling, others for snipping or gnawing, and, in the case of the rodents, incisors that continued to grow throughout the animal's lifetime.

Provided with the fundamental advantages of mammalian characteristics, and confronted with very little serious competition in their environment, the early insectivores evolved very rapidly, as indicated by the record of fossil teeth. Eventually the ancestral insectivores generated their own most serious competitors, as they gave rise to the rodents, multituberculates, and primates, and as a result they declined, perpetuating themselves in a few specialized lines such as the present-day hedgehogs and shrews.

The transition from insectivore to primate is not clearly documented in the fossil record. As noted earlier, the only evidence available for speculating about this phase is from the modern *Tupaia*, the tree shrews. It will be recalled that the tree shrews are, in most important respects, primates, but they have retained many features characteristic of the insectivores. Their diet is largely insectivorous, and they depend heavily on their sense of smell, as implied by their long snouts and the large olfactory areas in the brain, in comparison with other primates. Thus, it seems reasonable to view them as illustrative of the insectivore-primate transition, but it would be better if there were fossil evidence to reinforce this assumption. As it is, no fossil material has ever been conclusively identified as tupaioid. Two forms have been suggested (*Adapisorex* from the Eocene and *Anagale* from the Oligocene) as fossil tupaioids, but the status of each has been questioned.

The important features of the emergence and evolution of the early pre-primate insectivores can be summarized briefly as follows: 1) They are possibly the oldest placental mammalian order. 2) They evolved and diversified rapidly during the latter part of the Mesozoic, and, by early Cenozoic times, had given rise to three more mammalian orders, the rodents, multituberculates, and the primates. 3) The subsequent evolution of the insectivores is characterized by a decline in their diversity and habitat range. 4) While the fossil record of insectivore evolution is reasonably good in some lines, the transition from insectivore to primate is not documented by fossils. The basis of knowledge about the transition is by inference from living forms. 5) There is abundant reason to believe, however, that the major factor which served to distinguish the primates as a separate order was an arboreal adaptation. The adjustment made by the early primates to living in the trees is by far the most important event in the evolution of the primates, and there is a reasonable amount of direct fossil evidence bearing on the early stages of the evolution of the prosimians, which were the first primates to show the effects of this adaptation.

ARBOREAL ADAPTATION

Evolutionary Consequences

Enumerating the consequences of an arboreal way of life on the early insectivores that eventually evolved into prosimians is very nearly the same thing as listing the distinctive characteristics of the primate order, for, fundamentally, members of the order are like one another and unlike other mammalian orders because of the changes required for success in the trees. One could probably find evidence for the evolutionary effects of the arboreal adaptation in any and all aspects of primate features. The most significant and far-reaching consequences, however, were those affecting the limbs, the senses, and the brain. Further discussion of each of these should help to make more clear the enormous significance of the arboreal adaptation on the primates.

The Limbs.   That the primates are an unspecialized order of mammals has already been emphasized. Taking this view enables one to discern something fundamentally unique about the pattern of primate evolution, and that is the retention of generalized adaptations that may often be found in very ancient ancestral forms. Thus, when we find the primates adjusting to new circumstances, as the early prosimians did in adjusting to their life in the trees, we expect and find that they are not developing a variety of new and specialized traits, but rather that they are rearranging very old adaptive characteristics. This feature of primate evolution may be seen in the consequences of an arboreal adaptation of the limbs and the hands and feet, particularly when contrasted with other terrestrial mammalian orders. The presence of five digits on each of the hands and feet, the structural and functional differentiation of the fore- and hind limbs, and the functional versatility of movement of the limbs, hands, and feet are all attributes that may be found in reptiles and amphibians and might best be regarded as primitive terrestrial vertebrate characteristics. More recently, terrestrial mammals have specialized, with some reducing the number of digits, minimizing the differences between the fore- and hind limbs, and limiting much of the free range of movement in the limbs and extremities. In doing so, these terrestrial mammals have improved particularly in their speed ranges.

Thus, when one reads that as the primates took to the trees the fore-limbs and hind limbs became differentiated, it should be clear that this is not a brand-new characteristic, but rather a relative statement implying simply that the differentiation was carried somewhat further in the primates than it had been in their ancestors. The forelimbs, and particularly the hands, became much more actively involved in grasping, balancing, and directing the progress of the early primates as they moved through the trees. Too, the hind limbs and feet were active in grasping, balancing, and directing, but, more fundamentally, they provided structural support and strength for the animals' movements in the trees. Understanding the background of generalized vertebrate characteristics, the altered functional requirements imposed by the arboreal environments, and the way in which natural selection operates makes it possible to understand in a more profound way the simple statement that as the primates took to the trees their forelimbs and hands became structurally and functionally differentiated from their hind limbs and feet.

This differentiation was ultimately of great importance to man's origin and evolution, as will be seen in the next chapter. Even in the early stage of primate evolution, it resulted in an improved capacity to pick up, examine, and manipulate objects. While it is presently impossible to demonstrate conclusively how this by-product of an arboreal adaptation might have been advantageous to the prosimians, it is relatively easy to speculate that it was, for in the next evolutionary stage to appear—the monkeys —it may be seen as a refined and efficient capability.

The selective refinement of the ability to explore and manipulate objects in the environment can provide some assistance in our understanding of another feature of primate evolution: the development of nails as opposed to claws. Fingernails and toenails are specializations within the primates that require some special explanation. Unfortunately, there is no cogent standard argument which can be readily supported by the facts of the fossil record and contemporary primate variation. As an educated guess, Le Gros Clark (1960) suggests that the development of the nail in primates is probably associated with a relative advantage in solving problems of locomotion, since nails permit greater dexterity and greater tactile sense.

Taking to the trees, then, may be seen as an event that initiated important modifications in the limbs and extremities of the early primates. If the modern prosimians are fair representatives of this adaptation (and it must again be noted that they provide much more evidence on these questions than fossils), then in the context of overall progress in primate evolution only the first indications of the transition may be expected among the early primates.

The Senses. Insectivores depend primarily on the sense of smell to inform them about the features of their environment that are important to them. The evidence for this is clear and unambiguous; they have long noses with complicated and delicate internal structures that function to refine their smell discriminations. They have *rhinaria,* areas of moist skin surrounding the tip of the nose, that help to locate the direction of odors. And, finally, the olfactory areas of their brains are much more fully developed than the areas controlling the other senses. In the modern as well as the early prosimians, the sense of smell continues to be important, but less so in relation to the other senses when compared with insectivores. The olfactory area of the brain is large; the snout in most is long and its internal structure complicated; and some retain the rhinaria to the present time (see Figure 5-1).

While the olfactory sense is obviously important to both the insectivore and the prosimian, the other senses, particularly vision, are much more fully represented in the cortical areas of the prosimians. Thus, there are good structural reasons for concluding that a change in emphasis took place in the insectivore-primate transition, and there are good functional reasons for concluding that this change took place because of the requirements imposed by an arboreal adaptation. The functional basis for the increasing importance of vision is obvious: for an animal the size of even the small prosimians to move rapidly from branch to branch requires a knowledge not only that another branch is there and its direction, but also a knowledge of exactly how far away it is. In this situation stereoscopic vision is necessary to permit depth perception.

One of the most striking features in the appearance of the modern lemurs and tarsiers is the large size of their eyes. This development is apparently due not simply to the increasing importance of vision in the emergence of the primates, but to the fact that these modern prosimians are nocturnal. It might be tempting to conclude from this that all the early primates were nocturnal, but this would not appear likely since the photoreceptors, which are required for effective daylight vision, were certainly present in earlier forms. It would seem, then, that night vision among the primates is a secondary adaptation which, like fingernails, developed in primate evolution sometime after the order became distinct. Furthermore, it apparently took place twice, once in the line leading to the modern prosimians and again in the line leading to *Aotes,* a nocturnal New World monkey. Apart from these, all the modern primates have both rod (dark) and cone (light) photoreceptors on their retinas. In fact, beyond the prosimian level there are very few differences in the structure of the eyes of monkeys, apes, and men. Yet the evidence is clear that man's vision is much better than that of the others, which indicates that the improvements are related more to overall improvements in the areas of the brain that control vision and not to structural changes in the eye.

The evidence for the changes that might have taken place in the other special senses in response to an arboreal adaptation is not as abundant nor as easy to deal with as in the cases of vision and olfaction. With regard to the sense of touch, it should be noted that prosimians have well-developed tactile hairs, and in this feature they are like many other mammals and not like the higher primates. As we have noted already in connection with the development of finger- and toenails, the efficient arborealists developed sensitive feeler or digital pads and in the process lost the tactile hairs. Thus, again, an arboreal adaptation can be seen as the basis for modifying the sense discriminations among the primates.

There is even less to say about the senses of hearing and taste. Apart from the external ear, very little work has been done on the comparative anatomy of primate hearing apparatuses. The external ear does not vary a great deal from group to group, and, where variations occur, they seem often to be due to temperature regulation more than to differences in hearing discriminations. Again, however, there is an absolute and relative increase in the areas of the brain that control hearing, and from this, one might tentatively conclude that the sense has undergone improvements, but it is not something that can easily be related to the consequences of an arboreal adaptation.

When the early primatelike insectivores took to the trees, the successful ones, at least, underwent some changes in their dietary habits. This fact is implicit in the record of dental modifications. This may imply something about modifications to the sense of taste, but if it does, these implications are not at all clear.

The Brain. In addition to the changes in the senses, the earliest primates were subjected to selection for improved motor dexterity. These two factors are, of course, controlled by the brain; thus, improvements to them would seem to call for improvements in those areas of the brain that control them, and this is exactly what appears to have happened. Figure 5–1 illustrates the comparison of an insectivore and prosimian

Figure 5–1. Comparison of the side views of an insectivore (*Cententes*) brain with a prosimian (*Tarsius*) brain. The insectivore brain has been increased by two-thirds to make the comparison clearer. Note the greater development in the olfactory bulb in the insectivore brain. (After W. E. Le Gros Clark.)

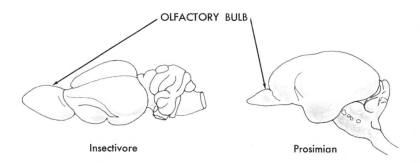

OLFACTORY BULB

Insectivore   Prosimian

brain. Motor dexterity and the senses are controlled in areas of the outer covering of the brain, the neopallium. It is clear from this illustration that although the center controlling olfaction is comparatively smaller in prosimians, the centers controlling vision are very much larger. This is even more obvious in higher primates.

The important implication here is simply that the brain underwent substantial changes as the early prosimians adapted to a life in the trees. Furthermore, these changes led to an overall improvement in the structure of primate brains over those of other mammals. Even the lowliest primates are alert, intelligent animals. This is an adaptive investment that has continually reaped dividends in primate evolution. Hopefully for man, intelligence will continue to hold its own in the ruthless, competitive marketplace of evolution.

Fossil Evidence

The earliest stages in primate evolution are better documented by fossils than are many of the later periods. (For a summary of the most important fossil primates consult Table 5–1.) From the Paleocene and Eocene epochs, there are fossil representatives of over sixty genera, which have been grouped into eight families. From the Paleocene, one of the most interesting and best-known forms is *Plesiadapis*, whose remains have been found in both North America and Europe. *Plesiadapis* had a specialized set of

Figure 5–2. Comparison of: a) the Paleocene *Plesiadapis* with b) the Eocene *Smilodectes*. (After E. L. Simons.)

TABLE 5–1

SUMMARY OF IMPORTANT TERTIARY DISCOVERIES OF
FOSSIL PRIMATES

Name	Location	Time	Materials Discovered
Plesiadapis	Europe, North America	Paleocene	One almost complete skull and an incomplete skeleton (Europe), several teeth and jaw fragments and an incomplete skeleton (North America).
Notharctus	North America	Eocene	Skulls, teeth, postcranial bones, and an almost complete skeleton.
Smilodectes	North America	Eocene	Several skulls and several postcranial bones.
Protoadapis	Europe	Eocene	Fragmentary mandibles.
Adapis	Europe	Eocene	Several skulls and teeth.
Necrolemur	Europe	Eocene	Several skulls and limb bones.
Parapithecus	North Africa	Oligocene	Lower jaw; though other fragments have been discovered, they are not described. Before 1960, misinterpretations were common due to the absence of the middle portion of the jawbone, which went unrecognized until then. Probably the earliest Old World monkey.
Apidium	Egypt	Oligocene	Originally a few fragments, additional material, including some juveniles, discovered recently. Perhaps a close relative of *Parapithecus*.
Propliopithecus	Egypt	Oligocene	Lower jaw and teeth. Small gibbonlike form that may be ancestral to gibbons, apes, and man.
Aegyptopithecus	North Africa	Oligocene	Five partial lower jaws and an almost complete skull.
Limnopithecus	East Africa	Miocene	Represented by several fragmentary remains, including limb bones. Perhaps more correctly included with *Pliopithecus*.
Proconsul	East Africa	Miocene	Considerable remains, including limb bones, a skeleton of a hand, and an almost complete skull. Probably an African member of the *Dryopithecus* group.
Dryopithecus	Europe, Asia, Africa	Miocene to Pliocene	Known mostly from a large inventory of jaws and teeth.
Mesopithecus	Europe, East Africa	Miocene to Pliocene	Abundant remains particularly from Greece.

TABLE 5–1 (*Continued*)

Name	Location	Time	Materials Discovered
Pliopithecus	Europe	Miocene to Pliocene	Several discoveries assigned to this genus including an almost complete skull. In the gibbon phylogeny.
Sugrivapithecus, Bramapithecus, Sivapithecus, Paleosimia	Africa, Europe, Asia (mostly India)	Miocene to Pliocene	Several fragmentary upper and lower jaws and isolated teeth. Probably all of these should be included with either *Dryopithecus* or *Ramapithecus*.
Kenyapithecus	Africa	Miocene to Pliocene	"*Kenyapithecus*" Africa Miocene upper jaw fragments with one lower tooth. Possibly an African variety of *Ramapithecus*.
Oreopithecus	Europe	Miocene to Pliocene	Abundance of remains including an almost complete skeleton.
Ramapithecus	Originally from India. Now believed to have had wide distribution over Old World.	Miocene to Pliocene	Originally, one fragment of an upper jaw; a few other jaws and teeth have been assigned to this genus.
Gigantopithecus	India, China	Pliocene	Very large teeth and jaws of an ape that is now extinct.

teeth. Its incisors were adapted for chiseling. Moreover, *Plesiadapis* had claws, and not nails, on its toes and fingers. Thus, it would appear that this is not a likely candidate for the ancestral line leading to higher primates. *Plesiadapis* does, however, represent one of the lines that lay along the transitional pathway from insectivore to primate, or, in other words, it represents a morphological translation of the early effects of an arboreal adaptation on the primates.

Whereas the Paleocene was of short duration, lasting approximately 15 million years, the Eocene continued for about 20 million years. Middle Eocene fossils found in North America, Europe, and Asia resemble in considerable detail some modern prosimians, particularly the lemurs. These include *Notharctus* and *Smilodectes* from North America, and from Europe, *Protoadapis, Adapis,* and *Necrolemur*.

Perhaps the most interesting feature of the early record of primate evolution is that in spite of the abundance of fossils, it is impossible to relate the evidence clearly either to the origin of higher primates or to the evolution of the modern prosimians. From Oligocene times on, the fossil record of the evolution of the prosimians is very sparse. No doubt

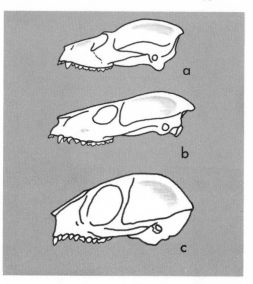

Figure 5–3. Lateral view of the skulls of: a) *Adapis parisiensis*, b) *Notharctus osborni*, and c) *Necrolemur*. (After W. E. Le Gros Clark.)

this is due partly to the fact that the prosimians themselves become more scarce as they came into competition with monkeys and rodents.

The details of the evolutionary background of the New World monkeys, the Platyrrhinae, would doubtless be informative and interesting, but unfortunately we know very little about them. Furthermore, no higher evolutionary stage of primates emerged in the New World. Thus, it is an area of less importance to the understanding of human evolution. For these reasons their evolution and fossil record are ignored by anthropologists.

In many ways the catarrhine monkeys are simply advanced prosimians. The trends in primate evolution initiated by the arboreal adaptation and represented by the prosimians are more obviously represented in the Old World monkeys. The monkeys, better than any other group, represent the generalized primate adaptation. Insofar as they embody in a more efficient way the effects of an arboreal adaptation, it follows that a listing of primate characteristics is a listing of monkey characteristics, much more so than characteristics for prosimians, apes, and man. Clearly, the fossil documentation of the emergence of the Old World monkeys could provide key insights into the general evolutionary picture of the primates, but, in fact, this record simply does not exist. Oligocene deposits from Egypt have yielded remains of two genera, *Apidium* and *Parapithecus,* which may represent the earliest catarrhines. The interpretation of *Parapithecus,* known originally only from one lower jaw, has been confused by the fact that it appeared to have only two incisors instead of four, as in other primates.. For this reason, some authorities felt that *Parapithecus* might not even have been a primate. A recent reinvestigation of the original discovery, however, in the light of the many new

Figure 5–4. The mandibles of: a) *Para-pithecus*, b) *Propliopithecus*. c) *Pliopithe-cus*, and d) modern gibbon. (After W. E. Le Gros Clark.)

Figure 5–5. Skull of a Pliocene monkey, *Mesopithecus pentelicus*. (After W. E. Le Gros Clark.)

finds of Simons' expeditions makes it appear that *Parapithecus* did indeed have four incisors, and may well be the oldest Old World monkey. The confusion appears to have come about as a result of the disintegration of the front part of the jaw at the time it was discovered. From the Pliocene, the catarrhines are represented by *Mesopithecus*, known from southern Europe. A form from the Miocene of East Africa has also been identified as *Mesopithecus*. This form is currently being relegated to a separate genus (*Victoriapithecus*) by von Koenigswald (in press). *Mesopithecus*, on the basis of dental homologies, appears to represent an ancestral stage in the evolution of the Colobinae, the modern arboreal monkeys that subsist on leaves.

Are the monkeys representative of an ancestral stage through which man's ancestors passed? The answer to that question is simple: We do not know. The fossil evidence needed to answer the question simply does not exist.

BRACHIATION

Evolutionary Consequences

The ability to get through the trees by means of swinging by the forelimbs under the branches is called *brachiation*. The apes are distinctive as a group among the Old World primates primarily because of the attributes they have acquired in the evolutionary process of becoming efficient brachiators. As previously discussed, it would appear that the arboreal adaptation was the first major event in primate evolution, producing, as it did, the prosimians and the monkeys. Brachiation is the second major event. As an adaptive response, it resulted in the morphological features distinctive of the apes, and some changes in the ways that brachiators related to and functioned in their environments can be inferred from this adaptation.

The consequences of brachiation have been reported by Virginia Avis (1962). She has carefully and thoughtfully explained the importance of brachiation and its significance in man's evolutionary past. The question she raises as to whether or not man's ancestors brachiated has long been warmly debated in physical anthropology (see Straus, 1949). Attempts to answer the question usually have resulted in simple lists of the pros and cons. On the pro-brachiator side of the issue is the fact that man and the apes have a similar conformation of the thorax, well-developed clavicles, and a variety of skeletal and muscular features that appear to be the result of a brachiating ancestry. On the other side are the proportions of the limbs, a well-developed and strong thumb, and another list of skeletal and muscular features that appear to be too generalized to have continued through the filter of a brachiating ancestry. The question is clearly fundamental to the solution of the problem of man's ancestry; since brachiation is the adaptive factor that is basically responsible for the emergence of the apes, then answering the question of whether or not man's ancestors brachiated is also answering the question of whether or not our ancestry includes apes.

Since the evidence both of fossils and from comparative anatomy appears to allow either alternative, it seems that the question cannot be answered. Some headway can be made, however, if the problem is approached in a modified way. Is it essential, for example, that brachiation necessarily implies a highly specialized animal? Or, in another way, was the brachiation adaptation necessarily a limiting one, or, as Avis claims, could it at one time have expanded the adaptive possibilities of the ancestral forms that gave rise to apes and perhaps man? Is it a reasonable likelihood that modern apes represent extremes in their adaptations that arose from an ancestry of less efficient, less specialized, perhaps more clumsy brachiators? If one admits the possibility of these alternatives, then the original controversy loses some of its meaning. It allows for the view that man and the great apes share a common ancestry beyond the monkey stage of primate evolution. The common ancestor would presumably be a brachiator, but not a very good one, and thus lacking many of the modern apes' specializations. There is a modest amount of evidence to support this view in a fossil known as *Proconsul,* which will be discussed later in this chapter.

There is a general question that seems to come readily to mind when discussing events such as an arboreal or a brachiating adaptation, and that is: Why should such changes take place? This same issue was raised in the last chapter when dealing with the emergence of mammals, reptiles, and amphibians, and the answer is probably the same. There is no need to presume some mystical force that motivates animals to evolve, nor is there any reason to presume that organisms are in any way purposive or directive of their evolution. As long as internal and external factors remain constant, evolution will not occur, but when modifications of heredity and the environment impose survival problems on living organisms, some members of a group survive while others do not. Those that survive are different from those that do not, and it is the accumulation of these differences that is the very act of evolution. In any event, brachiation apparently is an adaptation that is a ready possibility (as opposed to flying, galloping, or slithering) given the kinds of animals that primates are, for it apparently arose at least three times independently: once in the New World in the line leading to the spider monkey, again in the ancestry of the gibbons, and finally in the line leading to the great apes.

Fossil Evidence

The fossil record for the emergence of the apes is somewhat better documented than in the case of the catarrhines. For years, a fossil form known as *Propliopithecus* has been regarded as the earliest ape. Its remains are known from Oligocene deposits in Egypt, and the standard interpretation has been to regard *Propliopithecus* as the earliest known ancestor of the modern gibbon. Recently, Yale University conducted a survey of the Egyptian deposits, where an abundance of primate fossil material was discovered. There is reason now to believe that *Propliopithecus* is more generally apelike than was formerly thought. On the basis of new discoveries, Simons (1964) has questioned this standard interpretation of *Propliopithecus,* which he indicates "may well prove to be on or near the line of evolutionary development that led to the lower pongids and man." Whatever the status of *Propliopithecus* may be, another discovery, made in 1968, may represent a form ancestral to the diversified group of

Figure 5–6. Remarkably complete skull of *Aegyptopithecus* discovered in Egypt in 1967 and first reported by E. L. Simons in early 1968. *Aegyptopithecus* is Oligocene in date and interpreted as the oldest hominoid. (Photo of cast by J. H. McCullough.)

hominoids from Miocene times known as the dryopithecines. The discovery consists of an almost complete skull of an ape identified as *Aegyptopithecus*.

More complete remains of a gibbonlike form are known from the early Miocene of East Africa. The form is known as *Limnopithecus,* and its remains include parts of the postcranial skeleton, including the limbs. If one were to classify the animal on the basis of the limb proportions and features, it is likely that *Limnopithecus* would be included with the cercopithecoids. The limbs lack the expected specializations associated with the brachiation adaptation of the modern gibbons. *Pliopithecus* is also a fossil member of the gibbon-siamang group. It is Miocene to Pliocene in date and is known from remains found in Europe. Actually, *Pliopithecus* and *Limnopithecus* are very similar, and it may be that they should be regarded as members of the same genus. As a group, they fit rather well into a sequence of the evolution of the gibbons, which begins

Figure 5–7. *Proconsul* skull. (By permission of the Trustees of the British Museum, Natural History.)

with the affinities being apparent in the morphology of the teeth and is then characterized by modifications in the limbs brought about, undoubtedly, by the brachiating adaptation.

Apart from *Aegyptopithecus*, there are no fossil pongids from the Oligocene. The record of the ancestral forms of the modern apes and man does not become reasonably abundant until Miocene times. A group of fossils collectively known as *Proconsul* is known in its earliest phases from the Miocene of East Africa. They are in all likelihood the African varieties of the more broadly distributed form *Dryopithecus*. Not only are *Proconsul* forms widely distributed animals, but, in addition, are far from homogeneous. They include animals that range in size from that of a small chimpanzee to a large gorilla. For this reason it is perhaps misleading to refer to them by a single term. *Proconsul* lacks some of the specializations of the modern apes and, for this reason, occupies a position of considerable interest to human paleontologists. Here is a form that was as yet not clearly committed to a brachiating adaptation. The available evidence includes limb bones as well as teeth and jaws. The structure and proportion of the limb bones, like those of the *Limnopithecus* in the gibbon line, is very much like those of the monkeys. In its dentition, however, the *Proconsul* group is very much like the modern apes, particularly in the

Figure 5–8. Side view of a *Dryopithecus* skull. (Courtesy The American Museum of Natural History.)

morphology of the molars, the major differences being that the *Proconsul* molars are relatively smaller.

Clearly, *Proconsul* occupies a time and displays a morphology that makes it of special interest in the study of primate evolution. Not only is *Proconsul* like the modern apes in the shape of its molars, but it is in this respect also like man and his ancestors, differing again in relative size. Furthermore, *Proconsul* lacks the specialized adaptations of the post-cranial skeleton associated with efficient brachiation and thus could represent an ancestral stage shared by both the great apes and man. *Proconsul* is broadly distributed, morphologically diversified, and sufficiently unspecialized to be a reasonable candidate for perhaps the latest common ancestor to man, chimpanzee, gorilla, and orangutan.

Dryopithecus is interesting for many of the same reasons. This form is known from Miocene and Pliocene deposits from Europe and Asia, but, except for a single limb bone of questionable affinities, is known exclusively from teeth and jaw fragments.* In form, the dentition of the Dryopithecinae is more like that of the modern apes than that of *Proconsul*, which suggests that whereas *Dryopithecus* may represent an evolutionary stage one step beyond *Proconsul* in the phylogeny of the great apes, the line leading to the hominids may well have separated at an earlier time. This can hardly be regarded as much more than speculation, however,

* Leakey (1968a) reports briefly on a discovery he identifies as *Dryopithecus* from Fort Ternan in East Africa.

since the more fundamental, and presumably simpler, problem of the relationship between *Proconsul* and *Dryopithecus* is not at all clear. There are two main views on the problem, one regarding *Dryopithecus* as a highly varied group broadly distributed over the Old World and lasting in time from early Miocene to Pliocene times. Such a view then includes the numerous *Proconsul* finds as representative of a segment of the generalized dryopithecine group. Another view places them in an ancestral relationship with *Proconsul* the ancestor and the dryopithecines the descendants. Again and again, we are confronted with theoretical impasses such as this. Which of the two theories is more likely to be correct? By now it should be clear that it is not possible to know for certain, so it is largely a matter of choice. What is somewhat more fundamental is the suspicion that the problem of determining the relationship between *Proconsul* and *Dryopithecus* may never be solved. It is common in the face of such problems to claim that the questions cannot be answered without more fossils, and it is also common to wonder if this is indeed true, or simply a way of getting around a difficult problem. In fact, it would appear to be true; as the number of fossils increases, there is an increase in the range of agreement on fundamental issues and an increase in disagreements on more and more trivial issues. As more fossils are unearthed, the view that *Proconsul* and *Dryopithecus* are members of the same genus becomes more widely accepted. In view of the fact that they are similar in appearance and lived at the same time, it would seem logical to conclude that they may simply represent regional variants of the same genus. If this view is adopted, then the entire group may be included in the genus *Dryopithecus*.

Other recent discoveries have pointed to the need for a drastic reconsideration of the age of the hominids. Until recently, the hominids were

Figure 5–9. Lateral view of the left lower jaw of *Aegyptopithecus zeuxis*. (After E. L. Simons.)

Figure 5–10. Comparison of the upper jaw of: a) *Ramapithecus,* b) orangu-tan, and c) man. In each comparison the jaws have been made the same size. *Ramapithecus* is clearly more like man than he is like the orangutan. (After E. L. Simons.)

presumed to be very recent arrivals with an antiquity estimated at some-where between 1 and 2 million years. That they might be much older was indicated first in a reconsideration of a group of fossils known from India which had been interpreted as recent pongids. Identified first as separate genera, four are named after Hindu gods, *Sugrivapithecus, Ramapithecus, Bramapithecus,* and *Sivapithecus,* and the fifth is known as *Paleosimia.* These have been known since 1935 and until recently occupied a questionable position of secondary importance as evidence bearing on the evolution of the apes. This appears to be due to the fact that they were at first thought to be Pleistocene in date, and thus too late to be of much interest, but it now appears that some at least go back to early Pliocene. This has brought about a reconsideration of the fossils, and recently an analysis and reconstruction of the upper jaw of *Ramapithecus* has resulted in the startling conclusion that it is a hominid and not a pongid (Simons, 1964). The similarities are, of course, based on the jaw and teeth, specifically the form of the palate and the dimensions of the teeth (one of which, the canine, was reconstructed on the basis of the size of its socket), and it is this that is hard to accept. It is one thing to say that *Ramapithecus* is more like man, but the essential distinction be-tween the pongids and hominids is the fact that the latter are bipedal with erect posture, and this cannot be concluded with confidence from evi-dence of the jaw and teeth.

Further support for the great antiquity of the hominids has come from a recent discovery in Africa. *Kenyapithecus wickeri,* recovered in East Africa by L. S. B. Leakey in 1962, is strikingly similar to *Ramapithecus* and of comparable age. Both are dated at from 14 to 15 million years old. In further support of the hominid status of *Kenyapithecus wickeri,* Leakey has offered evidence recently (1968b) that the Miocene form may have been using bone tools. This remains highly conjectural. However, if *Kenyapithecus wickeri* turns out simply to be an African representative of *Ramapithecus,* then it appears that during the Miocene there were three major genera of higher primates: *Pliopithecus, Dryopithecus,* and *Ramapithecus. Pliopithecus* appears to be descended from *Propliopithecus* of Oligocene times and to be on or near the line leading to modern gibbons and siamangs. *Dryopithecus* and *Ramapithecus* may be the descendants of *Aegyptopithecus* of the Oligocene, and, as the evidence stands now, *Dryopithecus* appears to have given rise to the pongids and *Ramapithecus* to the hominids.

Another form, *Oreopithecus,* from the Pliocene, has been given many different interpretations. It has been regarded by various authorities at different times as an Old World monkey, an ape, a transitional form between the monkeys and apes, and a transitional form between the apes and man. It was first described in 1872, and, until 1958, all that was known about the form was based on fragmentary jawbones and teeth. In 1958, a most remarkable discovery was made in Italy of approximately fifty individuals of oreopithecine remains, including an almost complete skeleton of one individual. These remains have been dated as early Pliocene. The abundant remains seem largely to justify the earlier confusion, for in the rest of the skeleton may be found a surprising amalgamation of monkey, ape, and hominid traits. So far it would appear that the remains have done little more to clarify the phylogenetic and taxonomic position of *Oreopithecus* than to remove from contention the view that it was an ancestral catarrhine. The question now focuses more directly on the issue of whether it should be classified with the Hominidae or Pongidae or if it should be assigned to a separate family. William L. Straus, Jr. (1963),

Figure 5–11. Reconstructed skull of the August 2, 1958, discovery of Oreopithecus. (After J. Hürzeler.)

METRIC

Figure 5–12. Jaw of *Gigantopithecus*, a giant ape form that apparently became extinct. Its remains are known from China and India. This jaw from India was reported in the summer of 1968 by E. L. Simons. (Courtesy E. L. Simons.)

has made an extensive analysis of the *Oreopithecus* material and concludes that: "There is no valid reason for regarding [*Oreopithecus*] as belonging to the family Pongidae. Hence it must either be classified as a member of the family Hominidae or placed in a family of its own, the Oreopithecidae. . . . I am at present inclined to classify *Oreopithecus* as a primitive, aberrant member of the Hominidae." It is difficult to appreciate the basis for Dr. Straus's conclusion without some sophistication in comparative anatomy. However, it should be emphasized that his choice is essentially a matter of taste, and another competent investigator could easily conclude that *Oreopithecus* belongs in a separate family of its own. The ambiguity over its correct classification is probably due, in part, to the lack of other fossil forms from the same general time period.

A recent discovery in India is likely to contribute to our knowledge of primate evolution during the Pliocene. Announcement of the discovery was made by Elwyn Simons, and it consists of a very large lower jaw of a form identified as *Gigantopithecus*. This is truly a remarkably large and massive jaw with correspondingly large teeth. Simons believes that *Gigantopithecus* may be one of the Pliocene descendants of *Dryopithecus* that failed to survive up to the present time.

The Miocene-Pliocene border is clearly a most important chapter in primate evolution, but in many ways we know less about it than we do of earlier periods. The forces that drove man's ancestors out of the trees must have been gathering, but exactly what these were remains a subject of speculation with little data available.

PROBLEMS IN INTERPRETING PRIMATE EVOLUTION

In surveying the evidence bearing on primate evolution, one cannot help but realize that much of our understanding of the course of events is based on very little fossil evidence. Most of the better conclusions are reached by imposing the facts of modern primate variability onto the fossil record, rather than by the seemingly more logical process of interpreting the modern from the evidence of the fossils. Thus it is that we learn about the past from the present, rather than the other way around.

When one hears of interpretations of the phylogeny of the primates, it would be well for him to keep the following in mind: 1) The early periods in the Paleocene and particularly the Eocene are comparatively well known, being represented by many fossils of prosimians, divided into at least five families. 2) From Eocene times onward, the primates clearly underwent many important modifications; this much is clear from the comparatively sparse fossil evidence. How, where, and when these modifications took place are not questions that can be answered in most cases.

Certainly we need more fossils to increase our knowledge and to increase our confidence in our conclusions. However, it may be that even more important information is needed. What might be more important is a reevaluation of some fundamental issues, the answers to which have been presumed and unquestioned too long. For example, what are fossils able to tell us about phylogeny? About the significant evolutionary events in a particular line? Can we with reason expect to reconstruct phylogeny with a more complete fossil record, or is this too much to expect? If, again, we draw a parallel with artifacts and cultural evolution, the problem may become more clear. It is only under the most extraordinary circumstances that an archaeologist is able to make developmental connections between the artifacts of a particular site and the history of a contemporary group. Artifacts provide one basis for drawing inferences about the way in which culture has progressed along its many lines, and the general outlines of the picture are becoming more and more clear and more and more consistent with the facts of present-day cultural variation.

Similarly, it might improve our overall understanding if fossils were thought of in this way; that is, as bases for general statements about the way in which primates have evolved. No one, of course, claims that a particular fossil is ancestral to a particular modern form, but the step from a particular fossil to the presumption that it represents a population that may have been ancestral to a modern form is not a great one.

As others have noted, evolution is a two-faceted phenomenon (see Sahlins and Service, 1960, or Dobzhansky, 1962). One aspect of evolution is adaptive. Forms diversify and radiate into niches, and progress is relative to their success in meeting the requirements of the adaptive problems. Sahlins and Service call this aspect *specific evolution* and contrast it with *general evolution,* which results in the production of higher forms and where progress can be measured absolutely in terms of overall *adaptive capability.* They were writing particularly about cultural evolution, but clearly there is a parallel in biological evolution. Archaeological artifacts are used mostly to provide information about general evolution, and only rarely about specific evolution. Perhaps the limitations of the archaeologist are the same as for the primate paleontologist.

Finally, primate paleontology may have to rediscover evolution. While it is appealing to anyone with a sense of history to attempt to reconstruct the details of the phylogenetic record to try to answer the particular questions of which forms are related and in what ways, these are likely to be problems that will be with us forever. It would seem that it is the very process of evolution that makes that approach a practical impossibility. As living organisms adapt to their environments, they do so by continuing to diverge, converge, specialize, and generalize; in the process, they cover up the very tracks some would hope to follow in reconstructing phylogenetic histories. It is, however, this dynamic process of continual change that is recorded in the fossil record, and in retrospect it is this very thing that paleontology set out to study.

REVIEW

Prior to the appearance of hominids, primate evolution is characterized by the appearance of two evolutionary stages: 1) an arboreal stage, and 2) a brachiating stage. The arboreal stage may be subdivided into three phases: 1) prosimians, 2) Old World monkeys, and 3) New World monkeys. Some New World monkeys eventually became brachiators, but the adaptation among them did not result in as much difference within the group as it produced among Old World forms. In the Old World, the brachiating adaptation provided the fundamental distinctions between the apes and monkeys and produced two major phases: 1) the gibbons, and 2) the great apes.

The evidence for this sequence consists mostly of inferences from contemporary primates. The fossil evidence is not abundant, but, in general, it tends to support that from comparative anatomy.

REFERENCES AND
SUGGESTIONS FOR ADDITIONAL READING

AVIS, VIRGINIA
1962   Brachiation: the crucial issue for man's ancestry. *Southwestern Journal of Anthropology* 18:119–148.

BARTH, FREDRIK
1950   On the relationships of early primates. *American Journal of Physical Anthropology* (n.s.) 8:139–149.

CLARK, W. E. LE GROS
1957   *History of the primates.* Phoenix Books. Chicago: University of Chicago Press.
1960   *The antecedents of man.* Chicago: University of Chicago Press.

DOBZHANSKY, THEODOSIUS
1962   *Mankind evolving.* New Haven: Yale University Press.

EIMERL, SAREL, AND IRVEN DEVORE
1965   *The primates.* New York: Time, Inc.

GREGORY, W. K.
1922   *The origin and evolution of human dentition.* Baltimore: Williams & Wilkins.

HOOTON, EARNEST ALBERT
1947   *Up from the ape.* Rev. ed. New York: Macmillan.

LEAKEY, L. S. B.
1968a   Upper Miocene primates from Kenya. *Nature* 218:527–528.
1968b   Bone smashing by late Miocene hominidae. *Nature* 218:528–530.

MCKENNA, MALCOLM C.
1963   New evidence against tupaioid affinities of the mammalian family Anagalidae. *American Museum Novitates* 2158:1–16.

PATTERSON, BRYAN
1954   The geologic history of non-hominid primates in the Old World. *Human Biology* 26:191–209.

PILBEAM, D. R., AND E. L. SIMONS
1965   Some problems of hominid classification. *American Scientist* 53:237–259.

SAHLINS, MARSHALL D., AND ELMAN R. SERVICE
1960   *Evolution and Culture.* Ann Arbor: University of Michigan Press.

SIMONS, ELWYN L.
1960   New fossil primates: a review of the past decade. *American Scientist* 48:179–192.
1963   Some fallacies in the study of hominid phylogeny. *Science* 141:879–889.
1964   Early relatives of man. *Scientific American* 211, July, pp. 50–64.
1965   New fossil apes from Egypt and the initial differentiation of Hominoidea. *Nature* 205:135–139.

SIMPSON, GEORGE GAYLORD
    1940   Studies on the earliest primates. *Bulletin of the American Museum of Natural History* 77:185–212.
STRAUS, WILLIAM L., JR.
    1949   The riddle of man's ancestry. *Quarterly Review of Biology* 24:200–223.
    1963   The classification of *Oreopithecus*. In *Classification and human evolution*, ed. S. L. Washburn, pp. 146–177. Viking Fund Publications in Anthropology, no. 37. Chicago: Aldine.
WASHBURN, SHERWOOD L.
    1951   The analysis of primate evolution with particular reference to the origin of man. *Cold Spring Harbor Symposia on Quantitative Biology* 15:67–78.
    1967   Perspectives and prospects. Paper presented to Wenner-Gren Supper Conference on Primate Studies. April 27.

CHAPTER 6

ORIGIN AND EVOLUTION OF MAN

INTRODUCTION

Uniqueness of the Record

In evaluating the evidence of primate or mammalian evolution, paleontologists depend very heavily on the comparative anatomy of living forms as a crucial source of supplementary information. In the effort to understand the details of human evolution, the comparative anatomy of contemporary groups of modern men is of no value. Man is a single, highly varied species and, unlike the evolutionary stages reflected in the major groups of living primates, the so-called races of man do not represent phases in the evolution of man. Each is the end product of an evolutionary pattern characterized by intersecting phylogenies which has continually folded in upon itself. This pattern of evolution has provided for growth, diversification, and expansion within the species without resulting in the formation of new species. Thus, it would seem that the human paleontologist is limited to the strict details of the formal properties of fossils and, when available, the temporal coordinates. Time becomes particularly important, since the entire course of human evolution took place within a few million years. This implies that our scope of interest is to be focused on considerably smaller evolutionary units and processes when compared with the sweeping panorama taken in viewing the evolution of life and the evolution of the primates. It is one thing to conclude with some confidence that the Paleozoic reptiles included the ancestors of today's birds and mammals, but quite another to claim that an early Pleistocene fossil discovery is (or is not) a member of a species or population that ultimately gave rise to modern man.

These cautions are intended to remind the reader at the outset that when attention is directed at human evolution specifically, the scope implied is a very limited one indeed. The human paleontologist focuses on the evolution of one species that lived over 90 percent of its existence in some of the world's most inaccessible areas—an evolution which took place virtually overnight, geologically speaking.

These are useful cautions to keep in mind, but one should realize as well that the difficulties brought about by limiting the scope are made up for by the rather abundant fossil record of hominids and by the even more abundant archaeological record of culture. Even when the many sites yielding remains of modern man are excluded, say within the last 20,000 years, there are still over one hundred fossil-man sites and thousands of archaeological sites. It would, of course, be ideal if the sites were known equally well from all stages over the last few million years, but in fact most are known from the last 70,000 years.

As both the archaeological and paleontological records become more complete, and as man's understanding of the interrelationships between the biological and cultural factors improves, it will probably become less and less desirable to separate the two fossil records for consideration. As matters stand now, however, it is difficult or impossible to know what one implies concerning the other; that is, what archaeological remains may imply about the biological status of the hominids that made the objects, or vice versa. It is, however, becoming increasingly clear that man's biological variation is one expression of a complex of interdependent and interrelated factors that includes culture as well as the animate and inanimate aspects of the broader environment. All factors must be considered as a collective totality if we are to understand comprehensively the ways in which man and his ancestors have adapted, survived, developed, and thrived. Both theory and technique are at present too poorly developed to achieve this ideal objective. However, in what follows, an attempt is made to present not only the fossil evidence, but the relevant archaeological, paleontological, and, on occasion, geological and climatological information as well.

The Pleistocene

The Pleistocene began approximately two million years ago. On four separate occasions within that time, much of the Northern Hemisphere was covered with massive continental glaciers. There are several theories that attempt to explain the cause of the glaciers, but at present it is not possible to decide definitely on the correct one. Whatever the cause, it is clear that ice sheets gradually expanded outward from mountaintop elevations and southward from polar latitudes. On each occasion the process of expansion continued for thousands of years and then stopped; the climate moderated; the ice sheets receded; and the scenery returned to a condition much like that of today in the same areas. Indeed, most specialists claim that we are now in an interglacial period.

The same glaciations covered parts of both the New and Old World, but the sequences in each have been given different names. Table 6–1

TABLE 6–1

NOMENCLATURE OF EUROPEAN AND NORTH AMERICAN
PLEISTOCENE GLACIERS

Pleistocene		European	North American
	Fourth Glaciation	Würm	Wisconsinian
Late	Riss-Würm Interglacial		
	Third Glaciation	Riss	Illinoian
	Mindel-Riss Interglacial		
Middle	Second Glaciation	Mindel	Kansan
	Günz-Mindel Interglacial		
Early	First Glaciation	Günz	Nebraskan
	Pre-First Interglacial		

shows the correspondence and separate nomenclature. As shown in the table, the events of the Pleistocene are made to appear more stark than they really were. They are made to appear as sharp as Tuesday following Monday. However, the onset of any particular interglacial is never easy to recognize, undoubtedly begins at different absolute times in different parts of the world, and is a particularly difficult or impossible dating criterion to apply to fossil remains from the Southern Hemisphere. As evidence for dating, the effects of the glaciations are not limited simply to the areas covered by ice, but interpreting the evidence in the southern latitudes is an area of uncertainty and confusion. Until the last few years, it was widely held that the glacial-interglacial sequences of the north corresponded to alternating wet-dry periods in the south. This would have made relating events in the two hemispheres a straightforward problem if it were true, but there is evidence for only two such sequences of wet-dry periods, and these are not widely spread throughout the Southern Hemisphere. Furthermore, if and how they relate to the Pleistocene glaciers is not at all clear. What appeared to be a promising and simple relationship turns out to be much more complex and of questionable value, forcing geochronologists to use other techniques yielding more reliable, but often disappointingly limited, estimates of age.

The Archaeological Record

From time to time it will be useful in the discussion of the fossil evidence of human evolution to refer to the archaeological materials in association with the fossil skeletal material. The archaeological record is a reasonably continuous one beginning over one million years ago. It will be useful to digress briefly and consider the general outline of this record.

The sequence of glaciers implies something about the environmental challenges our ancestors were required to meet, and the archaeological record tells us something about how they met the challenges. The sequence of cultural remains from the Old World has been classified into two major stages, the Paleolithic and the Neolithic. The Paleolithic (Old Stone Age) begins with the origin of culture and ends with the origin of agriculture. Agriculture began between 10,000 and 15,000 years ago, and, since man had reached his modern form by that time, attention will be given here only to the Paleolithic (see Table 6–2).

There are five basic types of stone implements from the Paleolithic: pebble, chopper-chopping, core, flake, and blade tools. Later in this chapter an attempt is made to integrate the fossil record of human evolution with the archaeological record; so at this point these tool types are discussed only briefly.

Pebble tools are the oldest type of stone implement. They were made by the simple process of striking two rocks together until a sharp edge was obtained. They are known from several locations throughout Africa, where they are identified as the Oldowan industry. Core-tool traditions have been discovered in Europe, the Near East, southern Asia, and Africa. Core tools are made by shaping a large piece of stone (the core) by striking off smaller pieces (flakes) from all sides. Core tools are known also as hand axes, and improvements in the techniques of the manufacture provide the bases for distinguishing stages in development of the archaeological record. In Europe, the sequence is from Chellean through Acheulean; in Africa it is identified as the Chelles-Acheulean sequence.

Flake tools are smaller than core tools, more diversified in form and more specialized in function. They are found together with hand axes in Europe, Africa, and parts of Asia. In northern latitudes, there is a well-established sequence of flake-tool industries that lacks core tools. This is identified as the Clactonian-Levalloisian sequence. The presence of two distinctive traditions in Europe during Lower Paleolithic times has been interpreted by some as evidence for the existence of two groups of human beings. This is unlikely; it is possible that the flake-tool assemblages represent simply a cold-weather tool kit, whereas the hand-axe assemblages represent implements used mainly during warmer times of the year. Coalescence of the core- and flake-tool traditions in Europe represents the beginning of the Middle Paleolithic, which is identified with the Mousterian industry.

The chopper-chopping tools are similar, on the one hand, to pebble tools, in that they are rather crudely made, but this may be due simply to the fact that the stone used in making chopper-chopping tools is difficult or impossible to shape accurately. On the other hand, the chop-

TABLE 6–2

OLD WORLD PALEOLITHIC SEQUENCES

European Glacial Sequence	Paleolithic	Europe, North Africa, Near East, South Asia	Africa South of Sahara, Near East, South Asia	East Central Asia, Southeast Asia
Present	UPPER PALEOLITHIC 35,000*	Blade Industries	Blade Industries	Blade Industries
Würm	MIDDLE PALEOLITHIC 100,000*	Mousterian	Acheul	Chopper-Chopping Sequence
3rd Interglacial				
Riss	LOWER PALEOLITHIC 2,000,000*	Acheulean Sequence (Core Tool) — Levalloisian Sequence (Flake Tool)	Sequence	
2nd Interglacial				
Mindel		Chellean (Core) — Clactonian (Flake)	Chelles (Tool)	Choukoutienian
1st Interglacial			Oldowan (Pebble)	
Günz				

PLEISTOCENE

* Time (approximate beginning in millions of years ago).

per-chopping tradition is similar to the core- and flake-tool sequences to the west, in that the implements were used in similar ways, and in both areas the traditions lasted throughout most of the Paleolithic.

Blade tools are well-made implements that may be found throughout the Old World. Their appearance signifies the beginning of the Upper Paleolithic, and they are found with anatomically modern man.

The archaeological record of man in the New World extends back only to about 20,000 to 30,000 years ago. This indicates that when man first reached America, the Upper Paleolithic blade tools had already become established throughout most of the temperate zones in the Old World.

The Fossil and Archaeological Evidence

Commonly a discussion of human evolution is divided into four parts: 1) modern man, 2) Neanderthal man, 3) *Homo erectus*, and 4) *Australopithecus*. The discussion that follows is no exception, but the divisions themselves may be misleading. When only a few fossils were known, differences between them appeared more sharp and clear, but as more have been discovered, the distinctiveness of these groups has tended to fade into continuous gradations. It is convenient to talk about the groups separately, but bear in mind that the real subject under discussion is evolution, a dynamic and continuous process.

Modern Man

At first it may seem unimportant to consider fossil remains of modern man, but this would be a mistake. There is a fundamental division of opinion on the course of human evolution among professional physical anthropologists that comes from a disagreement over how old modern man is. Thus, if it is true that anatomically modern man was alive at the same time as, or earlier than, one or more of the other three types of hominids, then the types that overlap cannot be ancestral to modern man. If, for example, modern man had already appeared before Neanderthal man, then obviously Neanderthal cannot be an ancestor to modern man. This very issue is basic to the most common source of disagreement among human paleontologists, one side maintaining that none (or at least not all) of the other three types is ancestral to us because our type is too old, the other side claiming that modern man is very recent and that Neanderthal, *Homo erectus*, and *Australopithecus* are ancestral stages in our phylogeny. Without a knowledge of the record, it is impossible to reach any judgment, so we must take a look at the most important remains.

There is a second reason for considering modern man. The significance of variations displayed by fossil forms can be appreciated only after one has some awareness of the ways in which these traits vary in modern

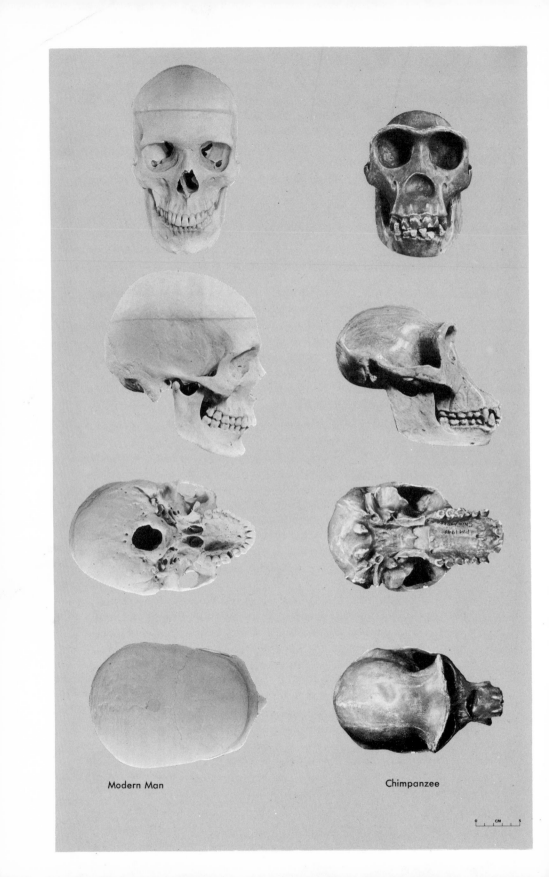

Modern Man   Chimpanzee

populations. Specialists undergo extensive training in an effort to learn as much as possible about modern man's morphology as a basis for comparison. Attention here is directed at only a few of the more striking and significant features of the skull. To make as sharp a contrast as possible, Figure 6–1 compares the skull of modern man with that of a chimpanzee from four views. In the first comparison, the frontal view, there are, as you would expect, some striking differences. The chimp has large brow ridges above its eye orbits, a broad and massive appearance to the face, projecting canines fixed in a dental arch that is more angular than that of man. If you look at the top of the skull in this view, a projecting bony ridge, the sagittal crest, may be seen to course along the midline of the head. This serves as an area for the attachment of some of the muscles that move the jaw. No such crest may be seen in the modern man; instead the skull of man shows a smaller and narrower face with a distinct forehead and a smooth, rounded contour to the top of the skull. It lacks the projecting canines and, in general, conveys a less rugged appearance.

From the side, the most striking feature distinguishing the two is the size of the brain case. In man it is very large and continuous with the front of the skull, and in the chimp it is rather a second area of the skull, attached as it is to the back side of the face. Looking down on the chimp's skull, one can see that it is more obviously separated in this view by the deep grooves running under the zygomatic arches (cheekbones) and behind the supraorbital ridges. Returning to the profile again, we may note the large mastoid processes in man, the differences in the chin contours, and the presence of another ridge of bone, the occipital crest, which, like the sagittal crest, serves as an area of muscle attachment, in this instance for the muscles that move the neck. In three dimensions we would again note the coarser, more rugged surfaces on the chimp as compared with man.

Looked at from below and without the lower jaw attached, the most striking features are the shape of the dental arch and the location of the foramen magnum, the large hole through which the spinal cord passes. Unlike the angular contour of the ape, the dental arch in man is open and rounded. The position of the foramen magnum implies erect posture in man, situated, as it is, well underneath the base of the skull and closer to the center of gravity of the skull. In the chimp it is located well behind the skull's center of gravity.

Looked at as a totality, the two skulls may be seen as structures that served different functions in the organisms' adaptive requirements. Apart from its common service as the entrance for food and the housing of the

Figure 6–1. (Opposite Page) Comparison of four views of a modern man skull with a chimpanzee skull cast.

Australian

American Indian

Euro-American

African

0   CM   5

olfactory, auditory, and visual sense receptors, the skull of the chimp is equipped with a face and with teeth that are built to pierce, crush, and tear. This is implicit in the projecting snout (prognathism), the long and pointed canines, the massive jaw, and the sagittal and occipital crests, attesting to the massive muscles that drive the movements of the jaw and neck. Clearly, the chimp's facial region may be effectively used for defensive as well as subsistence purposes. With this in mind, the comparison with man is difficult to make, for the striking distinction is the size of the brain case. This is the skull of a thinking animal, of a form that uses its brain to accomplish the objectives for which the chimp is equipped with sharp teeth and massive muscles.

Among contemporary groups of men there is tremendous variation. Figure 6–2 illustrates some of the variation, but the main features are common throughout: large brain, presence of a forehead, large mastoids, chin, smooth surfaces, and lack of sagittal and occipital crests.

The origin and antiquity of the modern-man type is still an unsettled question, which is another way of saying authorities disagree on the significance of some fossils. There have, in fact, been several remains that have been used as evidence for modern man's antiquity. Table 6–3 lists most of the evidence that has been used to support this view. At first, the evidence appears to be impressive, but careful reevaluation of the material during the last twenty years has caused some drastic revision.

No one takes the first five discoveries as serious contenders in the fossil record, and, apart from its discoverer, few if any consider Kanam as representative of early Pleistocene modern man. It is hard to understand why the discovery at Denise attracted as much interest as it did. Several authorities during the latter part of the nineteenth century and the first two decades of this century studied and restudied this material, and all concluded that it was perhaps early Pleistocene. What is remarkable, however, is that this conclusion was repeatedly reached even though the material is only partly fossilized and there is some evidence that it might have been a deliberate burial.

Moulin-Quinon seems to have been a fraud. Boucher de Perthes had done a great deal of important archaeological work in France. Indeed, he is responsible more than anyone else for providing the earliest cultural evidence through archaeological remains that man had lived in Europe in early Pleistocene times. He wanted very badly to discover fossil skeletal evidence of the men that were making the stone tools he had been discovering, and apparently someone deliberately provided him with the evidence by burying it and making him think he had discovered it.

Figure 6–2. (Opposite Page) Variations among modern man skull morphology. (African photos courtesy G. K. Neumann.)

TABLE 6–3

FOSSILS USED AS EVIDENCE FOR MODERN MAN'S GREAT ANTIQUITY

Name	Discovery		Materials Discovered	Status at Present
1. Denise	1844	France	Several skull fragments.	Discounted.
2. Moulin-Quinon	1863	France	Mandible.	Some evidence that this may have been a deliberate fraud. Discounted.
3. Bury St. Edmunds	1882	England	Skull fragment.	Discounted (see text).
4. Galley Hill	1888	England	Skull and parts of postcranial skeleton.	Regarded as recent burial.
5. Piltdown	1912	England	Skull and jaw fragments.	Deliberate hoax.
6. Mt. Carmel	1929–1934	Israel	Remains of several individuals.	In dispute (see text).
7. Kanam	1932	Kenya	Mandible.	Dating uncertain, relationships uncertain.
8. Swanscombe	1935, 1936, 1955	England	Two parietals and one occipital.	In dispute. Tendency to include with temperate third interglacial Neanderthals (see text).
9. Fontechevade	1947	France	Two parietals and two frontals.	In dispute.
10. *Homo habilis*	1960 et seq.	Tanzania	Skull, jaw, teeth, and hand fragments of a juvenile, and collarbone, hand, and foot remains of an adult.	Uncertain.

Three of the British discoveries, Bury St. Edmunds, Galley Hill, and Piltdown, have been removed largely through the persistent efforts of Kenneth Oakley and his collaborators. All three had been suspected by some experts as being more recent, and all were found to be recent by fluorine analysis.

The Bury St. Edmunds skull fragment may have been given greater significance than it deserved when it was discovered in 1882 in Suffolk. At that time fossils, and particularly human fossils, were scarce, and their importance was easily overemphasized. Looking back, it is clear that the remains were virtually useless for scientific purposes. The Bury St. Edmunds remains were found in association with an Acheulean archaeological assemblage; these are cultural remains that go back to second interglacial (Mindel-Riss) times. Considering these two facts is not, however, sufficient evidence of great antiquity. The discovery site was not examined by a competent geologist or paleontologist; the association of the bones with the Acheulean remains is not certain; the date of the Acheulean remains at this site has not been established (and the Acheulean lasted through the Pleistocene in some parts of the world); and, finally, the skeletal fragment is badly broken.

The story of Piltdown is widely known. It consisted of fragments of an ape jaw, an ape canine, and large fragments of the parietals, the occipital, and the nasal bone of a modern man. These had been stained and filed so that on reconstruction they could be made to fit together, forming the most peculiar anatomical assembly of modern-man-modern-ape characteristics ever known. Reinvestigation in 1950 and again in 1953 revealed it to be a deliberate hoax—made, buried, and probably discovered with the purpose of confounding the experts.

Reinvestigation of the Galley Hill site brought to light the evidence that this discovery, originally estimated as early Pleistocene in date, was in fact a recent burial probably no more than a few thousand years old.

The Kanam and Kanjera discoveries, reported in 1932 by L. S. B. Leakey, consisted of a fragmentary jaw (Kanam) and the fragmentary remains of the skulls of three individuals (Kanjera). The Kanjera materials do not differ from modern man. The Kanam jaw has a pathological growth on the chin region which obscures somewhat its morphological significance and relationships. Leakey claimed early Pleistocene antiquity for Kanam, but an attempt to reexamine the location for geological factors bearing on the antiquity of these remains was frustrated when the original site could not be definitely located. Leakey continues to hold to the view that Kanam is early modern man and, further, now claims to have additional fossil evidence to support his conviction. This additional material is part of the extremely interesting material he and his associates have been uncovering in Olduvai Gorge in East Africa for the last several years. It will make more sense to deal with the Olduvai discoveries after considering the other types of fossil man. At this point it should be stressed that the early Pleistocene levels in the gorge have not produced remains of modern man, but rather of a type that is morphologically more like man than like the other discoveries of comparable antiquity. This form he calls *Homo habilis*, and it will be discussed presently in connection with the problem of interpretation.

The evidence for the great antiquity of modern man, so abundant up to 1940, has declined, or in fact if one ignores the East African material for the time being, has disappeared. There remains, however, the consideration of the Swanscombe, Fontechevade, and Mt. Carmel discoveries.

Swanscombe, as you will note from the table, consists of only three bones. Remarkably, they fit together reasonably well, even though they were discovered over a twenty-year period. The interpretation of this material has been based almost entirely on a careful investigation of the first two discoveries by a special committee established in the 1930's to study the Swanscombe remains. The committee reported (Clark et al., 1938) that except for the unusual thickness of the bones, they did not differ in any important respect from those of modern man. They likewise affirmed that Swanscombe was second interglacial. Thus, here was evidence of modern man between the Mindel and Riss glaciations. Since then, a reinvestigation (Ovey, 1964) of the fossil material and the site has directed attention to the similarities between Swanscombe and some Riss-Würm interglacial fossil hominids. This has tended to emphasize the significance of Swanscombe as evidence for the great antiquity of modern man, but it continues to be a problem, since repeated investigations have continued to reaffirm its date as Mindel-Riss interglacial.

The Fontechevade discovery was made in 1947 in France in the province of Charenté. The fossil skeletal material consists of a few bones from the tops of the skulls of two individuals; no facial bones have been found. In form, the skulls are like those of Swanscombe. The interesting thing about this discovery is the fact that the remains were found beneath archaeological materials associated elsewhere with Neanderthal. Thus it appears that the more modern form precedes Neanderthal and thereby excludes Neanderthal from our ancestry. The remains are, however, fragmentary, and the interpretation has been questioned (Brace, 1964).

A similar issue was raised as a result of the Mt. Carmel discoveries in Israel. These were made in two caves, Tabun and Skhūl, between 1929 and 1934. Between them the caves yielded an extraordinary amount of fossil material. An almost complete skeleton, a lower jaw, and a few other postcranial fragments were discovered in Tabun, and Skhūl yielded the remains of ten individuals, some represented by almost complete skeletal remains, others by a few fragments.

Though the material is highly varied in form, it is basically like several other Neanderthal discoveries. The variability, however, has been bothersome, since some of the individuals show characteristics remarkably like modern man, and to those who maintain that Neanderthal man could not be in our ancestry, this is somewhat embarrassing. The remains were found together in association with the same kind of archaeological material, and apparently the two caves were occupied at the same or nearly the same time. From this it appears that the remains represent a variety of the Neanderthal hominid.

The evidence for the great antiquity of the present type of man is not very conclusive, or perhaps it might be better to say, is not as convincing now as it was thirty years ago. It is, however, a crucial question for the study of human evolution. Summarizing the issue of modern man's antiquity, one might say, excluding the Swanscombe and Fontechevade fragments, it appears that there is very little reason for placing the antiquity of anatomically modern man much farther back than from 50,000 to 25,000 years ago.

Since the formal and temporal factors of modern man as a stage in hominid evolution have been considered, the spatial and contextual aspects need only brief comment. At the present time, of course, man is global in his distribution, and it appears likely that he will eventually become interplanetary. This broad distribution is, of course, only recent. Up to about 25,000 years ago, he was confined in his distribution to the large continental land masses of the Old World. This implies the fact that he lived within a wide range of environmental contexts, and during the last 10,000 years his cultural adaptations have diversified enormously—so much so that it is impossible to say that man today lives in any context. He occupies many different environmental and cultural contexts.

In summary, modern man is variable in his formal characteristics yet morphologically homogeneous enough to be distinguished as a distinctive form of hominid. How old he is remains a problem; the old view, which supported his great antiquity, however, appears to be losing ground. Within the last 25,000 years, modern man has spread out laterally from Europe, Asia, and Africa to occupy his present global distributional range. He seems intent now on spreading out vertically.

Neanderthal Man

The first Neanderthal remains to receive substantial attention were found in 1856, three years before the publication of *The Origin of Species*. Little attention was given to the discovery until after the publication of Darwin's theory of natural selection, which implied that all animals and plants have descended from ancestral forms very different from their present-day descendants. That this might be true for subhuman forms of life seemed to make a mockery of the Book of Genesis. That it could be true for human beings was, to most, an absurdity. Yet a few of Darwin's supporters recalled this 1856 discovery and cited it as evidence in

Modern Man   Neanderthal

support of the view that man may have been subject to evolutionary processes, just as other forms of life had, and even the most critical skeptic, considering the appearance of the Neanderthal skull and further realizing that it must be very old, had to admit that at least it deserved an explanation.

Figure 6–3 illustrates a glacial Neanderthal skull in comparison with modern man. From the frontal view, Neanderthal impresses one with its massive face, large eye orbits, rather low-lying forehead, and the lowered position of the skull's greatest breadth. Yet it lacks the crest and large projecting canine teeth that give so much distinction to the fierce appearance of the chimpanzee. From the side, one again notices the sloping forehead and chin, the large supraorbital ridge, and the somewhat more sharply angled contour to the back of the skull. But what is most striking about the profile view is the size of the brain. Neanderthal brain size is comparable to that of modern man; in fact, on the average, the Neanderthal brain may be slightly larger.

Looked at from below, the differences between the Neanderthal and modern man are slight and difficult to discern. A closer inspection than is possible in an illustration would bring to light some differences in the size of the teeth, and, in larger samples, average differences in location and size of cusp patterns are also detectable.

In most respects, Neanderthal is very much like modern man, but where Neanderthal differs, it does so in the possession of apelike characteristics. This peculiar assemblage of traits required some explanation. At first, the Neanderthal discovery was regarded by most authorities as the remains of an individual with a grossly abnormal bone disease of some kind and thus not representative of an earlier type of man. However, during the 1880's fossil remains of two other individuals of the same general appearance were discovered in Spy, Belgium, and this did much to dispel the belief that the original discovery was a pathological freak. Since that time, Neanderthal remains have been discovered in more than eighty locations, leaving no doubt about the authenticity of Neanderthal man as a former inhabitant of the Old World.

As in the case of modern man, there is substantial variation within the category Neanderthal (see Figure 6–4). This is not at all surprising in view of the fact that Neanderthal remains have been found over a broad range in the Old World, including sites in Europe, North, South, and East Africa, the Near East, Russia, China, and Java (see Figure 6–5).* This

* Many investigators prefer to use the term *Neanderthal* to refer exclusively to the European discoveries.

Figure 6–3. (Opposite Page) Comparison of four views of a modern man skull with a Neanderthal skull cast.

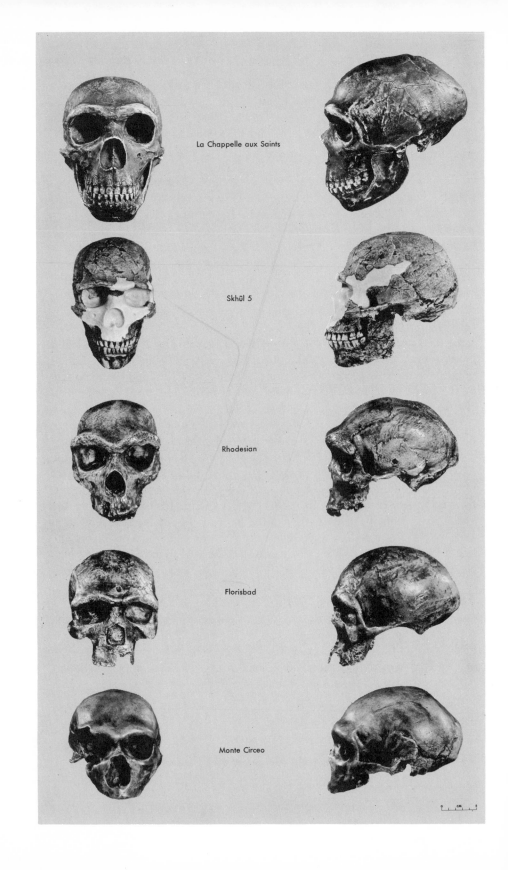

La Chappelle aux Saints

Skhūl 5

Rhodesian

Florisbad

Monte Circeo

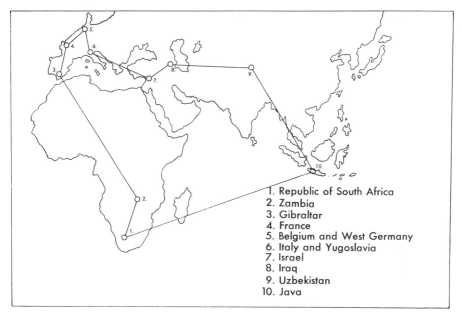

1. Republic of South Africa
2. Zambia
3. Gibraltar
4. France
5. Belgium and West Germany
6. Italy and Yugoslavia
7. Israel
8. Iraq
9. Uzbekistan
10. Java

Figure 6–5. Distributional range of Neanderthals.

distribution clearly indicates that Neanderthal was able to adapt to a wide range of environmental contrasts, including, for the first time in the evolution of the hominids, extremely cold climatic conditions.

If one includes only the remains with well-established absolute dates from among the many Neanderthal discoveries, the period within which it lived is rather sharply defined as between 110,000 and 35,000 years ago (see Oakley, 1964). This is a period which, in the Northern Hemisphere, began during the warmest phase of the third (Riss-Würm) interglacial and ended during the early major advance of the Würm glaciation.

As mentioned earlier, the most effective way of extending our information about fossil forms is by means of inferences drawn from the material itself and, more particularly, from the relationship between the material and the context in which it is found. As recently as ten years ago, it was a relatively simple matter to talk about the "way of life" of Neanderthal. Everyone "knew" that this was the hominid that lived around the Mediterranean toward the close of the Pleistocene, that made a characteristic inventory of implements known as the Mousterian industry (see Figure 6–6), and, since he lived during glacial times, his distinctive morphological features must have been due to the cold climate. During the last few years, it has become more and more obvious that such a view of

Figure 6–4. (Opposite Page) Variations in morphology among Neanderthal skulls.

Figure 6–6. Mousterian assemblage of stone implements. (After **Frederick Wulsin.**)

Neanderthal is not correct. A new view is only now beginning to emerge, based on the following propositions: 1) The Mousterian industry is internally more diversified and complex than it was formerly thought to be. 2) Likewise, the Neanderthal physical type is more heterogeneous than presumed, consisting of several presumably local, but recognizable, variants on the same morphological theme. 3) The distribution of the Mousterian industry is considerably more restricted than the distribution of Neanderthal variants. 4) Explaining "the Neanderthal physical type" as a product of an adaptation to cold climate is not only inadequate, but completely illogical. 5) Recognizing their broader distribution in space, the existence of variants through both space and time reopens the possibility that the form we have been calling Neanderthal man may be no more than the name for a stage through which our ancestors passed. 6) Perhaps not every Neanderthal population gave rise to modern man.

Clearly, then, the problem of extracting inferences from the contexts in which Neanderthal remains are found is not the straightforward one that it used to be. Mention should also be made here concerning two extreme points of view which have prevailed for a long time, each of which, in its own way, inevitably introduces distortion in any effort to draw inferences about either the Mousterian cultural assemblage or Neanderthal man. These are: 1) the very common presumption that Neanderthal must have hunted mammals similar to those that live in cold climates today, and 2) that Neanderthal's needs must always be thought of as having to be met in a cold climate.

These cautions should suffice as warning that we may not get very far in an attempt to draw broad generalizations about Neanderthal from contextual information, but keeping them in mind, it may be useful to subdivide Neanderthal's environment into two parts, the natural and the cultural, and to examine them briefly to see what more there is to conclude about Neanderthal man.

Two main factors should be kept clearly in view when considering Neanderthal man's natural environment. 1) It consisted, in the temperate latitudes, of sharp seasonal contrasts during a year, and over a longer period was affected in both hemispheres by shifting of the earth's climatic zones; and 2) the present-day mammalian fauna is regarded by paleontologists as an impoverished one, many species having become extinct during the last 10,000 years. In other words, one should not presume that everything was very much as it is now, only colder. From the distributional and temporal evidence we have already presented, we know that Neanderthal man lived under three major climatic conditions: temperate interglacial, temperate glacial, and subtropical to possibly tropical climates in Asia and Africa (see Table 6–4). Availability of food sources differed markedly in each zone, and this fact alone must have forced the inhabitants of each zone to adapt their ways of life accordingly, or to face inevitable extinction. Most certainly, plant food was more readily available (and present in substantial abundance) in the tropics, subtropics, and, for much of the year at least, in the temperate zone during the third interglacial than it ever was under the conditions in the fourth (Würm) glaciation in the north temperate latitudes. It is tempting, therefore, to conclude from this observation that, while the Neanderthalers of glacial conditions were hunters, the others were predominantly plant food gatherers. This may indeed be correct, but it would be a conclusion unjustified by the evidence. All that we can reasonably string together from the above is: 1) some Neanderthal peoples were living around glaciers; 2) edible plant life was scarce; and 3) large mammals were abundant. Therefore, the glacial Neanderthal people were hunters.

To say that the other Neanderthal groups were therefore not hunters, however, would not be justified. It is likely that the interglacial residents of the temperate zone were of necessity part-time hunters for the winter months, and thus could be expected to show greater contrast in their adaptations to the environment. The tropical and subtropical Neanderthalers could not be expected to show the same degree and kind of contrast due to climatic factors, simply because their environments lacked the sharp seasonal contrasts of winter and summer. What effect the

TABLE 6–4

SOME FOSSIL DISCOVERIES OF NEANDERTHAL VARIETIES

Name	Location	Head Length in mm.	Head Breadth in mm.	Date* Before Present	Cultural Association
1. Temperate Glacial					
Neanderthal	Germany	201	147	35,000–70,000	?
Spy I	Belgium	200	146	35,000–70,000	Mousterian
Spy II	Belgium	198	150	35,000–70,000	Mousterian
La Chapelle	France	208	156	35,000–70,000	Mousterian
La Ferrassie	France	209	158	35,000–45,000	Mousterian
La Quina	France	203	138	>35,000	Mousterian
Gibraltar	Gibraltar	190	148	35,000–70,000	Levallois-Mousterian
Monte Circeo	Italy	204	156	35,000–70,000	Pontinian (Micro-Mousterian)
Shanidar	Iraq	207†	155–158†	60,000–96,000	East Mousterian
2. Temperate Interglacial					
Skhūl and Tabūn	Israel	192‡	144‡	35,000–70,000	Levallois-Mousterian
Ehringsdorf	Germany	196	145	60,000–120,000	Mousterian
Steinheim	Germany	185	132	200,000?	
Fontechevade	France	194	154	70,000–150,000	Tayacian
Saccopastore	Italy	181	142	60,000	?
Krapina	Yugoslavia	178	149	?	Mousterian
Teshik-Tash (child)	Uzbekistan	185	144	?	Mousterian
3. Subtropical to Tropical					
Rhodesian	Zambia	208	144	35,000–70,000	———
Saldanha	Republic of South Africa	200	144	40,000	Fauresmith
Solo I	Java	196	148	?	Ngandongian
Solo V	Java	220	147	?	Ngandongian
Solo VI	Java	192	144	?	Ngandongian
Solo IX	Java	201	150	?	Ngandongian
Solo X	Java	203	155	?	Ngandongian
Solo XI	Java	200	144	?	Ngandongian

* These dates have been compiled from Oakley (1964).

† These figures were kindly provided by Dr. T. D. Stewart, senior physical anthropologist at the Smithsonian Institution. Dr. Stewart emphasizes that the overall dimensions have been distorted because of slight warping of the skull vault.

‡ These measurements were obtained on the most complete skull (Skhūl V).

northern glaciers had on the climatic conditions south of the equator is not clear. It may be that the corresponding change was reflected more in the decreasing amount of annual rainfall (from wet to dry) than in the decreasing average temperatures.

Undoubtedly other factors in the natural environment played important roles in the life of Neanderthal man—abundance and availability of marine resources, wind velocities, tides, currents, and many more. We have been able to consider only two (availability of land food sources and changing climatic conditions) that must have had an immediate effect on Neanderthal man's way of life, since they bear so directly on the basic survival requirements of nutrition and shelter. How, if at all, are these conditions of the natural environment related to the formal properties of Neanderthal man? For a very long time, two major "kinds" of Neanderthal have been recognized in the temperate latitudes, corresponding to two of the three climatic zones already discussed: 1) a temperate interglacial variant, variously called a pre-Würm, Würm, interglacial, and progressive form, with less distinctive Neanderthal features and thus with an appearance more like that of modern man than other "more typical" Neanderthal variants; and 2) a temperate glacial variety long regarded as the "typical" Neanderthal and characterized by having all the distinctive Neanderthal features in their most fully developed form. Thus, the earlier forms look more like human beings of today than the later forms, a somewhat surprising situation that led to uncertainties in assessing interrelationships between Neanderthal man and modern man.

In addition to these two, a third variety is now recognized from the tropical and subtropical regions of the Old World, combining distinctive Neanderthal features with characteristics more commonly associated with modern man in ways which cannot properly be called intermediate, but rather different from both northern Neanderthals and modern man. There are considerably fewer remains that fall into this category, but on the basis of what is known, it appears that they were living in the south from about 70,000 to 30,000 years ago, thus overlapping in time the two northern Neanderthal groups.

The contextual information provided by factors in the natural environment in relationship to the distribution of Neanderthal remains tends to support some modest and tentative but important conclusions: 1) Three variants of Neanderthal are recognizable—an interglacial, a glacial, and a tropical form. 2) Each one lived in an area which contrasted with the other two in climatic conditions and available food supply. 3) Only among the glacial Neanderthalers is it possible to conclude with confidence that hunting was the primary basis of subsistence. 4) In the interglacial and tropical areas, it seems likely that plant food constituted a more important part of the diet.

Cultural evidence provides more contextual detail and allows us to conclude more about how the various Neanderthalers lived. Until recently, it was easy to present the information about the culture of Neanderthal man. It was simply the assemblage of artifacts that has been known as the Mousterian. Accompanying this simple view were several misleading assumptions that together made up an unfortunately distorted stereotype of Neanderthal as a hairy, stoop-shouldered, long-armed, bull-necked ape of a man, staring stupidly off into the golden future, walking with a bent-knee shuffle, and usually dragging his wife along by the hair. Other views, based on only a tiny bit more information, pictured the same kind of stereotype dwelling in a cave and wearing skin clothing. We do not know how hairy Neanderthal was, nor if he was bull-necked, nor how he may have transported his wife; but we do know he was not stoop-shouldered, not particularly long-armed, and he did not walk with his knees bent. He did live in caves and rock shelters (at least some Neanderthalers did for part of their lives), and he almost certainly wore skin clothing, but beyond that the picture becomes hazy. It will be helpful to deal with each Neanderthal group separately.

The glacial Neanderthalers are the ones that have been thought of as "typical" and have for a long time been known as the manufacturers of a characteristic assemblage of stone tools collectively referred to as the Mousterian industry. In recent years, however, it has become increasingly clear that the Mousterian is a label for several different assemblages of artifacts. Fundamentally, the Mousterian is characterized by side scrapers (*racloirs*), knifelike flake tools, and points that may or may not have been hafted, and thus may or may not have been spear points. Beyond this common core of implements, Mousterian sites vary in terms of the proportions in which these implements occur, and also with respect to whether they are found in deposits containing bifacial core tools, the so-called hand axes. Single caves have been discovered with stratified sites showing these contrasting assemblages of Mousterian implements overlying one another.

At our present stage of understanding, it is impossible to know what, if any, significance the proportional differences of flake tools imply concerning how glacial Neanderthal man lived. Perhaps the dichotomy of Mousterian into assemblages with hand axes and those without may be more readily significant; the two kinds of sites are found in different localities. The hand-axe Mousterian sites are along the coast of Europe, and the assemblages lacking hand axes are situated farther inland on rivercourses and at higher elevations. Also, each tends to be concentrated in time, the non-hand-axe assemblages being more frequently associated with the glacial Neanderthal than the ones with hand axes. This is not intended to imply that the glacial Neanderthalers did not have or use hand axes, but rather that the "typical Mousterian" tools were much more common.

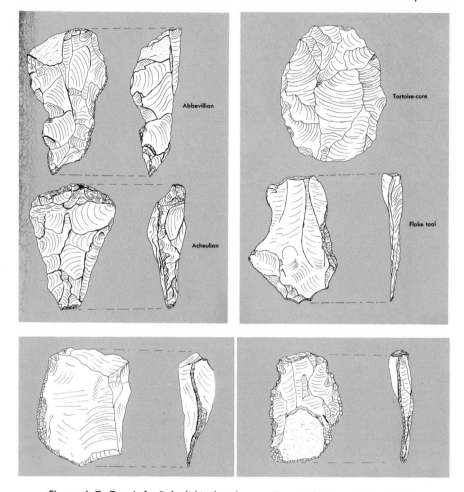

Figure 6–7. Top Left: Paleolithic hand axes. Top Right: Levalloisian tools. Bottom: Clactonian flake tools.

The temperate interglacial Mousterians are difficult to characterize archaeologically. The Riss-Würm interglacial is a period of great complexity in its archaeological content, particularly in the north. Older archaeological traditions, such as the Acheulean hand-axe and Clactonian-Levalloisian flake-tool assemblage (see Figure 6–7), some with very broad distributions, are replaced by the Mousterian. As a result there are "hybrid" industries particularly early in the interglacial followed by a period in which both hand-axe Mousterian and "typical" Mousterian are found together, often in alternate layers of the same cave deposits. These two coexisting Mousterian traditions are gradually replaced by a pre-

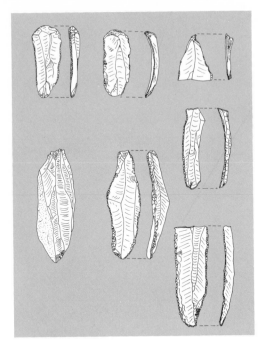

Figure 6–8. Upper Paleolithic blade tools.

dominance of the "typical" (i.e., without hand axes) Mousterian during the early advance of the last glaciation, but the hand-axe Mousterian is not completely obliterated until the entire Mousterian complex is replaced by the blade-tool industries (Figure 6–8) of more recent times.

The temperate-zone Neanderthalers are known also to have buried their dead—at least some of their dead—and to have placed implements in the grave. This practice is found commonly among contemporary people, and seems to imply rather clearly the belief in a life after death, and thus belief in a spirit and supernatural world.

The tropical variant of Neanderthal has been found in association with archaeological assemblages known as Fauresmith in Africa (Figure 6–9) and the Ngandongian in Asia, the latter being a local variant of a more broadly distributed industry, the Sangiran.

In Africa, south of the Sahara, the Paleolithic sequence preceding the Fauresmith is similar to the European sequence. On both continents, there was a long and well-established sequence of Acheulean hand-axe assemblages. In general, this part of Africa lacked the Clactonian-Levalloisian flake-tool sequence as a distinct and separate development, as it occurs in the north, where the flake-core tool traditions were replaced by the variants of the Mousterian during Riss-Würm interglacial times. In Africa, the Acheulean developmental sequence, at what appears to be very nearly the same time, is replaced in the densely forested regions of central Africa by the Sangoan industry (Figure 6–10) consisting of picks, cleavers, and crude hand axes. Although no good fossil evidence exists concerning the morphology of the peoples that made the Sangoan, it appears clear that it is in fact a forest adaptation assembly existing contemporaneously with the Fauresmith, which is distributed in the more arid, open areas, grasslands, uplands, and the savannahs of South and East Africa. Fauresmith assemblages include hand axes which are distinctive in being small, often heart-shaped, and usually made from shale, a type of rock with distinctive fracturing qualities that are reflected in the steplike appearance of the hand-axe edges. If, as would seem reasonable, Fauresmith and Sangoan were made by the same species of hominid, then, in Africa, Neanderthal was distributed throughout the continent, having adapted to both open country and forested environments, for there exists good evidence of association between the Saldanha tropical neanderthaloid and the Fauresmith archaeological assemblage. What is perhaps of even greater interest here is the fact that the ancestral sequence between tropical Neanderthals and modern inhabitants of the areas seems to be more readily accepted by human paleontologists, although in fact the actual evidence is no better than it is in Europe.

From Asia there is less evidence, and the background is quite different. Unlike Africa and Europe, the archaeological sequence throughout much of Asia does not contain the hand-axe sequences until recently. In some

Figure 6–9. Fauresmith implements. (After Sonia Cole.)

Figure 6–10. Sangoan implements. (After Sonia Cole.)

Flake knives   Pick

areas they do not appear until nearly the end of the European and African Paleolithic. Instead, there is a long period of development in assemblages of flake tools in association with a distinctive category of stone implements known as chopper-chopping tools. Although the name, chopper-chopping tools, may not seem to imply it, there are differences detectable between chopper tools on the one hand and chopping tools on the other. Choppers are usually made by taking a flattened, somewhat large pebble such as you might find along a stream bed or rocky beach, and then, depending on its size, either knocking off a piece at one side and then taking off smaller flakes to sharpen the exposed surface, or proceeding directly to sharpen one edge by knocking off small pieces. It is in many ways a scraper, but made by a core technique rather than a flake technique. The chopper has only one surface on which the flakes are removed, making it suitable as a tool for scraping hides, branches, or whatever. The chopping tool is generally larger and characteristically has both of its surfaces worked, producing a sharp, usually undulating, edge that is useful as a cutting and slicing implement; and since it is larger and heavier, it can also be thought of as serviceable in many of the same contexts as hand axes. Choppers and chopping tools are essentially core tools. They constitute a developmental sequence of their own, broadly spread in space throughout eastern Asia, and deeply rooted in time, extending back at least as far as one-half million years.

The chopper-chopping tools may have been used by some Neanderthalers, but, in all likelihood if they were, it would have been by one of the temperate variants. Figure 6–11 indicates the distribution of the chopper-chopping tools at the close of the Pleistocene. Indeed, recent fossil evidence from China indicates that Neanderthal man was living in Asia at the time, but as yet the evidence is either too fragmentary, the date unknown, or the associations with climatic and faunal evidence is too uncertain to be able to know if there is a distinguishable sequence of interglacial variants as in temperate zones farther west.

Our best evidence for Neanderthal man in tropical Asia was discovered in the Solo River valley in central Java and consists of the remains of several individuals. This Asian form of the tropical Neanderthal is morphologically very similar to the African and appears in an archaeological context of a rather poorly defined flake-tool industry consisting of points, scrapers, rounded stones possibly used as bolas stones, together with antlers that show some indication of having been put to use as pickaxes. This assemblage, known as the Ngandongian, was found in a deposit containing the remains of several forms of mammals now extinct in Java, but probably meat never was as abundant and important as a food basis as in temperate-zone glacial times. Apart from the meagerness of the archaeological and faunal record, one additional difficulty arises from the fact that the skeletal remains are only indirectly associated with the imple-

Figure 6–11. Distribution of chopper-chopping tools compared with the core-flake assemblages. (After H. L. Movius.)

ments, both having been found in the same layer and in the same general area, but not in direct association.

Combining all lines of evidence converging on Neanderthal, some general inferences seem reasonable in summarizing the material considered so far. 1) Neanderthal is the broad name given to various hominid forms that lived in the Old World from at least as early as third interglacial and to at least as recently as fourth glaciation times. 2) Three variants of the broad category are detectable: glacial temperate, interglacial temperate, and tropical to subtropical. 3) These variants made a variety of implements, some assemblages appearing essentially *de novo* with Neanderthal man, such as the Mousterian, which appears to be a cold-climate hunting industry, others being continuations of old traditions begun much earlier. 4) No evidence for deliberate shelter habitation exists outside the temperate zone; within that zone Neanderthal man occupied rock shelters and caves, sometimes apparently for long enough periods to be considered at least semisedentary, a condition presumably made possible by the abundant game or perhaps demanded by the cold weather. 5) Some, and perhaps all, buried their dead and, to the degree that this implies it, believed in an afterlife.

By way of general summary, it should be emphasized that Neanderthal is highly varied, broadly distributed, and deeply rooted in time. He adapted to several environments, manufactured a variety of implements, and thus, presumably, lived in different cultural contexts.

Now that we have considered some of the details of modern man and Neanderthal man, it seems only logical to consider the more interesting question of their relationship to one another. This involves the important problem of whether or not the Neanderthalers are the ancestors of modern man. In our view, the answer to this question is probably yes; Neanderthal is probably our way of designating our closest recognizably distinctive ancestor. By some this is rejected, usually because of evidence, such as the Swanscombe and Fontechevade material, which to them indicates that modern man's antiquity extends farther back in time than Neanderthal, and thus that Neanderthal could not be our ancestor. By others this answer is considered too conservative; they hold that Neanderthal is clearly in man's ancestry. These extremes indicate the ambiguity of the evidence.

Homo erectus

A perfectly reasonable concern following logically from the above is, where does Neanderthal come from? The most likely candidates for the closest recognizably distinctive ancestor include a variety of forms variously known as Java man, *Pithecanthropus, Sinanthropus,* Peking man, *Atlanthropus,* Chellean man, *Homo heidelbergensis,* and *Homo erectus* (see Table 6–5). We will classify them all together and refer to them by the last designation, *Homo erectus.* The earliest indication of a hominid earlier in time and more grossly apelike than Neanderthal resulted from a discovery made in Java in 1890 by Eugène Dubois. This, as it turned out, was the first of several discoveries of *Homo erectus* to be made in Java, the earliest ones by Dubois, later ones, beginning in 1936, by von Koenigswald, and most recently between 1960 and 1966 by Sartono and Jacob. Additional material of the same general morphology has been discovered in several other locations in the Old World. In spite of the fact that several locations have produced important indications of *Homo erectus,* the total fossil material available is not particularly suitable for reconstruction and the recovery of useful comparative formal characteristics. In many parts of the world, for example, the only available remains consist of jawbones, whereas in Java a large section of the facial skeleton has never been recovered. Nevertheless, putting together mostly what is

TABLE 6–5

LOCATIONS YIELDING EVIDENCE OF *Homo erectus*

Location	Date Found	Comment
1. Java	1890–1891	Original discoveries of skull fragment and femur. Originally designated as *Pithecanthropus erectus*.
	1936	Incomplete skull of an infant. Originally designated *Homo modjokertensis*.
	1937–1939	Three incomplete skulls found about forty miles from original 1890 discovery. Also identified as *Pithecanthropus*.
2. China	1927–1937	Several fragments of fourteen skulls and eleven mandibles. All were designated earlier as representative of *Sinanthropus pekinensis*.
	1963–1964	Mandible and skull fragments. Referred to as Lantian man.
3. Germany	1907	A mandible, also called Heidelberg jaw and *Homo heidelbergensis*.
4. Algeria	1954–1956	Fragments of three mandibles which have been designated *Atlanthropus mauritanicus*.
5. Morocco	1954	From Sidi Abderrahman, a fragmentary mandible.
6. South Africa	1949	Some jaw fragments, teeth, and two bones of the postcranial skeleton. Designated originally as *Telanthropus capensis*.
7. Tanzania	1960	Skull fragments referred to as Chellean man.
	1964	Identified by Leakey as "George," a skull reconstructed from many small fragments.

known from Java with material subsequently discovered in China, we can make some general statements concerning *Homo erectus* in comparison with modern man and Neanderthal man.

If one thinks of Neanderthal man as essentially like modern man but differing in some features in the direction of apelike characteristics, then *Homo erectus* is even more like Neanderthal. Figure 6–12 compares him with modern man, and Figure 6–13 with a Neanderthal form.

From the front, the contours of the face in *Homo erectus* are angular, as are those of the eye orbits. The forehead barely rises above the supraorbital ridges and slopes back, converging with the parietals, which themselves form an angle that, while clearly not a sagittal crest, is the suggestion of something similar to one. One may also notice from a frontal view that the greatest breadth of the skull is lower down and, as may be noted from the top, farther back on the *Homo erectus* skull than it is in modern man.

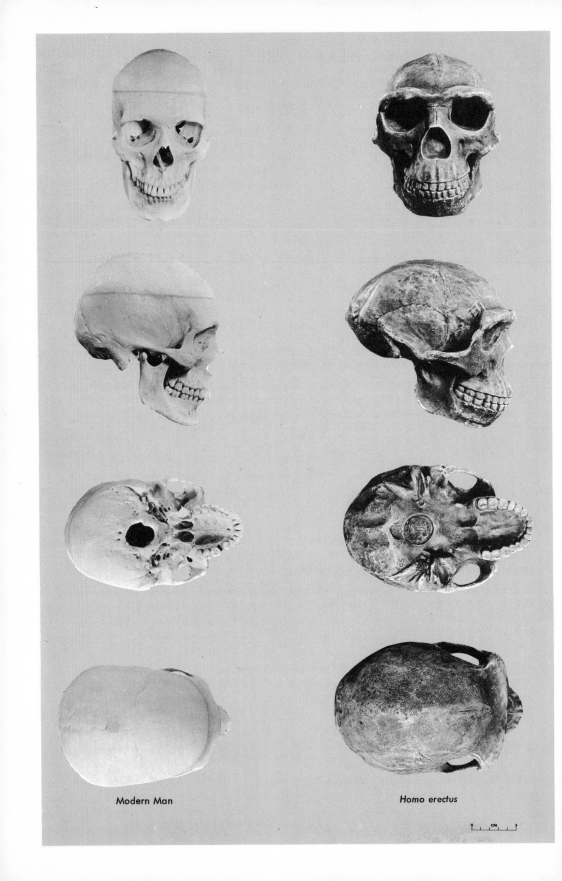

Modern Man   Homo erectus

From the side, the face can be seen to project farther forward than in modern man, and the relatively small brain is evident, as are the more fully developed brow ridges. The occiput shows a rugged surface and a sharply angled contour, and the mastoids are not well developed.

From below, there are few striking differences between *Homo erectus* and modern man apart from gross size. The foramen magnum is well under the base of the skull, and the teeth are set in a dental arch like that of Neanderthal and modern man and unlike the rectangular contour of modern apes. With one important exception, Neanderthal stands intermediate between modern man and *Homo erectus;* the factor of brain size is the exception. The cranial capacity of *Homo erectus* ranges between 900 cc. and 1100 cc., whereas the Neanderthal average is approximately 1400 cc. to 1500 cc., the same as in modern man. If, as would seem likely, *Homo erectus* is ancestral to Neanderthal, then clearly the most significant evolutionary forces acting to produce the Neanderthal descendants were those involved in increasing both the absolute and relative size of the brain. In some other respects not evident from the figures, Neanderthal and *Homo erectus* are similar to one another and unlike the general range of modern man. A more careful analysis of the teeth would show that the molar roots are often fused (taurodontism), and the tongue side of the incisors would show a pronounced spatulate groove (shovel-shaped incisors) (see Figure 6–13).

Again, one should keep constantly in mind that terms such as *modern man, Neanderthal man,* and *Homo erectus* are simply labels for widely varying hominids. As a demonstration, one needs to go no further than daily experience to know just how widely divergent can be the variation that is included in the category of modern man. Just look around you. There is no reason to presume that morphological variation among the earlier hominids was any less. Indeed, there is some evidence to the contrary, but since conclusive evidence on the total range of variation in these earlier forms is lacking, the issue cannot be resolved.

Two variants of *Homo erectus* are readily identifiable and distinguishable, one represented by the Javanese discoveries and the other by a series of discoveries that began to be made by Davidson Black near Peking, China, in 1927, and subsequently by von Koenigswald. Front and side views of each (Figure 6–14) demonstrate that the Chinese discoveries consist of individuals somewhat less brutish and apelike in their features than the Javanese remains. That is, each has essentially the same assemblage of distinctive traits setting them apart from modern man and Neanderthal man, but they are more marked in the Javanese material. Peking man has smaller supraorbital ridges, slightly more of a chin and

Figure 6–12. (Opposite Page) Comparison of four views of a modern man skull with a *Homo erectus* skull cast.

Homo erectus   Neanderthal   0 [scale bar] CM

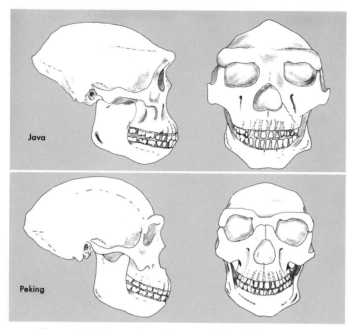

Figure 6–14. Comparison of two varieties of *Homo erectus*.

forehead, less prognathism, a slightly less marked gabling effect to his skull vault, and a moderately larger brain than Java man.

Recently, in 1963 and 1964, a lower jaw and skullcap were discovered in China in the Lantian district southwest of Peking. Although the evidence is meager, it appears that morphologically the Lantian fragments are more similar to the Javanese *Homo erectus* discoveries than the material from nearby Peking. There is evidence, likewise, that the Lantian discovery is older than those from Peking.

Spatial distribution of *Homo erectus* (see Figure 6–15) is in general the same as the distribution of Neanderthal man. The concentration of fossils is, however, different. In contrast to the scores of Neanderthal remains from Europe, only one jaw and one occiput of *Homo erectus* are known from there, and only a few Neanderthal remains are known from Asia.

Absolute dating estimates of *Homo erectus* made on materials from Africa, Java, and Europe all place him in time at between one-half and one million years ago. Unfortunately, the early discoveries from China were lost during an attempt to remove them to the United States at the outset of World War II, and thus they have not been evaluated in light of recent

Figure 6–13. (Opposite Page) Comparison of four views of a *Homo erectus* with a Neanderthal skull cast.

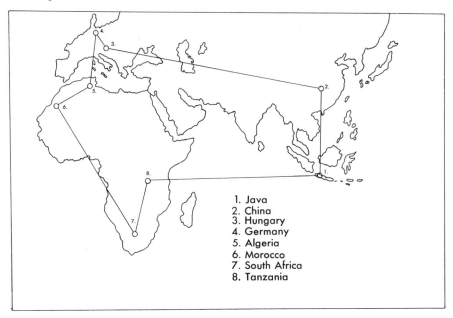

Figure 6–15. Geographic distribution of *Homo erectus*.

advances in geochronology. Subsequent work from the same deposits was begun in 1949 and to date has yielded a humerus and tibia that are said to be like modern man, and five teeth and a jawbone that are similar to the earlier Peking man material. Recent absolute dating estimates of the geological layer (Trinil) in Java that contained almost all of the *Homo erectus* remains have yielded dates of approximately 500,000 years ago, which is consistent with earlier estimates. No reliable dates for the lower (Djetis) beds are available; this layer will be of more significance later, since there is evidence of an even earlier hominid from Java in these beds.

Thus it is relatively simple and straightforward to estimate the time that *Homo erectus* was present, but very difficult to estimate his duration. About the only satisfactory estimate amounts to presuming that the 500,000-year estimate is at or near the mean, and from this to conclude that *Homo erectus* was on the scene during second (Mindel-Riss) interglacial times. The only evidence of duration—and it remains highly tentative—is the dating of the two *Homo erectus* forms from Leakey's excavations in Olduvai Gorge, one from near the bottom of Bed II ("George") and one from near the top (L.L.K.).* The volcanic rock that forms the bottom of Bed II has been dated at one million years old, the top at 490,000 years old. There is no reason to question the dating estimates here, but it is not clear as yet whether the two fossil discoveries

* *George* and *L.L.K.* are the names for the skulls and other bones.

actually are properly classified as members of the *Homo erectus* grouping. Presuming this to be true, however, the earlier estimates of 500,000 years would seem to date *Homo erectus* toward the end of his existence as an identifiable morphological unit and place his origin back to first inter-glacial or even earlier times. The East African dates are encouraging for a number of reasons, but most important among them is the fact that they provide us with a dimension that until now has been lacking in the interpretation of *Homo erectus,* the dimension of time depth.

From a survey of first-order morphological, temporal, and spatial in-formation, *Homo erectus* is sharply distinguishable from Neanderthal man and appears, at least in the main, to have existed one-half million years earlier. Their spatial distributions are the same, and both apparently existed over a long period of time. To obtain some information on *Homo erectus'* way of life, a consideration of context once again provides some interesting bases for tentative inferences.

While the fossil-producing locations are unequal in their content, it would appear that *Homo erectus* definitely preferred but was not re-stricted to warm climates. This is true in the case of European and Asian remains as well as those from Africa. Consider as evidence the fossil animals found with him in China; *Homo erectus* shared his habitat with tigers, elephants, rhinoceroses, ostriches, camels, and hyenas. In North Africa, the list is similar but includes also a giant baboon similar to forms previously known only from the earliest part of the Pleistocene from East and South Africa. The situation in East Africa is becoming more clear. The details differ from earlier reports, but the essential feature of the fauna is clear; it too seems to indicate a warm, moist climate.

The original discovery of the Java *Homo erectus* was made in a location which undoubtedly is not where the forms had died. The site is on the Solo River in a deposit which had been accumulated earlier by water action, and thus most everything in it had been moved, shuffled, and re-moved again. This makes it impossible to be very confident of context information, but what there is of it is in general very similar to the better-known African and Asian assemblages, including hippopotami, elephants, and fossil monkeys and apes. The remains from the lower levels are like-wise similar to the faunal assemblage from the Peking discoveries, in-cluding lions, tigers, hyenas, rhinoceroses, and hippopotami.

If one tried to make specific comparisons of fauna from one site to another, the resulting picture would probably be confusing. Undoubtedly many of the species were different and thus would show differing adap-tive capabilities, and further, since few good absolute dates are known from outside East Africa, the comparisons would be made between faunal groupings that lived at various times and with varying durations. Nevertheless, there is evidence from the Chinese and European discov-eries suggesting that *Homo erectus* was able to live in cold climatic conditions. From Peking, in addition to the remains of tigers, elephants, and camels, also discovered in the same deposits were fossilized remains of varieties of wolves, dogs, foxes, bears, horses, bison, and buffalo. The situation would doubtless be clearer if the deposits were stratified, but they are not; they are mixed up somewhat, having been extracted from what used to be caves, a fact that will be of importance to us again presently. Perhaps this peculiar assemblage reflects the faunal succession in an area once warm, moist, and densely vegetated, gradually changing to a colder, more typically temperate climate.

The evidence from Heidelberg suggests something similar to that from Peking. The European fauna was, of course, very different in earlier Pleistocene times, as evidenced by the different fossil species of elephants and rhinoceroses, as well as others not found at all in the China deposits, such as species of dogs, bison, horses, beavers, etc., found in association with *Homo erectus* from Heidelberg.

No doubt there is room for much speculation based on faunal evidence, and, in fact, we have already indulged in some by referring to some animals as warm-, others as cold-climate animals. It is certainly possible that earlier forms differed in their adaptive capacities from their modern counterparts, and thus one should be cautious in inferring such things from fossil remains. In careful terms, a summary of the faunal remains found together with *Homo erectus* could read as follows: in the North Temperate Zone, *Homo erectus* remains are found in association with remains of animals that today include both cold- and warm-adapted varieties. In today's tropical areas, *Homo erectus* remains are found in association with animals that today have only warm-adapted descendants.

Turning to the archaeological evidence, progress in reaching general-izations about *Homo erectus* is hampered by the fact that not all sites yielding fossil bones have produced cultural artifacts. Nevertheless, the available evidence is interesting and informative and is sufficient to allow some tentative generalized inferences. In Java, the fossil remains of *Homo erectus* have never been found in direct association with archaeological remains. The earliest evidence of archaeological material to be discovered in Java is an assemblage of crudely made flake and chopper-chopping tools that has been called the Patjitanian industry. Almost all of the materials discovered so far and assignable to the Patjitanian were recov-ered from a single large site of uncertain age in central Java. It is proba-ble—but circumstances of their location at the time of discovery make it impossible to know for certain—that they are from the Trinil stratum that yielded the remains of Java man. However, if this is true, they are found higher up and not at all clearly associated with the *Homo erectus* remains. Recall, however, that the fossil bones had been redeposited, and thus their original position likewise is not clearly known.

Apart from the associated fauna and the limited inferences it allows, there is little more to be extracted from the information provided by context from Java, perhaps largely because it was not discovered in its original context. Since the evidence is ambiguous, no conclusions are possible, but more reliable guidelines may be obtained by turning to other areas where richer sources of data exist.

In the recovery of the *Homo erectus* material from China, an abundance of archaeological remains was also discovered. The discoveries were made just outside of Choukoutien, a small village situated about twenty-five miles outside of Peking. The fossils were found within fissures in a massive limestone deposit that was being quarried at the time. Over the years, the fissures had filled up with debris either blown in by the wind or brought in by various animals frequenting the caves. *Homo erectus* was one of the animals that made use of the cave, and from the evidence of what he left behind, apparently used it for a long time.

The composition of the fossil material discovered is itself interesting and suggestive. There is a surprising disparity between the large number of skull fragments and the relatively few fragments of the postcranial skeleton. Furthermore, four of the five skulls appear to have been bashed in at the bases. This is interesting, and these two facts taken together have led others to speculate that this might imply that the Chinese *Homo erectus* remains were of individuals who were killed, probably outside the cave, their heads cut off, skulls bashed in, brains removed, and the fragmented bony remains tossed to the back of the cave. These speculations generate even more remote ones. Since it was probably other members of his species that did the deed, then here is a basis for concluding that *Homo erectus* was a cannibal. And, since cannibalism is rarely practiced outside a ceremonial context among contemporary primitive people, its existence may imply ceremonialism, and ceremonialism implies culture. Therefore *Homo erectus* had culture. That is a lot of speculation to emerge from so little empirical information. And, if the existence of culture is the crucial problem, it would seem completely unnecessary, since there is good evidence that he not only made tools but also knew how to make and use fire.

Having examined briefly the implements that collectively make up the Mousterian, one may get the comfortable feeling that he has seen a crude and primitive industry, and that having seen one, he has seen them all. Of course this is ridiculous, and a careful comparison of the Mousterian with the implements of the Choukoutienian (the name of the chopper-chopping tool assemblage found in association with the Chinese *Homo erectus*) reveals many obviously important differences (see Figure 6–16). The Mousterian implements are more diversified, more carefully manufactured, and the various kinds of implements are more standardized in the

Mousterian

Chopper-Chopping tools

Figure 6–16. A comparison of the kinds of implements found in association with the remains of Neanderthal man (Mousterian) and *Homo erectus* (chopper-chopping tools). (After H. L. Movius.)

ways in which they were made. The edges of Mousterian implements are sharper, and more deliberation went into their construction. The Neanderthal toolmaker worked on the edges of a flake by knocking off successive smaller flakes and thereby producing regularly a sharp-edged implement by a process known as secondary retouching. *Homo erectus* appears to have made tools more by dull plodding than deliberate design. In the cave deposits with *Homo erectus* there are many more flakes that appear to be discarded than there are flakes that were used. Indeed, there are so many flakes, and the tools are so crudely made, that paleontologists worked in the cave deposits for several years before some of the stones were identified as archaeological remains. The large proportion of discards to useful implements suggests that the tools were made by a simple trial-and-error process, whereby *Homo erectus* would knock off flakes from a piece of sandstone or quartz until either the core obtained a useful form, or a flake flew off having a useful shape.

The Choukoutienian is an early assemblage of implements in the chopper-chopping developmental sequence found throughout eastern Asia. (Figure 6–17 illustrates some differences between choppers and chopping tools.) As noted earlier, the assemblages that make up the sequence are like the hand-axe–flake-tool industries found elsewhere in the Old World in the sense that both include functionally-similar implements. They differ, however, in the technique employed in the manufacture of the core tools. The eastern Asian technique produced a chopping tool, the other a hand axe. The uses of the Choukoutienian implements may be easier to discuss after the other contents of the deposits have been considered.

That *Homo erectus* knew how to use and control fire is unquestioned. The evidence includes fireplaces found at several locations within the cave deposits, and many of the fossil bones of the other animals that apparently were brought in by *Homo erectus* have been burned and charred. From this it would seem reasonable to conclude that he ate meat, perhaps a lot of it, that he may have "cooked" it in some way, and thus that fire was important as a processing technique as well as a source of warmth. By extension of this reasoning, it would seem reasonable also to conclude that some, if not most, of the Choukoutienian implements must have been used to cut meat and scrape hides.

This is, however, only a small part of the story. *Homo erectus* was confronted with the problems of getting animals as well as preparing them. Hunting animals, particularly as large and fast as many of those found within the caves, requires either an elaborate technology or a more modest technology combined with a doggedness and determination such as that found among some contemporary primitive hunters such as the Australian aborigines and the Bushmen of the Kalahari Desert. These contemporary populations have, however, a technology which, although simple and meager, is far advanced over that of *Homo erectus*. Thus one cannot help but hesitate in labeling him, and presumably other members

Figure 6–17. Comparison of choppers with chopping tools. (After K. P. Oakley.)

of his species, as hunters. They could, for example, have been primarily dependent on the gathering of plant foods, while still obtaining a modest amount of meat from the remains left behind after a carnivore kill and from small, comparatively slow game they killed themselves. In short, the fact that *Homo erectus* is found within deposits which also include remains of animals he probably brought in does not necessarily imply that he was a hunter in the usual sense of that word. The artifacts found in the same deposits support the view that he was a meat-eater, but not that he was an efficient hunter of large game. Other implements made from more perishable materials such as wood could have been used, but these would not have been preserved. There are some who claim that markings on some of the deer antlers found in these deposits indicate their use as tools. Nevertheless, it seems unlikely that implements made from any materials sufficiently sophisticated in their design to enable *Homo erectus* to be an efficient hunter of the animals whose remains he is found with would be associated with such a crude assemblage of stone tools. Alternatively, he may have depended on communal hunting procedures wherein game animals are stampeded over cliffs or driven into traps where they can be readily killed, cut up, and then perhaps taken off to the caves for consumption. These methods usually call for the cooperative efforts of several individuals and result in irregular periods of abundance in animal food. This is a relatively common hunting technique among recent primitive people, but whether *Homo erectus* practiced it or not is unknown.

One final point of interest about the Choukoutien deposits yielding remains of *Homo erectus* is the observation that this location has served as a habitation site for hominids for a very long time. The deposits are about 160 feet deep, and artifacts and fossil bones are scattered throughout. Both the fauna and the Choukoutienian archaeological material remain decidedly stable from bottom to top, a fact which would seem to imply that *Homo erectus* lived there for a long time. It would be helpful if there were some reliable indications of the duration of his occupation in these caves, but this is not known. Of unusual interest also is the fact that evidence has been obtained from the same locality of modern man living in more recent times with an assemblage of implements that combines chopper-chopping tools with very well-made objects that, in Europe, are found in the Upper Paleolithic industries that succeed Neanderthal man. This is known as the Upper Cave industry, and, as the name would seem to imply, it has been found in a cave at the top of the same limestone deposits that farther down yielded *Homo erectus* and the Choukoutienian industry. The Upper Cave remains include four crania of modern-man morphology that in all likelihood are representative of the recent ancestors of the modern Asians from the area. There is a gap between the lower and upper caves—one large enough that some can still claim with justification that there is no proof of an ancestral relationship between the residents of the two levels. If one holds this view, it then becomes awkward to account for the continuity that would seem to be indicated by the presence of the same kind of chopper-chopping tools in both locations.

In summary, as indicated by the Peking remains, *Homo erectus:* 1) lived in caves, 2) had fire, 3) ate meat, 4) used chopper-chopping tools, and 5) continued his cultural adaptation over a long time.

In Europe, as already noted, the evidence for *Homo erectus* is meager. In 1965, a discovery was made of an occipital bone in Hungary that at first was assigned to the *Homo erectus* category, but which has recently been referred to as a Neanderthal that might be related to Swanscombe. This was at Vétesszöllös, a site that earlier had yielded chopper-chopping tools. As yet, it has not been described in detail, but, if the initial interpretation turns out to be correct, it is of interest simply because outside Asia most of the *Homo erectus* material recovered has been the remains of jaws and teeth. Thus, the basis of our comparison here is the Heidelberg jaw. This jaw was found in association with wild pigs, deer, elephants, woolly rhinoceroses, horses, bison, saber-toothed tigers, lions, wildcats, beaver, and elk. On the whole, this would seem to represent a heterogeneous fauna and thus imply a heterogeneous environment. The dating of the jaw has never been very clear. It was found at a depth of over eighty feet from the surface. On the basis of the associated fauna, the climatic circumstances appear to be temperate interglacial in a well-watered area with temperature fluctuations extending to greater average extremes in the succession of the seasons.

No archaeological material was found with the European *Homo erectus,* but there is no doubt that tools were being made at the time he was alive, whenever that may have been, and there is little doubt that he was a member of the population that made them. For over two hundred years, Europe has been producing indications of the existence of some people who occupied the Continent a long time ago and made sometimes crude, sometimes splendid stone tools, and who lived a way of life very different from that of today and from that of Neanderthal's day. The evidence has consisted almost entirely of stone implements. Apart from the controversial Swanscombe and Fontechevade fragments, little is known about the men who made the artifacts. As noted earlier, the Mousterian was the outgrowth of what has been interpreted as two separate tool traditions: 1) the hand-axe sequence which consists of sites containing both core and flake tools and is known as the Chelles-Acheul tradition, and 2) the flake-tool sequence made up of sites exclusively containing flake tools and called the Clactonian-Levalloisian tradition. The usual way of illustrating the relationship between these two is shown in Figure 6–7 on page 187. From this it can be seen that the Clactonian-Levalloisian and the Chelles-Acheul traditions are two separate and distinct traditions. The Clactonian began first, but, after the Chelles-Acheul began, the two were found over the same temporal and spatial distributions. It is becoming increasingly awkward to maintain this view, and the fact that very few skeletal remains have been discovered in these locations has made the problem more difficult to resolve. It now appears at least possible, if not probable, that the two sequences may in fact be aspects of one another, the hand-axe sequence reflecting a warm-weather subsistence adaptation and the flake tools a cold-weather adaptation.

Most important for our present interest, that of *Homo erectus* in Germany, is the observation that apparently the core- and flake-tool traditions were already under way in Europe by the time that he was living, and, while it is not by any means certain, it would not be surprising to learn that the European *Homo erectus* populations had adapted to their fluctuating environment, containing an abundance of game, in much the same way as the Asian populations, as illustrated by the Peking remains. If, as discussed earlier, the chopping tools served functions similar to the hand axes, then the Asian and European sequences may be seen as similar adaptations to similar environmental conditions, and thus, by extension, the European *Homo erectus* hominids were leading lives similar to their Asian counterparts in Peking. One final fragment of information bearing on this is the fact that some of the animal bones in the deposits again appear to have been broken, as in Peking. This is, of course, speculative. A recitation of the simple factual material concerning the Heidelberg jaw would read as follows: 1) The jaw was found at a depth of eighty feet from the surface near the village of Mauer in central Germany in 1907. 2) No archaeological evidence was recovered in the site. 3) Its age is uncertain, but the associated fauna indicates interglacial conditions, and, at that depth, it may be first interglacial. 4) Archaeological sequences in Europe go back that far and even farther. 5) It is not clear if the jaw belonged to a person who belonged to the species that made the tools, but, if it did, it may be that the European populations of that time were adapted to their environments in ways similar to those known in more detail from Peking.

Four, or possibly five, sites have yielded *Homo erectus* remains in Africa, two in North Africa, two in East Africa, and one uncertain form from South Africa. This is very little to go by, but it is sufficient to indicate that the range of *Homo erectus* is much broader than was believed a few years ago, when it was presumed that he was restricted to South and East Asia. Affinities between the Heidelberg jaw and the Asian discoveries had been noted, but it was not until the last few years, as indications of the range of *Homo erectus* became clearer, that he has been included within the group. In North Africa, the two sites that have produced the skeletal remains are at Ternifine in Algeria and Sidi Abderrahman in Morocco. The remains consist mostly of jaws and teeth, but include one fragmentary parietal, all of which in form are similar to the Heidelberg jaw and the Asian representatives of *Homo erectus*. Of particular interest is the Ternifine site which is that of a Pleistocene lake bed that existed at a time when the climate was apparently more moist than at present. The mammalian remains consisted of fossil elephants, rhinoceroses, zebras, giraffes, antelopes, lions, hyenas, very large baboons, saber-toothed tigers, and wild boars. This fauna indicates warm temperatures in a well-watered open savannah, an area which could include reasonably rich plant food resources as well as an abundance of large game. Today's baboons forage over areas that probably include many of the same features.

The archaeological material found in association with the fauna at Ternifine includes rather crudely made hand axes and an assortment of large flake tools. This industry is the same as that which in other areas is identified as the early stage of the Chelles-Acheul sequence and, if our earlier reasoning is correct, implies a versatile, largely unspecialized dietary adaptation that included animal and plant sources with proportional variations depending on availability, which, in turn, was probably controlled by seasonal variation in temperature and water resources.

A secondary but less complete indication of *Homo erectus* in North Africa comes from the Sidi Abderrahman site in Morocco. The fossil material consists of a jaw and some teeth found in association with faunal and archaeological materials similar to those at Ternifine.

Judging largely on the basis of the fauna, the North African remains appear to have been of individuals living toward the close of the European first interglacial or, as some would call it, early Middle Pleistocene. For the evidence from East Africa, we turn once again to the extraordinarily rich deposits of Olduvai Gorge in Tanzania. These are the same deposits that have provided so much material of importance to the study of human evolution in recent years. Much of it is not well known as yet, but the information available presently suggests that it may be necessary to make drastic revisions in the "standard" interpretations of man's phylogenetic history.

To obtain some appreciation for the indications of *Homo erectus* in this part of the world, it will be necessary to digress briefly and consider some of the important aspects of the geology of Olduvai Gorge. The gorge consists of a deep cut in the present surface plain which has exposed a series of geological beds in layer-cake order. These have produced an extraordinary series of fossils including the earliest known fully erect bipedal hominid and, in addition, a continuous sequence of cultural remains beginning with the oldest known stone tools and progressing through the Chelles-Acheul sequence of core and flake tools which continues in this part of the world up to relatively recent times. Figure 6–18 is a schematic illustration of the arrangement of the Olduvai Gorge geological beds. The *Homo erectus* fossils have come from Bed II. The lowest levels of Bed II have been dated at slightly older than one million

Figure 6–18. Stratigraphy of Beds I–IV along Olduvai Main Gorge. (After L. S. B. Leakey.)

years, and there are indications that the Bed II–Bed III juncture is datable at approximately one-half million years ago. Apart from the geological contrasts in the deposits distinguishing Beds I and II, Bed II includes indications that the climate was undergoing a substantial change at the time it was being deposited. On both faunal and geological evidence, there are good reasons for concluding that the area was much drier during the time Bed II was laid down than during Bed I times. There are, as well, indications of a change in the composition of the mammalian fauna that took place not at the outset, but *after* Bed II had already begun to be deposited. This change marks the appearance of an essentially modern group of mammals as replacements for the earlier fauna, known as the Villafranchian fauna, that extends well back into early Pleistocene, perhaps even Pliocene, times throughout many parts of the Old World. This is an interesting group of mammals whose appearance serves as a dating benchmark for the onset of the Pleistocene. The Villafranchian fauna is associated with warm weather in well-watered areas. It extends into Bed II in Olduvai Gorge, but is displaced during a phase when the area was drier—apparently not parched, but dry. At the top of Bed II, it appears from the evidence of river channels that the area was becoming humid once again.

The faunal assemblage displacing the Villafranchian in Bed II is similar in many ways to that found in association with the North African remains at Ternifine. The indications suggest again an open savannah type of terrain where a hominid would find himself once again in an area of considerable diversity in both plant and animal food resources. The faunal succession between the earlier and later stages of Bed II is accompanied by a change in the archaeological remains too. During the later stage, the first hand axes known from this area appear, and they are representative of the earliest phases of the Chelles-Acheulean core- and flake-tool traditions in East Africa. The remains of *Homo erectus* have been found in the later phase of the Bed II sequence, that is, in the same deposits that contain the savannah fauna and the early hand-axe archaeological remains. The discovery was made in 1960, at a point about twenty feet from the top of Bed II in an area where the entire bed is about eighty feet thick. The fragments recovered lack the face and jaw, but include the forehead, supraorbital ridges, and occipital crest. Measurements and observations made on these remains demonstrate their similarity to both Asian and European remains of *Homo erectus*. The discovery has been dated at 490,000 years old. One other discovery from the lower part of Bed II has been reported recently; the discovery, referred to by Leakey as "George," consisted of many small fragments and thus required a painstaking reconstruction, so that as yet no adequate description of the material has been made available. According to Leakey, it is the remains of a *Homo erectus* individual. If this is indeed true, then the African variants of *Homo erectus* go back in time to about one million years ago, since this discovery was made at very nearly the bottom of Bed II. This discovery may provide *Homo erectus* with "time depth" that heretofore has been hard to document except on morphological grounds.

The East African remains are too few to provide a basis for firm conclusions, but they tend to present a picture of *Homo erectus* that is consistent with the others considered so far, not only from the standpoint of morphology, but in more general adaptive terms as well.

The only other candidate for *Homo erectus* in Africa is from a South African site, Swartkrans, which has produced remains of australopithecines as well. This is the discovery which for many years has been known as *Telanthropus*. The material assigned to this group includes two incomplete lower jaws, a fragment of an upper jaw that may have belonged with one of the two mandibles, and a few other fragments. These are similar to the Peking and Heidelberg jaws and teeth, and, on morphological grounds, it would seem consistent and appropriate to include this

South African material within *Homo erectus*. There is, however, very little to go on, as was the case with the other African and European discoveries, particularly at Ternifine, Sidi Abderrahman, and Heidelberg. Furthermore, the deposits in which the Swartkrans material was discovered were such that it was impossible to estimate their age confidently or to ascertain details of their faunal and archaeological contexts. It would seem that all that might be inferred from the Swartkrans site is that *Homo erectus* may have resided there.

As indicated earlier, *Homo erectus* has in a more exaggerated form the same kinds of distinctive features compared with modern man that Neanderthal does. In fact, of course, it is not simply a matter of degree. Another way of relating the *Homo erectus* morphology with Neanderthal man is to see that the former is a smaller-brained, larger-toothed version of the latter. The question of whether the *Homo erectus* forms were ancestral to Neanderthal may be evaluated in terms of the evidence that has been presented: 1) Their territorial distributions overlap. 2) *Homo erectus* is found in association with industries of archaeological material that developed elsewhere, and in several places, into the industries found with Neanderthal man. 3) The temporal gap between them is formidable; the next most recent fossil whose age is well known is Swanscombe, which itself poses morphological problems, but, in any case, is dated at 250,000 years ago. This implies a gap of about one-fourth of a million years, during which time there is no clearly assignable fossil-man material. There are archaeological remains during the time, however. 4) Evidence against the view that *Homo erectus* is ancestral to Neanderthal man does not, in fact, exist in any concrete form. At present it would seem that the bulk of the evidence supports a permissive view. *Homo erectus* could be Neanderthal's ancestor, since no other well-documented hominid was around at the time; further, since the tools that Neanderthal used emerged from the same traditions as those *Homo erectus* used, the ancestral relationship seems rather secure. With the large temporal gap and the small amount of contradictory evidence, it is prudent, however, to keep an open mind on the problem.

The unevenness of the information available from the various parts of the Old World makes it difficult to summarize the general characteristics of *Homo erectus*, but some tentative generalizations can be reached. 1) He was distributed throughout the Old World. 2) Available dating estimates place him in time from about one-half to one million years ago. 3) He made tools. These differ in form between the African-European (Chelles-Acheul) and the Asian (chopper-chopping) *Homo erectus* associations, but it seems likely that both traditions served similar subsistence functions. Each would seem to be a generalized assemblage consistent with subsistence patterns that include both animal and plant food sources. 4) His appearance in the fossil record seems to be associated with a change in the mammalian fauna, and the newer fauna usually includes indications of a moderately warm, moist climate in open (as opposed to densely forested) terrain. 5) From China, we know that he was in control of fire, and further that fire seems to have been used for food preparation there. Since no such evidence exists with the Javanese, European, and African remains, it would not be justified to conclude that because Peking man had fire, the others did as well. 6) Likewise, *Homo erectus* occupied caves near Peking, and the South African material was from what was once a cave too, but the others are from open sites. A fair guess of the habitations of *Homo erectus* might be that he frequented caves where they were available, but probably not as a permanent resident. Seasonal or even daily fluctuations in the available plant and animal food sources must have kept *Homo erectus* on the move. Large kills of many animals at one time, such as were possible by driving a herd over a cliff, might have provided occasional periods of rest, as would seasonal variation in plant food abundance. Apart from these periods, the factor that determined much of the way of life of *Homo erectus* must have been his continual search for food.

Perhaps, then, Neanderthal is ancestral to us, and perhaps, again, *Homo erectus* is ancestral to Neanderthal. Who, then, is ancestral to *Homo erectus?* The most probable candidate for that distinction is the next subject of discussion.

Australopithecus

In 1924 the first of a continuing series of fossil hominid discoveries was made about eighty miles north of Kimberley, South Africa. The original discovery consisted of the fragmentary remains of the skull of an infant about five to seven years of age. It was brought to the attention of the energetic and imaginative young anatomist Raymond A. Dart, who judged it to be the remains of a type of hominid hitherto unknown, and thus a form that could be the "missing link." He called it *Australopithecus africanus,* which means, roughly, South African ape-man. These were the remains of a form old enough to precede modern man and the known forms of Neanderthal and *Homo erectus.* If, indeed, these were the remains of a hominid, then they were of great potential importance in understanding man's phylogenetic history and, further, could be expected to shed light on the origins of the *Homo erectus* and Neanderthal phases and how they might relate to modern man. Clearly, *Australopithecus* held out some hopeful possibilities; yet on superficial examination of the fossil material, it is perhaps difficult to see this potential. The skull looked very much like an infant chimpanzee's (see Figure 6–19), and not at all like what one might expect if the morphological trends indicated by the modern man–Neanderthal–*Homo erectus* sequence were projected back in

Chimpanzee   Taung

Figure 6–19. Comparison of an infant chimpanzee skull with Taung child skull cast.

time. Apart from the truly extraordinary fact that the skull had broken open and that, as a result of this, a cast of about one-half of the animal's brain became fossilized, it might have gone unnoticed. Dart, and eventually Robert Broom, were convinced that it was an infant hominid and not an infant chimp. They pointed out that, when compared with a chimpanzee, the *Australopithecus* child had a large brain for its age, that if it were a pongid, it should have begun to show some signs of the crests and ridges so characteristic of adults, and, more importantly, that the teeth were in many ways more like man's than like those of chimpanzees and gorillas. While the original discovery created considerable interest and concern, it was impossible to conclude anything definite about its significance. The discovery of one individual is not convincing. New discoveries of *Australopithecus* were made in 1936 and, except for a gap during World War II, have continued to occur ever since. Today the remains of over seventy-five individuals of this group are known. They have been recovered from sites in Africa, the Near East, Asia, and Java. Figure 6–20 shows a comparison of two australopithecines with modern man. In the facial view, the impres-

Figure 6–20. (Opposite Page) Comparison of four views of two adult australopithecine skull casts with a modern man skull.

Australopithecus africanus   Modern Man   (Australopithecus robustus)

sion is immediately conveyed that this is at once more apelike in its appearance than either Neanderthal or *Homo erectus*, yet its form, as mentioned above, is surprisingly different from what might be expected by "predicting" backward from modern man. Specifically, one can, on careful inspection, see a combination of manlike and apelike traits. Continuing with the facial view, note the small but clearly defined sagittal ridge, the very broad face, together with small nonprojecting canine teeth. From the side, the comparatively small brain falls within the range of modern apes and well outside the ranges of modern man, Neanderthal, and probably *Homo erectus*. The supraorbital ridges are well developed; the forehead is low-lying and slopes back abruptly from the brow ridges; and the snout projects forward, putting the incisors well out in front of the rest of the face. There is an occipital crest, small in comparison with that of modern apes, but, on the whole, the back of the head, including the poorly developed contour of the mastoids, is more like that of a chimpanzee than like man.

From the bottom, the australopithecine tooth row may be seen to be more sharply angled than modern man's. The foramen magnum is situated well underneath the skull as in modern man, indicating that *Australopithecus* walked completely erect.

In South Africa, australopithecine fossil material has been found at five sites (see Table 6–6 and Figure 6–21): Taung, which has produced only the original discovery of the child's skull; Makapansgat, like Taung, the site of a former cave located about 180 miles north of Johannesburg;

Figure 6–21. Geographic distribution of *Australopithecus*.

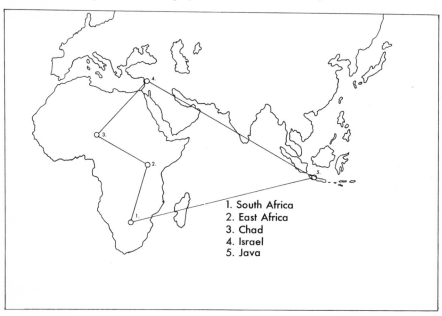

1. South Africa
2. East Africa
3. Chad
4. Israel
5. Java

TABLE 6–6

SITES YIELDING EVIDENCE OF *Australopithecus*

Location	Date Found	Comment
1. South Africa		
Taung	1924	Almost complete skull and mandible of a child. This was the original discovery that some felt was a fossil chimp.
Sterkfontein	1936–1957	Site yielding an abundance of skull fragments, teeth, mandibles, and postcranial bones. Among the most interesting remains are an almost complete skull and pelvis. The material was originally identified as *Plesianthropus transvaalensis*.
Swartkrans	1948–1952	Apart from the *Homo erectus* remains, this site has produced several fragments of skulls, jaws, teeth, and postcranial bones. Original designation: *Paranthropus robustus*.
Kromdraii	1938–1941	Compared with Swartkrans fewer and less complete remains but also identified as *Paranthropus robustus*.
Makapansgat	1947–1962	An almost complete skull, fragments of others, of mandibles, teeth, and postcranial bones, including pelvic fragments. Originally called *Australopithecus prometheus* (it was mistakenly thought that there was evidence for the controlled use of fire). The remains here are recognized as similar to those from Taung and Sterkfontein.
2. East Africa		
Olduvai	1959–present	According to Leakey (1965) these deposits indicate the coexistence of three hominids in early Pleistocene times: *Australopithecus* (originally *Zinjanthropus*), *Homo erectus*, and *Homo habilis*. Le Gros Clark (1967), among others, feels that *Homo habilis* and *Zinjanthropus* are both australopithecines.
Lake Natron	1964	An almost complete mandible found about fifty miles from Olduvai Gorge.
Lake Eyasi	1938	Three teeth and a fragment of an upper jaw.
Omo Basin, Ethiopia	1968	Three complete mandibles (two without teeth), one partial jaw with two teeth, and several dozen isolated teeth. Some teeth are at least 3½ million years old.
3. Chad		
Koro Toro	1960	The skull fragments here were identified by their discoverer as *Australopithecus*, but he and others now suggest that the remains may be more like those of *Homo erectus*.
4. Israel		
Ubeidiya	1959	Fragments of two skulls and a tooth.
5. Java		
Sangiran	1939–1953	Three mandibles and some teeth of alleged australopithecine affinity.

and three more cave sites within a few miles' radius of one another, Sterkfontein, Kromdraii, and Swartkrans, which, it will be recalled, was the site which also contained the two mandibles and associated skeletal material of *Telanthropus,* the possible *Homo erectus* form.

Efforts to relate the South African discoveries to one another and to other fossil hominids have been hampered by several serious obstacles. The early descriptions and subsequent discussions tended to magnify the differences not only between the australopithecines and modern man, but among the australopithecines themselves. If one were to take the literal interpretation implicit in the way these australopithecines have been labeled, he would have to conclude that within a very short geological period and within a comparatively small part of South Africa there were four separate genera of hominids. When you recall that chihuahuas and coyotes are within the same genus, you are able to get an idea of how striking the South African discoveries would be if this were indeed true. Today it is quite clear that it is not true, but the clumsy taxonomy that arose out of the emphasis on tiny and insignificant differences remains an obstacle to the interpretation of these forms. At present, all the South African discoveries are placed together with those of East Africa and other localities, and the skeletal material is classified into one genus, *Australopithecus.* Moreover, some taxonomists place them together with us in the genus *Homo.*

Another obstacle has been associated with attempts to establish some temporal relationships between and among the sites. Except for the Taung child, all of the remains have been recovered from unstratified cave deposits, but it is not entirely clear from these hominid remains whether or not *Australopithecus* was himself a resident of the caves. At any rate, the deposits are mixed up, and the fact that they were cut out during quarrying excavations and subsequently investigated makes it impossible to arrange the material in any satisfactory sequence. The only sequence suggested by association with climatic and faunal changes separates the five sites into two phases: 1) an early phase represented by the remains from Taung, Sterkfontein, and Makapansgat; and 2) a later phase, which includes the Swartkrans and Kromdraii sites. This division has some morphological justification in the fact that smaller variants of *Australopithecus* have been found in the early-phase sites, and the larger variants in the later-phase caves. The morphological differences between the large and small variants are not as great as those between male and female gorillas (Tobias, 1967). They are, however, localized in space and probably time, and this would seem to provide the necessary basis for distinguishing these as two separate species: 1) *Australopithecus africanus,* the smaller, apparently earlier form; and 2) *Australopithecus robustus,* the larger and later variant. Figure 6–20 compares the two with modern man. Apart from this mention, however, the australopithecines will be treated here as one group occupying one phase in the evolution of the hominids.

Apart from splitting the forms into too many taxonomic groupings, and from the vagaries of temporal considerations, another problem associated with *Australopithecus* which has beset students of human paleontology is the relationship between *Australopithecus* and other hominids. This is the most interesting question, and it will be taken up after some of the temporal, spatial, formal, and contextual information from each locality has been considered. It is sufficient perhaps to mention here only that no satisfactory means has been devised to relate with confidence the time of the South African australopithecine deposits to the glacial sequence in the north latitudes.

These problems are enough to make it difficult or impossible to be confident of any specific interpretations of the australopithecines, but, as if this were not enough, there is a more general and fundamental difficulty that arises from the fact that there simply is no modern-day analogue to them, nor to their way of life. Neanderthal can be "known" in a sense by drawing comparisons between his adaptation and that of efficient hunting peoples of contemporary or recent historic times. *Homo erectus* is, to be sure, more of a mystery, but not a total one. The situation of his day—the abundance of game and the crude status of his technology and undoubtedly inferior central nervous system—is almost certainly matched to some degree by the adaptations of modern-man populations with tremendously improved brains and more effective technological inventories in areas of scarcer game and shorter food supply. In the case of the australopithecines, there simply is no aspect of our experience that can readily be brought to bear on our attempt to understand him. Although several well-reasoned attempts have been made to do so, at our present state of knowledge we are more strictly limited to the ambiguities of temporal, formal, spatial, and contextual dimensions without modern-day parallels, and are able to offer only guesses about how *Australopithecus* may have lived.

Recognizing this should make it easier to summarize the available information and the problems created.

1) The five sites present different kinds of evidence. For example, apart from the australopithecine child, none of the species found at the Taung location is represented at Sterkfontein nor at Kromdraii, though many genera are common to all three. Stone tools of a pre-Chelles-Acheul type are known from Sterkfontein, Kromdraii, and Makapansgat, but not from Taung or Swartkrans. Taung appears to have been occupied at a time when the area was very dry; the others when it was more moist. These are features that make it difficult to generalize about the South African australopithecines.

2) All the remains have come from caves or fissures. These have filled up in whole or in part, and some have been tourist attractions for many years before they were known to contain evidence of *Australopithecus*. The Taung location has been completely destroyed by limestone quarrying operations.

3) The manner in which the deposits might have accumulated in the caves makes it impossible to be certain that remains found together are of forms that lived at or near the same time. In spite of this difficulty, most investigators presume a rough contemporaneity for the fauna within a cave but are reluctant to extend this presumption to the other sites in any precise way.

4) Collectively, the remains within these deposits include an extraordinary abundance of the bones of a small extinct variety of antelope and of a small extinct species of baboon, together with other mammalian forms that, while the deposits vary considerably in their composition, together make up the South African Villafranchian.

5) The abundance of baboons and antelopes raises the question of how they got there; neither is a cave dweller by choice. A number of explanations have been offered, but the one most consistent with the evidence is the explanation that *Australopithecus* brought them there. The support for this view is largely circumstantial but, taken as a totality, is moderately convincing. The vast majority of baboon skulls show evidence of having been killed by a blow on the head with the traditional blunt instrument, and of having had the skulls subsequently bashed open. This is decidedly not the way that carnivores kill their prey, but more distinctly the way that tool-using primates might. The antelope's long bones show signs of having been split open. Hyenas split bones to get at the marrow, but in the process usually leave distinctive tooth markings; such markings are lacking. *Australopithecus* may have been after the same thing with his hands or perhaps assisted by an implement. And, finally, there is an amount of peripheral "evidence" that conforms only in the sense that it permits the hypothesis that the australopithecines brought the animals into the caves: the baboons and antelopes are small enough, and it is not the kind of assemblage that carnivores (such as the scavenging hyenas), observed under natural conditions, leave behind in their lairs today. Furthermore, modern apes and some monkeys occasionally eat meat as part of their natural diet, thereby implying that the dietary precedent necessary for the australopithecines to have been able to eat meat is a trait that had been established among the primates for a long time. While it is clearly possible that the cave deposits in South Africa may have been laid down in a very different manner, the bulk of the evidence would seem to favor the conclusion that the australopithecines could have been and probably were responsible for bringing in most of the skeletal remains.

6) No good evidence exists to suggest a reliable conclusion concerning the manner in which the animals may have been killed. One reasonable view is that *Australopithecus* was a part-time scavenger, that is, that many of the animals were either killed by large carnivores or died as a result of other natural factors, and *Australopithecus* took what was left back to the caves for perhaps a more protected eating place and a locality in which he might share his food with other australopithecines. There is, of course, no evidence of sharing, but had he done so, *Australopithecus* would have had an easier time adapting, and thus surviving. In all, the sharing behavior might have bestowed as much survival potential at the australopithecine level of adaptation as erect posture and perhaps language, but such reasoning is clearly not direct evidence that it existed.

Scavenging is probably not a good way to describe the manner in which *Australopithecus* obtained his food. It implies that he lurked in the shadows waiting for a carnivore to kill a large animal and to eat his fill, and after the carnivore wandered off to rest, then *Australopithecus* moved in to take what was left. This is a common way for hyenas to obtain their food. Again the evidence is not direct, but since most modern primates, including modern man, depend heavily on plant food sources, it seems logical to conclude that *Australopithecus* did too. A view of *Australopithecus* as an animal that moved over large territories seeking food of any kind wherever it was available seems almost certainly to be closer to the real situation than the view suggested by calling him a scavenger. Perhaps it would be better to think of *Australopithecus* as an omnivore that was engaged in more or less full-time food collecting, whether from plant or animal sources.

7) Two opposing but not entirely contradictory views exist on the issue of whether or not *Australopithecus* lived in the caves as a regular tenant. They exist because it is clear, on the one hand, that he must have been on the move constantly to obtain food and therefore could not have lived in any one location as a permanent resident. On the other hand, it is clear that, if they brought the animals into the caves, then the australopithecines must have occupied the caves regularly to build up such an enormous quantity of bones. Both views could be true simultaneously if *Australopithecus*, at a time when animals were available, retired to the caves as protected areas in which to eat, whereas when he was not eating animal food, no such precautions were taken.

Professor Raymond Dart has proposed an interesting theory which, if it represents what in fact was happening, would have an important bearing on the way that *Australopithecus* lived and particularly on how he may have dispatched the animals and used the cave. He proposes to account for the large number of bones, particularly the antelope bones, by stating that they were used as implements—in other words, that the skeletal remains are, in fact, the implements that *Australopithecus* used to kill and cut up more animals. Thus, it would be at once an archaeological and a paleontological assemblage. Since archaeological assemblages are named, he calls this large assemblage of bones, horn cores, and teeth the Osteodontokeratic (bones, teeth, horn) culture. It is an interesting theory, but an impossible one to demonstrate conclusively as true or false with present evidence.

8) Careful studies have been carried out on the climatic conditions prevalent at the time the caves were used, but these have not produced much new information because of the problems already discussed with regard to temporal and distributional factors. These have resulted in the observations stated earlier that Taung appears to have been occupied during hot, dry, desertlike conditions; the other areas are better watered. During much of the time the caves were frequented by the australopithecines, the climatic conditions do not appear to have been markedly different from those prevailing there today.

9) Irrespective of the validity of the Osteodontokeratic theory, australopithecines have been found in association with stone tools of the earliest of the pebble tool traditions, the Oldowan or pre-Chelles-Acheul. The assemblages consist of crude hand-axe-like pebble tools and crudely made flake implements (Figure 6–22). Earlier objections that *Australopithecus* was too dull to have made the implements seem to have been overcome by the recent evidence that chimpanzees are toolmakers, and if they are able to do as well as alleged, then the accomplishments of the australopithecines are more reasonable to expect. The Oldowan is the earliest known stone tool assemblage, and it is the first stage in a continuous development that goes through the Chelles-Acheul, Clactonian-Levalloisian, Mousterian, etc., sequence.

From the South African materials, answers to the most interesting questions concerning the australopithecines would have to run as follows: Did they make tools? Yes. Were they hunters? No, not in any usual meaning of that word. Did they eat meat? Yes. When did they live? The evidence is inconclusive. Were they ancestral to *Homo erectus*? The direct

Figure 6–22. Kafuan or Oldu-
wan pebble tool.

evidence is again inconclusive, but possibly yes, and if not, then who was? Leakey may have an answer to this. The evidence on *Australopithecus* that has been recovered at Olduvai Gorge bears directly on these problems; it is interesting; most of it is recent; and very little systematic descriptive material is available on which to draw conclusions concerning its significance. Some of the East African discoveries were mentioned earlier in the context of *Homo erectus,* the L.L.K. discovery, and "George."

The first of the recent discoveries came from Bed I and consisted of a relatively complete skull, which at first was thought by Leakey to be a completely new genus of hominid. He named it *Zinjanthropus boisei.* Subsequently, it was renamed *Australopithecus boisei* (Tobias, 1967). The discovery attracted a lot of attention, since it was felt to be a new genus and thus a possible candidate as the "missing link," but what really caused confusion was the publication of the potassium-argon age estimates of *Zinjanthropus* placing him at 1.75 million years old. Up until then, most authorities presumed that the Pleistocene had not lasted more than one million years, and that it was within this period that the hominid phase of primate evolution took place. Here, however, was evidence of an erect bipedal hominid roaming around East Africa about 750 thousand years earlier. The consequences of the age estimate were perhaps predictable; many authorities flatly denied the validity of the discovery. Others claimed contradictory evidence was available, but most quietly accepted the new estimates and revised their view of the Pleistocene accordingly. In fact, the effect was in some ways welcome, since the many major events known only by relative age and formerly sandwiched within one million years could now justifiably be spread out over two.

Figure 6–23 shows three views of *Zinjanthropus.* Material now regarded as *Australopithecus boisei* includes the cranium, the tibia and fibula discovered a year later, and two teeth discovered in 1964, but in a much more recent location. In his most striking features, *Zinjanthropus* is grossly apelike. He has a massive face with clear evidence of a heavy musculature including sagittal and occipital crests. His brain size is within 600–700 cc., a range that includes the largest brain sizes of modern gorillas. These are features which he shares with the australopithecines from South Africa, particularly those from Swartkrans and Kromdraii. What deserves special attention here is that found within the same layer, Bed I, are the remains of a child located at a lower level than the australopithecine but still within Bed I. Leakey calls this form *Homo habilis* and thus implies that he is more like us than he is like *Australopithecus.* Furthermore, Leakey has found evidence of both *Australopithecus* and *Homo habilis* in Bed II contemporary with the *Homo erectus* forms discussed earlier. Finally, Leakey has recently referred to a circular stone habitation hut right at the bottom of Bed I! The implications of these discoveries

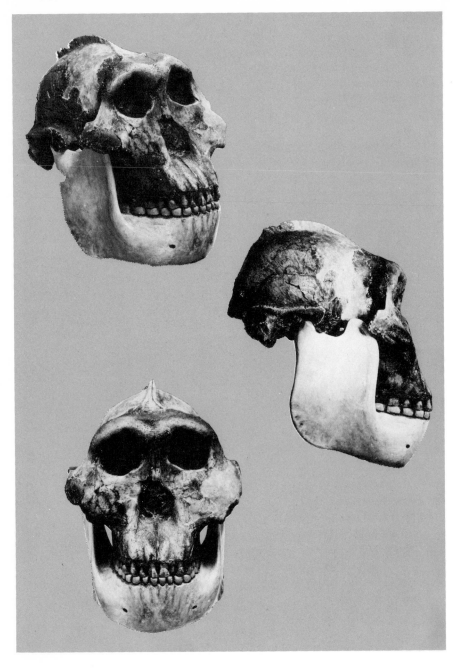

Figure 6–23. Three views of a *Zinjanthropus* skull cast. (Reconstruction by Phillip V. Tobias and R. Clarke, photo by R. Campbell and A. R. Hughes.)

are astounding, and Leakey has drawn attention to them repeatedly and forcefully, but how they might fit in with the rest of our information is not at all clear. The record implies that two hominids were living side by side during the time that Bed I was deposited. These persisted into Bed II times, when, with *Homo erectus,* there are three hominids living at the same time in the same area. The evidence for his view is not very compelling; it consists of the following: 1) Citations by Leakey that the existence of two or more similar but distinct species occupying the same geographical zones is not an uncommon event, as formerly believed. Thus, if this is the case, *Homo habilis* and *Australopithecus* could have lived side by side. 2) Resurrection of the Kanam mandible, which, as Leakey readily admits, only he seems to have taken seriously as evidence for early Pleistocene modern man. Thus Kanam is evidence for a more modern type of very early hominid, as is *Homo habilis,* according to Leakey. This is not very convincing, but since only a very small amount of descriptive material has been made available on the Bed I hominids, one is forced to rely heavily on the interpretations of the discoverer. Le Gros Clark (1967), a distinguished British human paleontologist, discounts *Homo habilis* and concludes that only *Australopithecus* resided during Bed I times, and that he persisted up to the Bed I–Bed II juncture. This is a view that meshes more consistently with the paleontological facts considered so far, but consistency is often misleading, and it may well be necessary to modify the view of human evolution in the direction of Leakey's claims. At present, however, there would seem to be very little evidence to support such a shift. Again, what is needed urgently now is not more fossils, but a complete description and comparative analysis of the material already recovered.

The archaeological evidence from Olduvai Gorge has not been completely analyzed as yet, and thus it is not possible to discuss it with confidence. Some points of information have been made available, and they, like the fossil bone material, contain some surprises. The existence of a circular stone structure down at the base of Bed I contemporary with *Homo habilis* is indeed astonishing. Deliberate manufacture of shelters has long been presumed to be a very recent cultural accomplishment occurring within the last 100,000 years. Previously man and his ancestors were believed to have lived out in the open or at times to have occupied natural shelters such as the rock shelters and caves in which the fossil material is often found.

Stone flake tools and crude chopper tools, collectively known as Oldowan pebble tools, have been reported as abundant in Bed I, giving way to a pre-Chelles-Acheul and eventually to a regular hand-axe sequence that apparently continues up to relatively recent times. The cultural picture has been confused recently by a report that Leakey now has evidence for *three* cultural assemblages in Bed II.

In indirect support of the Osteodontokeratic culture in South Africa, there have been indications that bone tools were in use in East Africa at the same time that the pebble tool sequence was developing. Indeed, the East African cultural assemblages are similar in most fundamental features to those from South Africa, but until more complete information becomes available from East Africa, specific comparisons are impossible.

The geological and faunal makeup of Olduvai Gorge has been reported in the first of a proposed three-volume survey (Leakey, 1965). The fauna from Bed I make up a characteristic series of late Villafranchian genera and species. This continues into the lower part of Bed II, after which a shift occurs, involving an increase in the variety and abundance of giant herbivores. Eventually, and presumably during the time when Beds III and IV were being deposited, the modern fauna characteristic of East Africa today took over in their present form and proportions. The faunal assemblages are not easily integrated with the archaeological and hominid fossil remains for the reason mentioned above, namely, comprehensive descriptions of the latter are not yet available. Thus it is that, with the exceptions noted, there are no striking contrasts between the South African and East African archaeological and paleontological remains.

The evidence for australopithecines outside of South and East Africa, while still rather meager, is accumulating steadily. It consists of the following: 1) a jaw with some teeth from Java of a form which formerly had been called *Meganthropus;* this was found in the bed (Djetis) below the one yielding *Homo erectus* (Trinil); 2) material from a few scattered sites from elsewhere in Africa, specifically near Lake Chad and Lake Eyasi; and 3) material from the Jordan Valley in the Near East. At present the total material available is very small and thus could easily result in conclusions that ultimately turn out to have been misleading. Perhaps the only justifiable conclusion one might reach with regard to these discoveries is that it appears likely that *Australopithecus* had a broader distribution in the Old World than formerly he was thought to have. Its limits are as yet unclear, however.

The history of human evolution merges with the evolution of the primates as one goes back in time beyond the australopithecines. For a long time, the Pliocene was a dark void in the fossil record. This gap is beginning to be filled as more is learned about *Kenyapithecus* and *Ramapithecus,* forms discussed earlier that may serve to join from opposite directions the evolution of the primates with human evolution. Furthermore, additional Pliocene deposits were discovered in Africa in 1969. Before proceeding to contemporary human variation, however, a review and recapitulation of the evidence for human evolution would seem to be in order.

During the past fifteen years, there has been a great increase in the number of fossils directly relevant to the record of man's origin and evolution. The full impact of these discoveries and of the reanalyses of older discoveries may not be felt for several years, but even now they have begun to cause some major shifts in the interpretations of the course of man's evolution. The earlier view of modern man's great antiquity has given way first to a period of extensive confusion and ambiguity, and only now does it appear that the situation is clearing again, and the view that is emerging tends to include all the earlier forms as representatives of phases in man's ancestry. If this is indeed the direction in which interpretations are moving, then they have shifted to polar extremes in approximately twenty years, the earlier view rejecting Neanderthal, *Homo erectus,* and *Australopithecus* as man's ancestors on the grounds that man was already on the scene contemporary with or antecedent to these forms. The later view claims all of them as ancestors of modern man. Certainly not everyone shares this view, and, at present, the evidence from paleontology is ambiguous, and, more particularly, the Olduvai Gorge material is contradictory.

The archaeological evidence, however, seems to be clearer. There is a reasonably complete and essentially unbroken sequence of development from pebble tools to space vehicles, and it is this that compels us to view the paleontological material found in association with it at various points in time and space as representative of the ancestral stages of our evolution.

Based on this reasoning, and recognizing the limitations, we may tentatively conclude that man's ancestors are in fact represented by Neanderthal man, *Homo erectus,* and *Australopithecus.*

REFERENCES AND
SUGGESTIONS FOR ADDITIONAL READING

BOULE, M., AND H. V. VALLOIS
  1957   *Fossil men.* Translated by Michael Bullock. New York: Dryden Press.
BRACE, C. LORING
  1964   The fate of the "classic" Neanderthals: a consideration of hominid catastrophism. *Current Anthropology* 5:3–43.
  1967   *The stages of human evolution.* Englewood Cliffs, N.J.: Prentice-Hall.
BRACE, C. LORING, AND M. F. ASHLEY MONTAGU
  1965   *Man's evolution: an introduction to physical anthropology.* New York: Macmillan.
BROOM, R., AND G. W. H. SCHEPERS
  1946   *The South African fossil ape-men: the australopithecinae.* Transvaal Museum Memoir no. 2. Pretoria, South Africa: Transvaal Museum.

BUETTNER-JANUSCH, JOHN
1966   *Origins of man: physical anthropology.* New York: John Wiley & Sons.

CLARK, W. E. LE GROS
1964   *The fossil evidence for human evolution.* 2d rev. ed. Chicago: University of Chicago Press.
1967   *Man-apes or ape-men?: the story of discoveries in Africa.* New York: Holt, Rinehart & Winston.

CLARK, W. E. LE GROS, ET AL.
1938   Report of the Swanscombe committee. *Journal of the Royal Anthropological Institute* 68:17–98.

COMAS, JUAN
1960   *Manual of physical anthropology.* Rev. and enl. English ed. Springfield, Ill.: Charles C. Thomas.

COON, CARLETON S.
1962   *The origin of races.* New York: Alfred A. Knopf.

DART, RAYMOND A.
1925   *Australopithecus africanus:* the man-ape of South Africa. *Nature* 115:195–199.
1957   The Makapansgat australopithecine Osteodontokeratic culture. In *Proceedings of the Third Pan-African Congress on Prehistory,* pp. 161–171.

DART, R. A., AND D. CRAIG
1959   *Adventures with the missing link.* New York: Harper.

DAY, MICHAEL H.
1965   *Guide to fossil man: a handbook of human palaeontology.* London: Cassell.

DUBOIS, EUGÈNE
1894   *Pithecanthropus erectus, eine menschenähnliche Ubergansform aus Java.* Batavia: Landesdruckerei.

EMILIANI, CESARE
1968   The Pleistocene epoch and the evolution of man. *Current Anthropology* 9:27–47.

HARRISON, RICHARD J., AND W. MONTAGNA
1969. *Man.* New York: Appleton-Century-Crofts.

HEMMER, H.
1969   A new view of the evolution of man. *Current Anthropology* 10:179–180.

HOOTON, EARNEST ALBERT
1947   *Up from the ape.* Rev. ed. New York: Macmillan.

HOWELL, F. CLARK
1959   The Villafranchian and human origins. *Science* 130:831–844.
1960   European and Northwest African Middle Pleistocene hominids. *Current Anthropology* 1:195–232.

HOWELL, F. CLARK, AND THE EDITORS OF LIFE
1965   *Early man.* New York: Time, Inc.

HOWELLS, WILLIAM W.
    1966   *Homo erectus. Scientific American* 215, November, pp. 46–53.
HULSE, FREDERICK S.
    1963   *The human species.* New York: Random House.
KENYON, KATHLEEN M.
    1957   *Beginning in archaeology.* Rev. ed. New York: F. A. Praeger.
KROEBER, A. L.
    1948   *Anthropology: race, language, culture, psychology, prehistory.* Rev.
           ed. New York: Harcourt, Brace & World.
LAUGHLIN, W. S., AND R. H. OSBORNE, EDS.
    1967   *Human variation and origins: readings from* Scientific American.
           San Francisco: W. H. Freeman.
LEAKEY, L. S. B.
    1965   *Olduvai Gorge, 1951–1961* (vol. 1). London: Cambridge Univer-
           sity Press.
MAYR, ERNST
    1950   Taxonomic categories in fossil hominids. *Cold Spring Harbor Sym-
           posia on Quantitative Biology* 15:109–118.
MONTAGU, M. F. ASHLEY
    1960   *An introduction to physical anthropology.* 3d ed. Springfield, Ill.:
           Charles C. Thomas.
OAKLEY, KENNETH P.
    1964   *Frameworks for dating fossil man.* Chicago: Aldine.
OVEY, C. D., ED.
    1964   The Swanscombe skull. Royal Anthropological Institute, *Occasional
           Papers,* no. 20.
SIMONS, ELWYN L.
    1963   Some fallacies in the study of hominid phylogeny. *Science* 141:879–
           889.
SPAULDING, ALBERT C.
    1960   The dimensions of archaeology. In *Essays in the science of culture
           in honor of Leslie A. White,* ed. G. E. Dole and R. L. Carneiro.
           New York: Thomas Y. Crowell.
TAX, SOL, ED.
    1960   *The evolution of man: man, culture, and society.* Vol. 2 of *Evolution
           after Darwin.* Chicago: University of Chicago Press.
TOBIAS, PHILIP V.
    1967   *Olduvai Gorge* (vol. 2): *the cranium and maxillary dentition of*
           Australopithecus (Zinjanthropus) boisei. London: Cambridge Uni-
           versity Press.
WASHBURN, SHERWOOD L.
    1960   Tools and human evolution. *Scientific American* 203, September,
           pp. 62–75.

PART III

Human Heterography

A COMPARISON OF THE BASIC UNITS and fundamental divisions of human heterography with human paleontology reveals some unexpected similarities. The primary units of analysis in human paleontology are the fossils, or, more precisely, the traits that are used to compare them to one another. Profound comparative analysis of paleontological material requires more than just information on the formal variations of the traits; it calls for the recovery of data on time, space, and context as well. Except for spatial factors, these latter dimensions tend to be ignored in most discussions of contemporary human variation, but they are nevertheless important factors bearing on the ways in which we view, and the manner in which we interpret, the facts of man's variation. To be sure, formal variations and their distributions are of primary importance, but the other dimensions are relevant, and notice of their significance should be taken when considering the various ways in which human heterographic variations have been viewed and grouped.

The primary dimension of interest to both paleontology and heterography is that of form. Much more data on formal variation are available for heterographic analysis, and this offers a more solid empirical basis for the testing of hypotheses and the formulation of generalizations or theories. Details of function, context, and distribution can, for example, be observed directly. This abundance of information might lead one to suspect that heterographic analyses must be considerably advanced over those in paleontology; that is, theories should be more fully developed, and there should be substantially more agreement on basic issues, concepts, and principles. Yet, what one actually finds is an almost complete lack of theory, and, in place of agreement, a sea of confusion. This situation has come about because: 1) the study of human variation is inextricably woven together with the concept and study of race; 2) race is an ambiguous concept, and thinking on the subject often begins with incorrect assumptions which can only lead to error, however logical the route; and 3) even scientists approach the subject with strong emotional and moral commitments, with the result that disorder and lack of direction occur in place of ordered, systematic, and dispassionate analyses. The situation does not come about because of a lack of data or a lack of interest; there is perhaps too much of both. The crucial need at the moment is to recognize how ignorant and confused we are of the processes reflected by the facts of human variation.

Ideally, we might find that the study of human variation would be served best if we were able to approach it with no preconceptions, no idea of how variable mankind is, no idea of how the variation is distributed, and no idea of what the variation and its distribution imply. For example, we "know" that skin color ranges from very dark to very light, that dark skin color is African, or, if we have looked more carefully, equatorial, and that light skin color is temperate in its distribution. Moreover, we "know" that, for the most part, dark skin color is associated with prognathism, kinky hair, thick lips, and broad noses, whereas light skin is found in association with contrasting characteristics. We "know" that these traits identify races, and we think, with confidence, that common membership within a race implies a close historical connection between peoples and a shared phylogenetic past. These are common beliefs and, of course, there are many others, most of them held with such conviction that they are considered obvious or self-evident. For this reason, it is probably unrealistic to ask that the beliefs be suspended. It would be, for example, like asking many seventeenth-century New Englanders to question their attitudes and beliefs about witches. For the present, however—and this may be too much—it would be helpful if one could at least question the belief that these races are fixed, eternal, and real things. If they are anything at all, races are fundamentally clusters of characteristics brought together through normal evolutionary processes. The individual traits have emerged at different times as the products of different evolutionary factors operating at varying intensities. Moreover, these processes of evolution are continually changing, forcing traits that exist now to change in form and frequency. From the standpoint of evolution, a race, if it is anything, is a transitory thing, and what it implies about its members, the traits that distinguish it from others, and its relationship to other races is not at all clear. It may indeed be that it implies nothing about these things. But these are problems that will be taken up in Chapter 9.

To obviate some of the difficulties inherent in most discussions of human variation, the basic material on human heterography is presented in as objective a manner as possible. The data are presented neither to justify a particular classification nor to support one point of view. The discussion is centered first on traits of unknown inheritance which have been used extensively by physical anthropologists to describe man's variation, and then secondly on traits of known inheritance. In both instances some consideration is given to the range of variation in the trait's expression and how this is distributed. In the case of traits of known inheritance, attention is also given the matter of how the trait is inherited. Chapter 9 considers the final step in attempting to derive significance from the range and distribution of human variation by examining and evaluating some of the most common ways of classifying that variation.

Before beginning the discussion of specific ways in which human beings vary, it should be emphasized that perhaps the most extraordinary thing about the human species is how alike all of its members are. Consider that man's distribution is global and that he occupies many sharply contrasting environments, and it is possible to appreciate more clearly the extraordinary fact that man is one species only. No other animal even approximates a rival to man in this respect. Man extends his adaptive range primarily by nongenetic means (by culture), and in this way he has been able to retain biological homogeneity while adapting to ecological heterogeneity.

In the past few chapters, attention has been given to filling in some background and reviewing the highlights of the fossil record of human evolution and how it has been interpreted. In the next three chapters the general area of human variation, or, as identified earlier, human heterography, will be the center of interest. In the final chapter, the evidence bearing on the question of evolution in human populations today is considered.

REFERENCES AND
SUGGESTIONS FOR ADDITIONAL READING

COON, CARLETON S., WITH EDWARD E. HUNT, JR.
    1965   *The living races of man.* New York: Alfred A. Knopf.
COUNT, EARL W., ED.
    1950   *This is race: an anthology selected from the international literature on the races of man.* New York: Henry Schuman.

Downs, James F., and H. K. Bleibtreu
  1969   *Human variation: an introduction to physical anthropology.* Beverly Hills, Calif.: Glencoe Press.
Garn, Stanley M.
  1965   *Human races.* 2d ed. Springfield, Ill.: Charles C. Thomas.
Kelso, A. J.
  1967   The concept of race. *Improving College and University Teaching* 15: 95–97.
Livingstone, Frank B.
  1962   On the non-existence of human races (with comment by Theodosius Dobzhansky). *Current Anthropology* 3: 279–281.
Montagu, Ashley, ed.
  1964   *The concept of race.* New York: Free Press.

CHAPTER 7

HUMAN HETEROGRAPHY AND
MORPHOLOGICAL VARIATION:
TRAITS OF UNKNOWN INHERITANCE

INTRODUCTION

A literal interpretation of the title of this chapter might lead one to believe that it will not deal with inherited characteristics, but will examine the ways in which human groups vary. Since man varies in an infinite number of ways, obviously it is impossible to treat the subject comprehensively; a choice must be made at the outset on the kinds of traits to be considered. Basing our decision largely on tradition, and thereby including the ways in which physical anthropologists usually describe human variation, some illustrations of each of the following kinds of characteristics will be considered: physical, physiological, and developmental; a very brief comment on psychological characteristics will conclude the chapter.

PHYSICAL CHARACTERISTICS

Since human groups vary widely in their physical characteristics, a further choice must be made at this point on the traits that are to be considered. Attention will be given to the following measurements, indexes, and observations: 1) stature and weight; 2) head breadth, head length, and cephalic index; 3) nose length, nose breadth, and nasal index; 4) skin color; 5) hair form; and 6) distinctive morphological characteristics of restricted distribution. The discussion of the first three is based largely on a statistical analysis of the anthropometric data on approximately three hundred samples of adult non-European males reported in Biasutti (1959). The data on European populations have been drawn from Martin and Saller (1955–1966). This represents a deliberate attempt to report anthropometric data in a form similar to that used for genetic characteristics in the next chapter. The discussion on the rest of the traits is less detailed.

Before beginning a discussion of the traits, it may be useful to distinguish measurements, indexes, and observations. A *measurement* represents numerically the expression of a trait in terms of an independent scale of fixed intervals. Thus, stature, weight, head length and breadth, and nose length and breadth can be measured, that is, expressed numerically in terms of independent scales (inches, pounds, centimeters, etc.). Measured—or, as they are more commonly called, quantitatively variable —traits provide some of the most interesting questions in human heterography, but investigation of them has been hampered by the absence of information about how they are inherited. There are no proved, well-documented, readily accepted hypotheses on the mode of inheritance of quantitative traits in man. There exists a general theory which has been applied with some success to the hereditary variations of quantitative traits in some lower organisms. For the most part, it presumes that such traits are controlled by several loci occupied by genes with equal and additive effects. The theory is interesting and its applications fascinating, but it must remain a theory until it can be related in a clearer way to the better-established theory of gene action. Genes act to produce polypeptide chains, and, so far as we know, that is all that genes do; how this fits in with the theory of the inheritance of quantitative traits is not at all certain at the present time. Relating these concepts may be the next outstanding advance in the science of genetics. (Figure 7–1 shows some of the instruments used to measure man's physical characteristics.)

Indexes express numerically the proportional relationships between two or more measurements. The cephalic index, for example, expresses as a percentage the relationship between head length and head breadth, and the nasal index expresses the proportional relationship between nose length and nose breadth. Indexes are useful in describing human variation, in that they express relative differences. All measurements reflect gross body size; indexes do not. A person with a large head can have the same cephalic index as one with a small head, if head length and head breadth are in the same proportions.

Anthropometer

Spreading caliper

Sliding caliper

Figure 7–1. Anthropometric equipment.

Observations record qualitative variation; thus any particular observation is classified into a category. For example, observations of variation in hair form are usually classified into one of the following categories: straight, low wave, wavy, curly, tightly curled, kinky, and peppercorn. This is an elaborate illustration; commonly a trait will be noted simply as present or absent. The distinction between measurements and observations is due, at least in part, to the status of the techniques of measurement. Skin color, for example, has for many years been presented in the form of observational data. Now, with the development of reflectometers, it may be measured in terms of light reflectance units. Thus, what today may be regarded as a characteristic of several qualities may, as our measurement skills improve, be measurable in quantitative terms tomorrow. The primary purpose of scientific instruments is to assist the investigator in quantifying his experience.

Stature and Weight

Average variation in height in normal males ranges from 140 cm. to 185 cm. The geographical distribution of this variation is by no means random. Table 7–1 shows how this variation is distributed throughout the major areas of the world.

TABLE 7–1

MEAN STATURE AND STANDARD DEVIATION
BY MAJOR AREAS OF THE WORLD*

Area	Mean Stature cm.	Standard Deviation cm.	Number of Samples
1. Africa	164.9	7.24	115
2. Asia	163.0	4.13	74
3. Europe	167.2	3.00	149
4. Oceania	167.3	5.24	26
5. American Indians	163.7	5.79	55

* The mean is, of course, the average, and the values given here have been arrived at after weighting for sample size. Thus a sample of ten persons contributes one-tenth what a sample of one hundred does in calculating the mean. The standard deviation is a figure that provides information about variability in the population; the larger the standard deviation, the greater the variability. Except for Europe, these data have been compiled from Biasutti (1959) and weighted for sample size. The figures for Europe have been estimated from a graph of data obtained from Martin and Saller (1955–1966).

In Europe, the second-tallest average stature is combined with a comparatively small range of variability. The way in which the variation is distributed in Europe is clearly not random, but also it fails to follow any clear and simple pattern. Both the tallest and the shortest average statures occur in the north: the shortest Europeans are the Lapps of northern Sweden, Norway, and Finland; the tallest Europeans are the non-Lapp populations of these same countries. In the central areas, intermediate-to-tall statures may be found, whereas in the south, average statures do not vary much from the mean for the Continent.

In Asia the distribution is again a complex one and is characterized by a wider range of variation as well as the lowest overall mean. An inspection of the distribution reveals no clear north-south gradient in stature; the shortest Asian populations are found at both extremes (see Table 7–2). The significant feature of the distribution is that from west to east stature shows a gradual decline. The correlation† between longitude and stature ($-.51$) for these populations is highly significant.

The tallest and the shortest human populations in Africa reside within a zone marked approximately by the equator and 10° north latitude. Although it may appear from Table 7–3 that the Bushmen are the shortest Africans, in fact the Pygmies scattered throughout the northern Bantu

† Correlation coefficients range from -1 to $+1$. Negative correlations imply that as one variable (stature, for example) increases, the other decreases. Positive correlation coefficients imply that as one thing increases, so does another. Values at or near zero mean that one variable changes independently of changes in the other. Actually another judgment needs to be made in evaluating a correlation coefficient. However, understanding this is beyond the scope of this book. For those interested, the coefficients have been tested for significance and the results taken into account in the discussion.

TABLE 7–2

MEAN STATURE AMONG ASIAN POPULATIONS*

Area	Mean Stature cm.	Standard Deviation cm.	Number of Samples
1. Malay Peninsula and Archipelago	155.62	3.92	16
2. North Asia	158.82	2.32	14
3. Vedda	159.35	2.26	4
4. Southeast Asia	160.32	3.10	17
5. India, Castes	162.67	2.13	3
6. Far East	162.97	1.98	8
7. Central Asia	164.30	2.14	9
8. India, Various Locations	164.45	3.53	13
9. Iran, Armenia, Assyria	165.28	2.51	11
10. Asia Minor	167.26	1.80	9

* These data have been compiled from Biasutti (1959) and weighted for sample size.

TABLE 7–3

MEAN STATURE AMONG AFRICAN POPULATIONS†

Area	Mean Stature cm.	Standard Deviation cm.	Number of Samples
1. South Africa (Bushmen, Hottentots)	157.93	2.81	4
2. Northern Bantu (Equatorial)	161.95	7.40	42
3. Madagascar and Indian Ocean	164.55	1.94	4
4. North Africa	166.64	3.90	14
5. East Africa	168.17	2.70	26
6. Sahara	168.64	3.21	9
7. Central Bantu	168.75	2.35	11
8. West Africa	169.07	3.65	30
9. East Sudan	173.76	5.85	14

† These data have been compiled from Biasutti (1959) and weighted for sample size.

TABLE 7–4

MEAN STATURE AMONG PACIFIC POPULATIONS‡

Area	Mean Stature cm.	Standard Deviation cm.	Number of Samples
1. New Guinea and Melanesia	156.69	6.83	8
2. Australia	168.45	2.24	8
3. Polynesia and Micronesia	169.41	3.70	11

‡ These data have been compiled from Biasutti (1959) and weighted for sample size.

peoples of central equatorial Africa fall considerably under the average Bushman stature with mean values commonly below 150 cm. Adjusting for this clustering of extremes near the equator and looking at the entire continent, there is a significant correlation (.22) between stature and latitude. Thus, average stature increases as one moves either north or south from the equator. An inspection of the distribution reveals that the rate at which this occurs is more rapid to the north.

The data from Oceania are fragmentary (see Table 7–4), but they suggest that, in contrast to the distribution in Asia, there is among Pacific populations an *increase* in average stature from west to east. The correlation between stature and longitude in these Pacific groups is .54. The tallest peoples are the Samoans, Tahitians, Hawaiians, and Marquesans of the eastern Pacific, and the shortest are the Pygmy groups of New Guinea in the west. Moreover, there is a correlation between stature and latitude (.57) in Oceania, indicating that as distance (north or south) from the equator increases, average stature likewise increases.

Although, once again, the data are not too extensive among the Indians of North and South America, a correlation between stature and latitude appears (.52) like that found in the Pacific populations. With the conspicuous exception of the Eskimos, who are similar in stature to other circumpolar peoples, populations of shorter American Indians cluster around the equator within a zone roughly 20° wide from 10° north to 10° south latitude (see Table 7–5). Outside of this zone average statures increase to maximum values in both the north and south temperate latitudes.

Discounting for the moment the complex European situation (and it will be necessary to do this regularly), it is clear from the above that the

TABLE 7–5

MEAN STATURE AMONG AMERICAN INDIAN POPULATIONS*

Area	Mean Stature cm.	Standard Deviation cm.	Number of Samples
1. Central America	159.06	4.15	10
2. Andes	159.50	6.52	4
3. Eskimo	162.80	3.04	4
4. Amazon Basin	163.39	4.45	17
5. Patagonia and Tierra del Fuego	163.93	8.38	7
6. Northwest Coast	163.99	3.57	10
7. Plains and Prairie (North America)	167.50	2.88	4
8. Southwest United States	168.87	3.80	3
9. Eastern United States	171.45	1.06	4

* These data have been compiled from Biasutti (1959) and, with the exception of the Eastern United States, where a raw mean and standard deviation are used, are weighted for sample size.

distribution of stature over each of the major habitation zones is distinctive. In Asia, stature is correlated with longitude; in Africa and North and South America with latitude; and in the Pacific with both longitude and latitude. Apart from this, one other general observation appears justified: equatorial zones include extremes in average stature.

Stature is a complex trait, the resultant of a variety of environmental forces acting upon an underlying genetic structure. To what extent is stature inherited? That is, to what extent is it determined by genes? If one asks this question in reference to any particular individual, there is no way to answer it, since we know neither how many alleles nor how many loci are involved. However, some progress can be made if one asks the question in a different way: How much of the variation in stature that is found in a population is due to genetic factors? One can obtain some estimate of this by comparing correlations in stature between identical and fraternal twins. The higher the correlation between pairs of identical twins, the greater the contribution the genetic component makes in determining the variation. Such comparisons yield heritability estimates and are expressed numerically as the coefficient of heritability.*

Identical twins are highly correlated for stature, thereby indicating that the genetic component plays a major role in determining stature variation. Osborne and De George (1959) report a heritability coefficient of .79 for males and .92 for females. Shields (1962), reporting only for females, calculates an h value of .89, and in their classic study, Newman, Freeman, and Holzinger (1937) calculate a value of .81 on a total sample including males and females. Why it is that values differ between the sexes (if indeed they do) is not clear, but it is clear that genetic factors are responsible for much of the variation in stature.

Weight, in contrast to stature, has a low heritability (.05 for males, .42 for females [Osborne and De George, 1959], .57 for females [Shields, 1962], .775 for a pooled sample [Newman, Freeman, and Holzinger, 1937]). Although the variability in heritability coefficients between the sexes and among the samples is not readily explainable, it is clear that the environment plays a larger role in determining the variation of weight than it does in the case of stature. Mainly because of this, weight has never been particularly useful to physical anthropologists, since it is difficult to know what differences in weight signify.

If both weight and stature are considered together and attention is given to the distribution of total body form, it has been presumed for a long time that a lean, linear body conformation is characteristically tropical, whereas a more rotund, corpulent form becomes more common as distance from

---

* Where r_I is the correlation coefficient for identical twins and r_F is the correlation coefficient for fraternal twins, then:

$$h = \frac{r_I - r_F}{1 - r_F}$$

the equator increases. If this were an accurate way to characterize the distribution of body form in man, then human beings would represent a special case of a more general regularity in the distribution of body forms among mammals. Bergmann's rule (1847) notes that in mammals the larger animals within a particular species could generally be found in the colder regions of the species' range. If one interprets this to mean simply stature, then obviously it does not apply to human populations. To take such a view would be inappropriate, since stature measures body size in but one dimension. What Bergmann was describing was the relationship between body volume and surface area, which appears to reflect efficiency of heat regulation. A low surface area to high volume proportion is efficient in retaining heat; the reverse, high surface area to low body volume proportion, is efficient in dissipating heat.

Allen's rule (1877) refers more specifically to the relationship between temperature and the size of extremities and appendages. It specifies that in the colder regions of a species' distribution the parts of the body most conspicuously susceptible to frostbite (noses, ears, fingers, toes) tend to be shorter than they are in members of the species situated in warmer areas. By considering both Bergmann's and Allen's rules, it is readily deduced that the cold-adapted variants of a species would tend to be rounded and globular with relatively slight interruptions to their contours made by the extremities and appendages. Those found in the warmer zones would be expected to be more linear and to have more pronounced irregularities to their contours. These rules are simplifications and overly generalized. Nevertheless they tend to be reasonably correct descriptions of the ways in which body form is commonly distributed among mammals, particularly large ones. In man the situation is complicated by culture, and the available data on body form are more impressionistic than quantitative. In one study Newman and Munro (1955), reporting on a large sample of soldiers, suggest that the regularities specified in Bergmann's rule may be found in the distribution of American males.

In recent years, investigators have become more interested in measuring the components of body weight. For example, fat fold calipers have been developed to measure total body fat, and X-ray photography has been used to measure the contribution that bone weight makes to total body weight and volume. These and other refinements have so far been applied to only a few human populations, but they illustrate one of the lines along which anthropometry is developing and suggest how it is likely to be applied in the future.

Head Length, Head Breadth, and Cephalic Index

If our skulls were perfectly spherical, variation in head form and head size could be expressed in one diameter, but, of course, this is not the case. To describe head form completely would require an infinite number head length   head breadth

Figure 7–2. Measurement of head length and head breadth. Regarding head length, Hooton (1947) mentions that some observers prefer to work from the left side, holding the caliper horizontally. "However," he continues, "there is some advantage in holding the caliper vertically so that its hinge is above the subject's head and the horizontal scale falls in the sagittal or median front-to-back line of the head." In measuring head breadth, Hooton (ibid.) notes that the operator stands behind the seated subject, and that the caliper can be held either horizontally with the hinge toward the observer or vertically with the hinge above the head of the subject. (Courtesy G. W. Hewes.)

of measurements, but one can obtain a crude overall estimate from just two: head length and head breadth (see Figure 7–2). Each could be taken up separately, but more commonly they are considered together and expressed in the form of the cephalic index, thus:

$$\text{Cephalic index} = \frac{\text{head breadth}}{\text{head length}} \times 100.$$

A low cephalic index implies a narrow head, whereas a broad head is expressed as a large cephalic index. Human population averages vary from 70 percent to 90 percent. Table 7–6 summarizes the distribution of cephalic indexes by major habitation areas of the world.

Africans have simultaneously the narrowest heads and least variation (see Table 7–7). There are two notable characteristics of the distribution of cephalic indexes in Africa: 1) a gradual decline in average values from west to east within the continent, and 2) a striking negative correlation (−.51) with stature, or, put more simply, taller Africans have narrower heads. This is an observation made on an impressionistic basis by several investigators, some of whom have assumed that it is true for all human beings; but, as we will see presently, in the Pacific and in the New World

TABLE 7–6

MEAN CEPHALIC INDEXES AND STANDARD DEVIATIONS
BY MAJOR AREAS OF THE WORLD*

Area	Mean Percent	Standard Deviation Percent	Number of Samples
1. Africa	76.17	2.33	115
2. Asia	80.32	4.38	74
3. Europe	81.60	3.00	49
4. Oceania	78.76	3.92	26
5. New World	80.58	2.85	57

* Figures in the table have been compiled from data contained in Biasutti (1959) and Martin and Saller (1955–1966). Mean and standard deviation for Europe have been estimated from a plot of the data; the others have been calculated and weighted for sample size.

TABLE 7–7

MEAN CEPHALIC INDEXES AMONG AFRICAN POPULATIONS†

Area	Mean Percent	Standard Deviation Percent	Number of Samples
1. Central Bantu	74.14	1.96	11
2. East Sudan	74.66	2.67	14
3. Sahara	74.73	1.59	9
4. East Africa	74.90	1.24	26
5. South Africa (Bushmen, Hottentots)	75.10	1.39	4
6. North Africa	75.96	2.15	15
7. West Africa	76.22	2.09	30
8. Northern Bantu	77.21	1.90	41
9. Madagascar and Indian Ocean	78.75	2.08	4

† These data have been compiled from Biasutti (1959) and weighted for sample size.

there is no indication of this. Indeed, there is a suggestion that the reverse might be the case: taller peoples in these areas may have broader heads.

The distribution of cephalic indexes in Asia is like that of Africa in one respect and unlike it in another (see Table 7–8). In Asia, as in Africa, there is a negative correlation between stature and cephalic index (−.24). Likewise there is a gradient from west to east, but, in contrast to Africa, the correlation between longitude and cephalic index in Asia is positive (.24). Thus there is a tendency for cephalic indexes to increase as one goes from the Middle East to the Far East. Although, again, the distributional pattern in Europe is extremely complex, there is some indication that the west-to-east trend is the same as in Asia. This is not to say, however, that the gradient is continuous from Atlantic to Pacific, for it is

TABLE 7–8

MEAN CEPHALIC INDEXES AMONG ASIAN POPULATIONS*

Area	Mean Percent	Standard Deviation Percent	Number of Samples
1. Vedda	75.65	7.16	4
2. India, Various Locations	76.49	2.94	13
3. India, Castes	77.33	1.27	3
4. Asia Minor	79.87	4.68	9
5. Iran, Armenia, Assyria	80.22	5.29	11
6. Malay Peninsula and Archipelago	80.83	2.75	16
7. Southeast Asia	80.94	3.28	17
8. Far East	81.06	1.72	8
9. Northern Asia	81.26	2.64	14
10. Central Asia	82.49	3.69	9

* These data have been compiled from Biasutti (1959) and weighted for sample size.

TABLE 7–9

MEAN CEPHALIC INDEXES AMONG PACIFIC POPULATIONS†

Area	Mean Percent	Standard Deviation Percent	Number of Samples
1. Australia	72.66	1.49	8
2. New Guinea and Melanesia	77.74	3.49	8
3. Polynesia	80.66	2.93	11

† These data have been compiled from Biasutti (1959) and weighted for sample size.

TABLE 7–10

MEAN CEPHALIC INDEXES AMONG AMERICAN INDIAN POPULATIONS‡

Area	Mean Percent	Standard Deviation Percent	Number of Samples
1. Eskimo	78.08	1.00	4
2. Patagonia and Tierra del Fuego	79.10	3.17	7
3. Eastern Woodlands	79.65	.65	4
4. Amazon Basin	80.14	1.73	17
5. Central America	81.10	3.67	10
6. Southwest United States	81.30	3.48	3
7. Plains and Prairie	81.35	2.67	4
8. Northwest Coast	83.20	3.85	10
9. Andes	84.08	4.27	4

‡ These data have been compiled from Biasutti (1959) and weighted for sample size.

clearly bimodal; some of the people with the broadest heads in the Old World reside in central and eastern Europe.

In the Pacific islands, an east-to-west increase in cephalic index may be observed. The narrow-headed Pacific populations are in the east, the broad-headed in the west, and the intermediate ones in the middle (see Table 7–9). The correlation coefficient between longitude and the cephalic indexes of the twenty-seven populations included in the analysis is .34. In this respect, Oceania is like Asia and unlike Africa, and in another respect it is unlike both: the negative correlation between stature and cephalic index does not exist in the Pacific. In fact, there is a suggestion that with more information one might confirm a significant positive correlation between them.

The American Indians have the second-highest average cephalic indexes, and among them there are no significant large-scale distributional regularities (see Table 7–10). The Eskimos have the narrowest heads among indigenous Americans, and the Andeans have the broadest. The Eskimos combine narrow skulls with broad faces, and in this respect are like some Asian populations. These features provide them with a decidedly distinctive head form as compared with other native American populations. The American Indians are like the peoples of the Pacific with respect to the correlation between stature and cephalic index; they, too, show a weak positive correlation (.11) between them.

Table 7–11 shows the various heritability coefficients that have been calculated on identical-twin samples for the cephalic indexes. The coefficients are similar to those obtained for stature (see discussion beginning on page 238) and support the conclusion that the majority of variation in cephalic index is due to genetic factors.

TABLE 7–11

HERITABILITY COEFFICIENTS FOR CEPHALIC INDEX

Sex	h	Source
Males	.90	Osborne and De George (1959)
Females	.70	Osborne and De George (1959)
Males and Females	.75	Newman, Freeman, and Holzinger (1937)

Nose Length, Nose Breadth, and Nasal Index

Often lurking behind the more pristine reasons for classifying mankind into races is the desire to scale groups of human beings; that is, to locate them on an imaginary ape-to-advanced-modern-man scale. The procedure behind this is simple: the larger the number of traits like the modern ape, the lower the position on the scale. The population with the highest number is therefore the most apelike, and the one with the fewest is the most advanced. The outcome is, of course, entirely manageable, and thus the exercise is meaningless, and even if one were "objective" and chose for comparison traits selected at "random" and "independent" of one another, it is not at all clear what the results would mean. Suppose, for example, that it could be demonstrated that you are more like a mouse than I am. What could be reasonably inferred from that "fact"? Nothing, of course. In any case, nose form has been extensively used in descriptions and classifications of human variation, not merely because it distinguishes some groups from others, but further because some forms are much more "apelike" than others. In fact, the forms of the nose found in man are substantially different from those found in the apes. As E. A. Hooton (1947) put it: "To have a nose like an ape, you would have to be one."

Classifying nose forms has been done in four ways: 1) from a profile view (Figure 7–3), 2) from underneath (Figure 7–4), 3) from the front, and 4) by calculation of the nasal index, thus:

$$\text{Nasal index} = \frac{\text{nasal breadth}}{\text{nasal length}} \times 100.$$

Most commonly, the classification involves a simultaneous judgment concerning the length and breadth of the nose, two continuously variable traits that may well reflect two distinctive adaptations. It is possible on the basis of the distribution of these features that the length of the nose is mainly controlled by selective factors imposed by variations in temperature, whereas the breadth is controlled more by the forces imposed by variations in humidity. The details here may be argued, but if the principle is sound, that is, if nose length is largely independent of nose breadth in terms of the selective agencies impinging upon them, this would be a suitable reason for distinguishing them as separate traits. Since, however, the data on the measurements are not as often reported as nasal index, we will have to violate our own cautions and examine the distribution of the index as though it were a single trait.

The nasal index expresses nasal breadth numerically as a percentage of nasal length. Martin and Saller (1955–1966) report the range of variation among human beings as from 40 percent to 147 percent, i.e., from individuals whose nose breadth is less than half their nose length to persons with noses which are almost half again as broad as they are long. Mean variation among human populations ranges from 60 to 110 percent (see Table 7–12).

How does nose form vary over the face of the earth, and how does its variation compare with the distributions of stature and cephalic index? Consider Africa, which has: 1) the largest average nasal index, and 2) the greatest range of variability. This is the reverse of the situation with cephalic index, where Africa had the lowest average and the least varia-

CONCAVE CONTOURS

STRAIGHT CONTOURS

CONVEX CONTOURS

Figure 7–3. Variations in nasal profiles. (After R. Martin and Karl Saller.)

Figure 7–4. Variations in nasal flatness. (After R. Martin and Karl Saller.)

bility. In Table 7–13 one can see that once again the Bushmen and Hottentots of the Kalahari Desert come out at one extreme, but, as noted in the instance of stature, it should again be emphasized that the Pygmies, included within the northern Bantu group, commonly have mean nasal indexes over 100 percent. Since these large values occur at the equator, it is of interest to determine whether there is any consistent pattern in the distribution of values to the north and south, and in fact there is a striking negative correlation (−.64) between latitude and mean nasal index in Africa. A negative correlation with latitude implies that as one moves away from the equator, mean nasal index declines. It appears from an

TABLE 7–12

MEAN NASAL INDEXES AND STANDARD DEVIATIONS BY
MAJOR AREAS OF THE WORLD*

Area	Mean Percent	Standard Deviation Percent	Number of Samples
1. Africa	84.67	13.88	115
2. Asia	71.85	9.09	74
3. Europe	66.00	2.00	20
4. Oceania	82.77	9.82	26
5. New World	74.78	6.35	57

* Figures for this table have been compiled from data contained in Biasutti (1959) and Martin and Saller (1955–1966). The mean and standard deviation for Europe have been estimated from a plot of the data; the others have been calculated and weighted for sample size.

TABLE 7–13

MEAN NASAL INDEXES AMONG AFRICAN POPULATIONS*

Area	Mean Percent	Standard Deviation Percent	Number of Samples
1. North Africa	70.29	4.32	14
2. East Africa	74.27	8.72	26
3. Sahara	75.17	7.72	9
4. East Sudan	88.04	3.65	8
5. Central Bantu	93.84	4.61	11
6. West Africa	95.21	6.81	18
7. Northern Bantu	95.53	7.81	27
8. South Africa (Bushmen, Hottentots)	103.93	3.85	3

* These data have been compiled from Biasutti (1959) and weighted for sample size.

TABLE 7–14

MEAN NASAL INDEXES AMONG ASIAN POPULATIONS†

Area	Mean Percent	Standard Deviation Percent	Number of Samples
1. Asia Minor	61.54	4.40	9
2. Iran, Armenia, Assyria	63.66	2.97	11
3. Central Asia	69.21	7.15	9
4. India, Various Locations	74.18	6.30	12
5. Far East	74.75	1.85	2
6. Northern Asia	78.90	3.77	8
7. Southeast Asia	82.80	5.21	3
8. Malay Peninsula and Archipelago	84.44	6.60	13
9. India, Vedda	85.52	5.55	4

† These data have been compiled from Biasutti (1959) and weighted for sample size.

TABLE 7–15

MEAN NASAL INDEXES AMONG PACIFIC POPULATIONS‡

Area	Mean Percent	Standard Deviation Percent	Number of Samples
1. Australia	99.58	4.23	8
2. New Guinea and Melanesia	85.26	6.62	7
3. Micronesia and Polynesia	79.08	3.58	11

‡ These data have been compiled from Biasutti (1959) and weighted for sample size.

inspection of the data that the values decline more rapidly to the north. The pattern is the opposite of that observed in the distribution of stature, and this is reflected in a significant negative correlation between nasal index and stature ($-.36$).

Looking at the distribution from the standpoint of longitude, there is a tendency for average nasal indexes to decrease at any particular latitude from west to east. This means that whereas the mean values of nasal index differ from north to south at any point along that continuum, the smaller averages can be expected in the east. This pattern is the same as the one observed in the distribution of cephalic indexes in Africa, and thus it is not surprising to find a positive correlation (.13) between nasal and cephalic indexes.

Europeans have the narrowest noses and display the least variability of any of the major areas. If Europe is regarded as a part of the Euro-Asian continent, then the low average nasal indexes of Europeans may be seen as the western extreme of a marked west-to-east increase in average nasal index among Euro-Asians (see Table 7–14 for more detail). Thus, in contrast to Africa, where the larger values are in the west, the large Euro-Asian nasal indexes are in the east. Stature may be thought of similarly, with the Europeans representing the western extremes of a continuous west-to-east decline. From this it follows that for the Euro-Asian area, stature increases as nasal index decreases. This is expressed in the results of a correlation analysis conducted on the Asian populations which yielded a striking negative correlation between stature and nasal index ($-.75$). Thus, if you enter Asia from eastern Europe and travel eastward to the Pacific, you will likely observe on the way that the residents become shorter, and their noses become broader.

As noted earlier in the discussion of cephalic index, there is in Asia a gradual increase in mean cephalic index from west to east, just as there is in mean nasal index. This positive correlation (.13) implies that in Asia, populations with broad heads tend to have broad noses.

The striking characteristic of the distribution of nasal index in the Pacific is the fact that it is bimodal; that is, there are two decidedly different distributions, one in Australia and one among the rest of the island populations. The Australian aborigines have nasal indexes similar to those found among African Pygmy and Bushman populations (see Table 7–15).

When the two distributions are separated, too few populations remain in each group to enable one confidently to draw conclusions through statistical procedures. However, it would appear that among the non-Australian populations, nasal index increases from west to east as cephalic index does, and in this regard the distributions parallel those in Asia.

Although the picture remains unclear in Oceania and complicated in Europe, it appears that for the rest of the world, nasal index and stature are negatively correlated. This observation is confirmed in the distribution of nasal indexes among the Indians of North and South America (see Table 7–16).

TABLE 7–16

MEAN NASAL INDEXES AMONG AMERICAN INDIAN POPULATIONS*

Area	Mean Percent	Standard Deviation Percent	Number of Samples
1. Eskimo	68.45	3.16	4
2. Andean	69.98	2.11	4
3. Plains and Prairie	71.98	2.01	4
4. Patagonia and Tierra del Fuego	72.80	3.33	7
5. Northwest Coast	78.85	6.33	10
6. Southwest United States	79.45	2.45	2
7. Central America	81.06	3.02	9
8. Amazon	81.44	4.97	16

* These data have been compiled from Biasutti (1959) and weighted for sample size.

The correlation coefficient between stature and nasal index obtained on the data reported here is −.50. Stature among the American Indians, it will be recalled, increases as the distance from the equator increases; nasal indexes are largest among American Indians living near the equator, and they decline as distance from the equator increases. The correlation coefficient expressing this distribution pattern is the one between nasal index and latitude, which for the populations included here is −.32. This is the same relationship noted in the distribution of nasal index by latitude in Africa. Also paralleling the African distribution, it appears once again that at any particular latitude in the New World, the larger nasal indexes are to be found in the west.

The most conspicuous exception to the north-south distribution among the American Indians is the low average nasal index reported from the Andean populations living near the equator. Since these are people living at high altitudes, and thus subject to cold temperatures, it suggests the likelihood that their narrow noses are of some adaptive advantage in cold, low-oxygen, dry climates.

The distribution of nasal indexes among American Indians is not significantly correlated with the distribution of cephalic indexes; the two vary independently of each other.

One further point on the subject of nose form deserves consideration before turning to skin color, and that is the ecological rule known as Thompson's rule. Thompson's rule refers to nose breadth and notes that in cold climates noses tend to be narrow, whereas in hot climates they tend to be broad. The underlying explanation usually provided to account for the distribution of nasal breadth is the function of the nose in regulating the temperature of the external air before it reaches the lungs. It is based on the simple impression that the narrower the nose, the warmer the air that reaches the lungs, while broader noses have less effect on the temperature of inspired air. This rule is consistent with the distribution of nasal index in Africa and in the New World, but not particularly consistent with the pattern in Asia, where longitude appears to have substantially more influence on nasal index than latitude.

Skin Color

Among normal persons, variation in skin color is due largely to differences in the amount of melanin in the skin. Melanin is a large and complex pigment molecule formed by specialized cells, melanocytes, located beneath the superficial layers of the skin. The melanocytes produce the dark-brown-to-black melanin in the form of granules which are excreted into the intracellular spaces in the deep and outer layers of skin. There is no substantial difference between dark- and light-skinned persons in the number of melanocytes, but there is a great difference in the density of melanin granules.

Until recently physical anthropologists have been forced to judge skin color variation instead of measuring it, but in the past decade instruments that measure light reflectance (reflectometers) have begun to be used. Reflectometers allow for greater precision, comparability, and objectivity. However, at present there are comparatively few reports of data obtained using the reflectometer. In discussing variations in skin color, it continues to be necessary to rely upon the subjective and qualitative data that have accumulated over hundreds of years.

The distribution of skin color can be summarized best by means of a map (see Figure 7–5). A casual inspection of the map reveals nothing startling. Dark skin color is tropical, and depigmentation increases as distance from the equator increases. On closer inspection one could note complexities in the distribution, but since the data on which the map is based are imprecise, it is of little value to consider these in detail. A discussion of the complexities would focus on the exceptional areas, i.e., tropical areas inhabited by light-skinned peoples. The exceptions are usually understandable on cultural grounds. As Hulse (1955) has pointed out, many of the irregularities in the distribution appear to be due to the relatively recent expansion of agricultural people into new areas.

The distribution of skin color in man is a special case of an ecological regularity called Gloger's rule. Originally Gloger's rule was formulated

Figure 7–5. Distribution of skin color. (From Renato Biasutti, *Le Razze e I Popoli Della Terra*, courtesy UTET.)

Very Light   Light   Intermediate   Dark   Very Dark

to point out distributional regularities observed in the pigmentation of feathers and furs. The rule stated that the darkly pigmented varieties within a species are found in the warm and humid parts of the species' range.

Is it obvious why pigmentation decreases as distance from the equator increases? Not at all. In one way the distribution is the opposite of what one might "obviously" expect. In hot, humid areas one might expect light skin color, since it reflects rather than absorbs heat as dark skin color does. Two proposals are presently in competition to explain the distribution of skin pigmentation in man. One notes that pigmentation increases as solar ultraviolet radiation increases and concludes from this that skin color is essentially a protective shield against the harmful effects of radiation. The equator is exposed to the greatest solar ultraviolet radiation, for the simple reason that there is most daylight there, and the sun is more directly overhead than in any other part of the earth. This proposal has been around for a long time but has failed to gain general acceptance, mainly because it fails to explain the distribution. To be sure, the intensity of solar radiation decreases as distance from the equator increases, but the intensity of exposure to the radiation does not necessarily decrease. The thick overgrowth that prevails throughout much of the equatorial tropics provides a kind of protective umbrella, so that the actual amount of radiation reaching the ground is less in many areas of the tropics than it is in Denver, Colorado.

The other proposal says that pigmentation acts as an adjustment mechanism in the production of vitamin D. This, too, is not a new idea, but interest in it has been revitalized recently by an article written by W. F. Loomis (1967), a biochemist at Brandeis University. Vitamin D is known as the sunshine vitamin; what this means is that solar radiation activates the synthesis of the vitamin in the skin. Once synthesized, the vitamin diffuses throughout the circulatory system and functions in the absorption of calcium and in the deposition of the inorganic matrix in bone. Vitamin D is an unusual vitamin in that too much of it as well as too little can result in death. Heavy pigmentation, according to this view, filters out a large percentage of the activating radiation and thereby inhibits the overproduction of vitamin D. Light skin facilitates the synthesis of the vitamin and thus assures that minimum quantities are produced in areas where exposure to the sun is considerably reduced. Skin color from this point of view is seen as essentially a regulating device that makes it possible for human beings living at different latitudes to obtain a constant amount of vitamin D.

How is skin color inherited? No one knows. On this issue, there is general agreement on only two points: the inheritance of skin color 1) is complex, and 2) involves more than one genetic locus.

Hair Form

Hair form has been used frequently in standard racial classifications, since the various forms of the hair correspond in their distribution to the common notion of race, going back to the time of Blumenbach. If one were to classify man's variation on the basis of hair form alone, one would end up with classes very much like the old fivefold classification. In many respects the distribution of hair form corresponds better to this kind of classification than does skin color. Like all of the "racial" characteristics, however, hair form displays considerable variation within and between the areas where one form may predominate.

Hair form varies from straight to tightly wound spirals with intermediate forms of low wave, wavy, deep wave, and kinky. These are illustrated in Figure 7–7. Variations in hair form tend to be associated with variations in the thickness of the individual hair strands. Among dark-haired people, the thickest cross sections occur among people with very little or no wave, and the thinnest are found among those with tightly spiraled hair. Very little is known of the evolutionary significance of hair form. About the only theory presently available to account for the variations states that hair form provides a kind of general protection to the brain against damage through trauma and through the effects of radiation. Perhaps this is true, but, if so, the work of demonstrating its validity remains to be done.

Figure 7–6. Europeans. Top: Left, Swede; Center, Lapp; Right, Irishman. Bottom: Left, Basque; Center, Magyar; Right, Albanian. (Courtesy Carleton S. Coon.)

Figure 7–7. Variations in hair form. (Redrawn from an illustration in Rudolf Martin and Karl Saller, *Lehrbuch der Anthropologie,* by permission of Gustav Fischer Verlag.)

Morphological Traits of Restricted Distribution

The list of observed physical characteristics could be extended indefinitely. Indeed, only a meager sample of facial and skull traits has been mentioned to provide an introductory familiarity with the distribution of heterographic variability and the kinds of problems that have confronted physical anthropologists in their efforts to describe man's morphological variation. Before considering the physiological aspects of heterography, some mention should be made of a few characteristics that are clearly distinctive, but with restricted distributions. The traits to be considered briefly here are the epicanthic eye fold, shovel-shaped incisors, and steatopygia. The first two traits range predominantly among Asian and American Indian populations. Steatopygia is African, or, more specifically, South African.

Epicanthic Fold. The epicanthic fold is one of several factors contributing to the characteristic appearance of the mongoloid eye. In extreme form it consists of a fold of skin that, when the eye is open, comes

Figure 7–8. Comparison of eyes having the epicanthic fold with eyes lacking that trait.

down over and runs on a line with the edge of the upper eyelid (see Figure 7–8). Together with a depressed nasal bridge, wide and projecting cheekbones, and deposits of fatty tissue overlying the cheekbones, the epicanthic fold is responsible for the slant-eyed appearance of the mongoloid eye. It is commonly found among infants from all over the world and, among adults, more commonly found among females than males, and particularly, of course, among people of Asian origin (see Figure 7–9).

Shovel-shaped Incisors. Shovel-shaped incisors (Figure 7–10) have a distribution among contemporary human beings similar to that of the epicanthic fold. It is known, however, as a trait with a broader distribution in fossil-man times, having been found commonly among European and African fossils as well as Asian remains. The folding inward of the incisor teeth increases their chewing surfaces without increasing their breadth in relation to the size of the dental arcade. To the extent that increased chewing surface is in itself functionally desirable and improves the durability of the teeth, the adaptive value of shovel-shaped incisors is not too difficult to see. The problem, however, comes up in trying to account for its distribution today. Why is it retained in some modern populations and not in others? Brace (1963) puts forth structural reduction as the explanation, reasoning that in those parts of the world where the functions of the incisor teeth are displaced by other factors (food preparation techniques, sharp cutting tools) the genes that determine their structure become free to vary in their composition. The most probable consequence, he reasons, is a structural reduction in the form of the incisors. In distributional terms, there is some support for this. Shovel-shaped incisors are less frequent among the descendants of those people who have solved, by cultural means, the problems that incisors usually solve biologically and who have done so for the longest period of time.

0   1000   2000   3000 km.

(1 Kilometer = 0.621 mile)

High frequency,
extreme form

Low frequency,
extreme form

Variable frequency,
weak form

Rare frequency,
weak form

Figure 7–9. Distribution of the epicanthic fold. (From Renato Biasutti,
Le Razze e I Popoli Della Terra, courtesy UTET.)

shovel-shaped   no shoveling

Figure 7–10. Comparison of shovel-shaped incisors with incisors lacking that trait.

Among the modern populations with high frequencies of the trait and whose histories and cultural adaptations are known to be grossly diversified, the pattern is not at all clear.

Anthropology has had a long and time-honored tradition of noting and doting on the unusual, the weird, the bizarre. Perhaps it was felt that unusual things needed to be emphasized, but unfortunately, because they are unusual, little effort to do anything more than report their discovery and perhaps estimate their frequency has ever been done. Such traits as epicanthic folds and shovel-shaped incisors fall into this category. An attempt was made by Virginia Carbonell (1963) to deal with shovel-shaped incisors in a comprehensive way. Her efforts were frustrated by the lack of standards and the absence of simple correlative data that would have made the older studies so much more useful (for example, the absence of family studies). Her paper illustrates the underlying complexities of an attribute thought to be a single trait and shows the distributional details of shoveling in modern and fossil-man populations.

Steatopygia. Steatopygia is another of the biological curios that usually manage to get into discussions of racial variation. The trait consists of an extraordinary enlargement of the upper thighs and buttocks due to the accumulation and localization of fat in these regions of the body. Today it is generally thought of as a feature distinguishing the Hottentots of South Africa. It is particularly developed in Hottentot females (see Figure 7–11). There are some reasons for believing that during Upper Paleolithic times in Europe steatopygia may have been a relatively common attribute. The evidence for this is the discovery of figurines (Figure 7–12) which have clear indications of the trait. It could, of course, be merely the artistic stylization of the form, or perhaps simply representative of generalized obesity, which in the closing days of the glaciation of Europe might have been regarded as a desirable attribute in females.

Nothing is known concerning the significance nor the inheritance of steatopygia. It represents an instance of another ecological regularity called Rensch's rule, which notes that in mammals, the members of a species adapted to hot climatic conditions have localized deposits of fat. This

Figure 7–11. Steatopygous female Bushman of southern
Africa.

Figure 7–12. Ancient steatopygous figurine, drawn from a
photograph of "Venus" of
Lespugue.

fails, of course, to explain the significance of steatopygia; it merely notes that when peculiar localized accumulations of fat occur in mammals, they tend to occur in hot climates. The Hottentots live in South Africa and raise cattle as their principal means of subsistence. They are similar and almost certainly closely related to their desert hunting and gathering neighbors, the Bushmen.

The discussion of heterographic variation has become progressively more general as it has passed from metrical to observational to uncommon traits. From this point on, the discussion will deal with physiological, developmental, and, briefly, psychological characteristics, and, at present, there simply is not an extensive body of data on the range of human variation in any of these areas; so the discussion will continue to be at a general level.

Physiological Characteristics

Adaptations are usually thought of as a consequence of the activity of evolutionary mechanisms on evolving units. Selection continually scans the variability presented by mutation, rejecting most of it, but on occasion favoring a variant and thus causing it to become more and more common over time. Size, structure, mating patterns, and movements in and out of the population may act to cause lasting evolutionary consequences too, but selection and mutation would seem to be more continuous and systematic, thus over the long range more forceful. There is, however, another kind of adaptation with which we are all familiar: the adaptations we each make to the daily variations occurring in our environments. Our body temperatures remain extraordinarily constant in environments that vary widely in humidity and temperature. Our cells receive abundant oxygen to carry out their functions over a broad range of altitude variation. The ability of our systems to adapt to changing environmental conditions is known as *physiological plasticity,* and it is a phenomenon that can be found to occur under many more circumstances than simply variations in temperature, moisture, and altitude. We are continually responding in physiological ways to internal and external stimuli such as fear, crowding, and dietary imbalances, as well as to the usual activities required of us daily, such as walking, talking, and even resting. There are, indeed, far too many facets to physiological plasticity to be concerned with them all here, but the important points to be emphasized are: 1) that plasticity is itself variable, 2) that some adaptive responses are more efficient than others, and 3) that these tend to occur in spatial clusters. For example, some groups adjust more successfully to high altitude than others, whereas other peoples may be able to sustain themselves better under the stress conditions of crowding, cold, heat, wetness, dryness, etc. In general, as one might expect, the more efficient plastic responses tend to be found in areas where the stresses calling for them are more common, more severe, or both. Tropical people, for example, tend to be able to regulate their heat loss in hot, humid environments more efficiently than people from more temperate zones.

The evolutionary significance of these plastic responses is at one level obvious and at another not at all clear. It is obvious that plasticity makes survival possible; otherwise we would all have to live in impossibly constant environmental conditions. What is not clear is the cause or causes of the different qualities of physiological plasticity. Is a native of the Congo jungle able to adjust more efficiently to extremes of heat and humidity than, say, a native of North English, Iowa, because he was born there and grew up there, or because, through selection among his ancestors over a long time, he has come to have some special genetic capacities? The resolution is not to be made here, and we will not take even a middle-of-the-road view that "it's probably some of each," for there is as little evidence for that view as for either extreme. It is clear, however, that before deciding on this issue, we should have some awareness of the work that has been done.

Apart from casual observations (and on the subject of adaptation to environmental extremes, there are many of these), evidence on man's physiological adaptations has emerged from two sources: 1) distributional studies showing correlations between anthropometric characteristics and selected ecological variables such as temperature, humidity, and altitude; and 2) experimental studies on human subjects selected because of their somatic characteristics and observed for the limits of their variability (tolerance) under varying, but usually extreme, environmental conditions. Distributional studies tend to be concerned with more interesting problems but provide much less convincing results. For example, D. F. Roberts (1953) has demonstrated a high negative correlation between mean body weight and mean annual temperature by going through the available figures on each variable from around the world. As is the case with the correlations reported above between anthropometric traits and longitude and latitude, it is difficult to conclude what the significance of such a correlation may be. Does it mean that some systematic evolutionary pressures have been applied to human populations living in hot climates to weed out those individuals with the genetic determiners to become heavy (or, conversely, pressures on populations living in cold climates to reduce the thinner variants)? Does it mean that temperature variations affect the quality of metabolism, causing fat to be stored in colder climates more efficiently than in the tropics? Does it mean that the persons living in warm climates have less to eat, or, perhaps, simply eat less? There are at present no clear and unambiguous answers to these questions. As Roberts points out, much more work is necessary; body weight is often not reported in anthropometric surveys; mean annual temperature is a crude estimate at best of the thermal variations the peoples of the world are subjected to; and reasonably comparable nutritional surveys are almost entirely lacking. Assuming that the work gets done, and eventually it will, this would seem to be potentially a most productive way to investigate man's adaptive characteristics. The approach makes no assumptions about racial clusters.

Experimental studies on physiological variations in man are usually made to determine if races are the same or different in their abilities to tolerate and in the ways they adjust to environmental stress. Thus, the experimental work begins by presuming that, if physiological plasticity varies in man, the variation should be maximized in interracial comparisons. Empirical studies on reactions of Negroes and Caucasians to heat and cold stress tend to support this presumption, although the noting of any kind of differences between the races would tend to support it, since there are virtually no other comparisons available. Would the differences in heat regulation and sweat loss noted between Negroes and Caucasians subjected to variable conditions of moisture in hot climates be greater than differences between the sexes within one race? Most of the empirical work on experimental physiological plasticity has been done on male military subjects and, as noted earlier, the resulting contrasts are not readily assignable to genetic or nongenetic causes, although Baker (1958) argues forcefully in favor of genetic causation.

Other experimental work has been directed at ascertaining the physiological reactions of peoples living regularly in climatic extremes. Particular attention has been given to cold-habitat groups, such as the Eskimo and the Australian aborigines, and high-altitude dwellers, such as the

Figure 7–13. Asians. Top: Left, Tamil; Center, Rajput; Right, Kalmuck. Middle: Left, Vedda; Center, Ainu; Right, Japanese. Bottom: Left, Tungus; Center, Formosan; Right, Andaman Islander. (Courtesy Carleton S. Coon.)

peoples of the South American Andes. These field studies usually compare the reactions of the inhabitants to those of a control group, this consisting most frequently of the European and American scientists who conduct the investigation. Although the studies are too few in number to be conclusive, they suggest the following: 1) There are two fundamentally different types of adaptation to cold. The first, characteristic of the Eskimo, results in an increase in heat near the skin by means of increased metabolic activity and peripheral blood flow. The other adaptation, which has been known for other mammals and recently demonstrated in Australian aborigines, is based on insulation of the vital organs. Unlike the Eskimo, the peripheral surfaces do cool, but as they do, they serve further to insulate the deeper organs of the chest and abdomen. 2) The controls showed responses similar to those of the Eskimo, that is, increased metabolic activity as exposure to cold continued. The Eskimo began with elevated metabolic rates, their body temperatures fell lower, and their skin temperatures remained higher than the Europeans'. 3) Comparatively few studies have been done on residents of high-altitude environments, and the few comparisons available are on small samples. They indicate what would be reasonable to expect and look for, that the major unusual adaptive requirement at high altitudes is the decreased oxygen pressure. This requirement results in a large number of differentiating features between people living at sea level and at high altitudes, including subtle differences in gas concentrations in the body, in lung volume and chest expansion, in proportions of components of blood, and in ability to do work in low-oxygen tension environments.

Studies of man's ability to adapt to changing environmental circumstances by means of physiological plasticity are accumulating rapidly (see Newman, 1961, and Baker and Weiner, eds., 1966). In general, they suggest the expectable result that: 1) residents of an area show greater tolerance to the environmental stresses of that area than do nonresidents; 2) nonresidents' acclimatization varies in degree and quality; and 3) these variations are commonly associated with racial variations.

The discussion to this point makes it appear that temperature, humidity, and altitude are the only environmental factors of interest in the study of man's physiological adaptation. This is not the case; these features have been emphasized because they are of somewhat immediate interest to physical anthropology, and, further, physical anthropologists have contributed substantially to our understanding of man's adjustment to the stresses they provide. Physiologists have been interested in a wide variety of other factors that may, in time, attract more interest from physical anthropologists, such as space capsules, injury, disease resistance, motion, noise, crowdedness, and silence.

Before concluding this brief consideration of physiological characteristics, some special attention should be given to nutrition. Physiological

Figure 7–14. Oceania: Left, Tiwi; Right, Micronesian.
(Tiwi Courtesy Carleton S. Coon.)

traits are considered not only because they constitute an additional basis for describing human variation, but also because, in some ways, they provide a means for explaining variation as well. If, for example, two groups are compared and found to have significantly different chest circumferences and further found to contrast in the altitudes of their environments, the known relationship between high altitude and large chest circumferences may explain the contrast. Such relationships probably occur very commonly in connection with nutritional factors. Two populations may differ significantly in all their body dimensions not because they are adapted differently nor because their relationship is remote, but simply because they eat differently, either in quantity or quality of food. Thus, the effect of nutritional variation is important in interpreting relationships between and among human populations, but, in fact, is often neglected due to lack of information or to the complexity it introduces into an analysis. For example, there are clear indications of metabolic differences between groups of men. Eskimos not only eat more fat, but their physiological systems break it up, store it, and use it in ways that differ from Caucasians. Some groups live on daily diets with compositions that, with the same energy output, would be starvation diets for others. Since it is clear that overall body size is affected by the quality and quantity of food, then it follows that two or more populations may be *alike* because of either similar food sources or differential physiological utilization of different food sources. Likewise, it is possible for two or more populations to *differ* in some respects from one another either because of different food sources or differential physiological utilization of the same food sources. Clearly, in attempts to describe and explain man's heterographic variation, it is important to know not only what foods people eat, but how they are digested, stored, utilized, and what effects they have on the phenotype. This is a large order, and, for practical purposes, it will probably continue to be necessary, usually, to deal with heterographic variation under the assumption either that nutritional variations have no relevant effects or that their effects on man's variations can be recognized and taken into consideration. This will undoubtedly prove too simple, but even considering their limitations, these assumptions accommodate only food-source variation and, to some extent, physiological variation in the metabolic processes. What specific effects foods have on the phenotype are essentially unknown; some general impressions have begun to accumulate in studies of growth and development. Birth weight, for example, would seem to be more a reflection of environmental factors (such as the mother's health, nutrition, parity, and twinning) than of the genotype of the child. Furthermore, the striking trend in increasing stature observed in European and American communities over the last one hundred years seems to be due mostly to dietary improvements. These, however, are topics that might more properly be considered under the next category of morphological variation— developmental characteristics.

DEVELOPMENTAL CHARACTERISTICS

The study of growth and development is itself a highly diversified enterprise, containing within it several specializations. It is, perhaps, more accurate today to think of growth studies as a part of a rather new branch of science known as developmental biology, which includes such apparently diverse areas as reproductive and perinatal biology, developmental genetics, developmental psychology, and gerontology. The major thread of consistency that holds these areas together is a common interest in the interaction through time of genetic and environmental factors in producing the form and behavior (the phenotype) of the individual. This is an objective which, at present, seems idealistic and perhaps unrealistic, but there are several good reasons for being hopeful. Investigations in developmental genetics are beginning to provide some understanding of gene action and how the activity of genes is correlated with morphological changes in the structure of chromosomes. Developmental embryology has, in the last few years, made discoveries that have brought about a reevaluation of the older views of fertilization and implantation. Pharmacology is more and more concerned with the effects of drugs on the normal processes of growth.

Taken together, these are encouraging signs, but clearly only a beginning; their implications for human biology and the practice of medicine are not yet clearly understood, and it is only because they are helping to shape some new research orientations in the older, well-established field of human growth that they are at all relevant to physical anthropology.

Unfortunately for present purposes, most of the information that has been collected in growth studies deals with modern European or American populations. Thus, we lack extensive data on how growth patterns, rates, and velocities may vary from one population to another. Judging largely from modern populations, there are impressive indications that such factors, particularly growth patterns, are remarkably similar from location to location, and there are reasonably clear indications that environmental factors can and often do affect the absolute dimensions.

Do other populations grow in ways different from modern urban populations? This is not an easy question to answer, particularly with regard to primitive populations. Obtaining readily usable data on growth is usually done by means of longitudinal or cross-sectional sampling. Longitudinal studies measure the same persons at regular intervals throughout their lives and are obviously impractical for use with primitive populations. An investigator would need either to remain with the group for several years or to return at regular intervals to locate and identify the members of his sample. Neither is impossible, but both are impractical.

Cross-sectional studies can be done over a short period of time, since they involve sampling several persons of different ages and making inferences about growth regularities. For example, a cross-sectional study might proceed by measuring all the five-year-olds, six-year-olds, and seven-year-olds in a school. A growth curve could then be plotted for the ages from five to seven. This approach would be more practical than a longitudinal study in primitive populations, but, in addition to limitations inherent in all longitudinal studies, would be handicapped in most cases by the inability to determine age with precision. Using either method, one is still hampered in making comparisons between widely scattered populations, if they have been measured at different times, by the fact that in urban communities there has been a steady increase in size over the last one hundred years. Thus, if one were to compare seven-year-old boys from central Michigan who were measured in 1918 with seven-year-old boys measured in 1968, he would probably find greater differences between them than he would between seven-year-olds in different races measured at the same time. Thus, making comparisons within the category of developmental characteristics is a difficult task. Roberts (1960) made empirical comparisons between and among some African and European groups. He considered the technical problems confronting such studies and also the role that major environmental factors might play in influencing the results.

To summarize the foregoing discussion in its relationship to human heterography, the following points are of greatest interest: 1) Individuals differ considerably in such features as the rate and velocity of growth and in the time at which developmental events occur. 2) These individual variations seem to cluster together with other racial characteristics, but the details are not at all clear. 3) To what degree the variations are due to genetic, and thus evolutionary, differences or to environmental agencies is not known. 4) The most striking result of growth studies has been the indication that, no matter how much variation there may be in the ways of accomplishing growth, the overall growth pattern is similar for all groups of human beings and, indeed, between man and the rest of the primates when obvious and appropriate corrections are applied.

PSYCHOLOGICAL CHARACTERISTICS

This is a troublesome topic. The strength of beliefs on the subject, many of them contradictory, tends to be inversely proportional to the amount of evidence in support of them. This is not a situation in which there can be a dispassionate discussion of the evidence, for two good reasons: 1) people are not dispassionate about racial differences in psychological traits, and 2) there is no unambiguous evidence to bring to bear on the subject. The only correct statement one is able to make about the distribution of psychological variation is to say that, indeed, it does occur (perhaps one might state the situation more precisely by saying that persons get different scores on psychological tests), but how the variations are associated with other attributes is not known. Furthermore, the significance and source of variation in psychological characteristics are not known. To continue the discussion further would be analogous to taking an unmarked trail to an unknown destination—an intellectual random walk.

REFERENCES AND
SUGGESTIONS FOR ADDITIONAL READING

ALLEN, J. A.
> 1877   The influence of physical conditions in the genesis of species. *Radical Review* 1:108–140.

BAKER, PAUL T.
> 1958   The biological adaptation of man to hot deserts. *American Naturalist* 92:337–357.

BAKER, PAUL T., AND J. S. WEINER, EDS.
> 1966   *The biology of human adaptability.* London: Oxford University Press.

BARNICOT, N. A.
> 1957   Human pigmentation. *Man* 144:1–7.

BERGMANN, C.
> 1847   Über die Verhältnisse der Wärmeökonomie der Thiere zu ihrer Grösse. *Göttingen Studien* 3.5:95–708.

BIASUTTI, RENATO
    1959   *Le razze e I popoli della terra.* 2d ed. 4 vols. Torino: UTET.
BIELICKI, TADEUSZ, AND Z. WELON
    1964   The operation of natural selection on human head form in an East European population. *Homo* 15:22–30.
BRACE, C. LORING
    1963   Structural reduction in evolution. *American Naturalist* 97:39–49.
BRUES, ALICE
    1959   The spearman and the archer—an essay on selection in body build. *American Anthropologist* 61:457–469.
CARBONELL, VIRGINIA M.
    1963   Variations in the frequency of shovel-shaped incisors in different populations. In *Dental anthropology,* ed. D. R. Brothwell, pp. 211–234. New York: Macmillan.
GARN, STANLEY M.
    1965   *Human races.* 2d ed. Springfield, Ill.: Charles C. Thomas.
GARN, STANLEY M., ED.
    1960   *Readings on race.* Springfield, Ill.: Charles C. Thomas.
HARRISON, G. A., J. S. WEINER, J. M. TANNER, AND N. A. BARNICOT
    1964   *Human biology: an introduction to human evolution, variation, and growth.* New York: Oxford University Press.
HOOTON, EARNEST ALBERT
    1947   *Up from the ape.* Rev. ed. New York: Macmillan.
HULSE, FREDERICK S.
    1955   Technological advance and major racial stocks. *Human Biology* 27:184–192.
LOOMIS, W. F.
    1967   Skin pigment regulation of vitamin-D biosynthesis in man. *Science* 157:501–506.
MARTIN, RUDOLF, AND KARL SALLER
    1955–1966   *Lehrbuch der Anthropologie.* 3d ed. 4 vols. Stuttgart: Gustav Fischer Verlag.
NEWMAN, HORATIO H., F. N. FREEMAN, AND K. J. HOLZINGER
    1937   *Twins: a study of heredity and environment.* Chicago: University of Chicago Press.
NEWMAN, MARSHALL T.
    1961   Biological adaptation of man to his environment: heat, cold, altitude, and nutrition. *Annals of the New York Academy of Sciences* 91:617–633.
    1962   Evolutionary changes in body size and head form in American Indians. *American Anthropologist* 64:237–257.
NEWMAN, RUSSELL W., AND ELLA H. MUNRO
    1955   The relation of climate and body size in U.S. males. *American Journal of Physical Anthropology* (n.s.) 13:1–17.
OSBORNE, RICHARD H., AND FRANCES V. DE GEORGE
    1959   *Genetic basis of morphological variation: an evaluation and application of the twin study method.* Cambridge: Harvard University Press.

PARNELL, R. W.
   1965   Human size, shape, and composition. In *Human body composition: approaches and applications,* ed. Josef Brozek. Symposia of the Society for the Study of Human Biology 7:61–72.
ROBERTS, D. F.
   1953   Body weight, race and climate. *American Journal of Physical Anthropology* (n.s.) 11:533–558.
   1960   Effects of race and climate on human growth as exemplified by studies on African children. In *Human growth,* ed. J. M. Tanner, pp. 59–72. New York: Pergamon Press.
SHIELDS, JAMES
   1962   *Monozygotic twins.* London: Oxford University Press.
WENT, F. W.
   1968   The size of man. *American Scientist* 56:400–413.

CHAPTER 8

HUMAN HETEROGRAPHY AND MORPHOLOGICAL VARIATION: TRAITS OF KNOWN INHERITANCE

INTRODUCTION

One conclusion that seems clearly to be supported by the distributional evidence of man's morphological variation is that traits tend to be found in clusters of association rather than randomly distributed over the surface of the earth. On reflection, this is not surprising, since groups of people living within an area can be expected to display their common evolutionary background in the form of similar adaptations which, translated into morphology, imply similar anatomical, physiological, and developmental characteristics. If this is a reasonable expectation, then it would seem logical to anticipate not only that genetic characteristics would tend to cluster together, but also, to the extent that they reflect common evolutionary episodes, that they should be found in association with clusters of morphological traits as well. This raises an interesting question: Are genetic characteristics of any more value in solving the traditional problems of physical anthropology than measurements and observations on morphological traits? The simple observation, for example, that human beings have various blood types, while it may have important clinical implications, is in principle no different from the well-established fact that men have various forms of hair, various skin colors, etc. Furthermore, to the extent that physical anthropology concerns itself solely with purely historical problems (for example, Are the Hopi more closely related to the Zuni than to the Santa Clara Pueblos?), inherited traits are probably of no greater value to it than the usual anthropometric measurements and observations. In the past twenty years, however, physical anthropology has become increasingly involved with problems of evolutionary process and the dynamics of adaptation, and in these, inherited characteristics have properties that make them much more useful than the traits of unknown inheritance. The advantages are in some ways obvious, but will in any event be easier to comprehend after some background details are presented. The best-known (and thus most interesting) inherited characteristics in man are the blood groups and the hemoglobins, and these will be discussed in some detail, to be followed by a brief discussion of other traits of known inheritance in man.

THE BLOOD GROUPS

If you prepare a slide of your blood and look at it under a microscope, you will find no basis whatever for distinguishing between it and that of any other normal person's blood. The components are all there: red cells in large numbers and considerably fewer white cells, all supported by a relatively clear liquid medium called plasma. If the blood is allowed to clot, the plasma loses some of its components (those needed to form the clot), and the remaining liquid medium is then referred to as serum. Furthermore, if you examined the functions of the clotted elements, you would find no basis for distinguishing one person's blood from another's. The red cells transport oxygen from the lungs to the tissues and carry away carbon dioxide as a waste product. The white cells provide one major physiological defense against infection, and the plasma functions in bringing nourishment to the cells of the body, in removing the waste products of metabolism, in clotting the cells on injury, and, in a different fashion than the white cells, in resisting the effects of infection.

Suppose, however, that you mixed a drop of your blood with a drop of someone else's—what would happen? Nothing from the above would lead you to suspect that anything would occur, but it is likely that clumps of cells would form islands in the solution, as illustrated in Figure 8–1. This is agglutination; the cells would have, by some means, become attached to one another, and if you were given this blood in a transfusion, the result could very well be fatal. Clearly, the conclusion based only on microscopic observation and functional analysis is incorrect: one person's blood is not the same as another's.

From this evidence, one might be tempted to believe that every person's blood is unique, which would imply that any person's blood would agglutinate the blood of everyone else. In fact, however, the correct interpre-

no reaction   antigen-antibody reaction
in a drop of blood

Figure 8–1. Comparison of nonagglutination with agglutination.

tation requires more information. What causes the agglutination? If you take out the cells and mix them together, do you observe agglutination? Does the serum or plasma from one person agglutinate the cells of another? If so, would the reverse always be true?

These are the problems that confronted Karl Landsteiner when he recorded a series of observations inquiring into the same problems, for which he eventually won the Nobel Prize. His discovery (1900) consisted of the following observations: 1) the serum of some individuals will agglutinate the cells of others; 2) the reactions are not always reciprocal; and 3) these observations have clear implications for medical practice. Thus, Landsteiner made it clear that not all bloods were the same, nor were they all different; rather, there are types of blood. He had discovered the ABO types.

The discovery of the blood types implied the presence of: 1) compositional differences (known as antigens) in the red cells and 2) substances in the serum called antibodies, which distinguish particular antigens from others in a very specific way, causing the agglutination of the cells. This antigen-antibody phenomenon is very widespread as a physiological defense mechanism against the effects of exposure to foreign proteins. It is, for example, this mechanism that protects us against bacterial infections. Infectious microorganisms also introduce foreign substances (antigens) which stimulate the production of antibodies that attack the antigens and thereby the microorganisms themselves.

The ABO blood groups discovered by Landsteiner have come to be known in detail, and as more has been learned about the system, it has become evident that it has characteristics which make it unique. Since the time of Landsteiner's discovery, a number of other blood group systems have been discovered, and, with a few exceptions, these are all controlled by genetic loci that segregate independently. The red blood cell is indeed a complicated thing having several different antigenic properties.

The medical implications of different blood types have been obvious since Landsteiner's original discovery, but the anthropological implications became evident only gradually as it was learned that these types (or, more particularly, the genes responsible for them) occurred with varying frequencies in different populations. This implied that they might be useful to anthropologists in classifying races and in solving a multitude of specific historical problems. In addition, and unlike the usual anthropometric measurements, the blood groups are traits that can be determined with precision (a person is either type A or he is not) by relatively simple procedures. Also, they have other assets of anthropological significance: 1) they are constant throughout an individual's lifetime; 2) no one has any preconceived prejudices about them, as they do other morphological traits; and 3) at the outset at least, they appeared to be totally uninfluenced by selection. These properties imply enormous anthropological potential.

ABO Blood Groups

Every person's red blood cells can be typed into one, and only one, of the following four types: A, B, O, and AB. These were the groups that Landsteiner discovered in 1900. Implications and ramifications of the discovery continue to be investigated today; yet, basically, the original observations were quite simple. There are two antigens, A and B, and two antibodies, anti-A and anti-B, and they are combined as indicated in Table 8–1.

TABLE 8–1

ANTIGEN-ANTIBODY COMBINATIONS IN THE ABO BLOOD TYPES

| Type | Antigen* | | Antibodies | |
	A	B	Anti-A	Anti-B
A	+	−	−	+
B	−	+	+	−
O	−	−	+	+
AB	+	+	−	−

* + means present; − means absent.

Thus, when a sample is classified as blood type A, it means the following: 1) the cells have the A antigen and do not have B; and 2) the serum contains anti-B antibodies and lacks anti-A. Type B is the reverse of type A; type O blood has neither antigen and both antibodies; and type AB the reverse, both antigens and neither antibody.

How does a person become blood type A, as opposed, say, to blood type O? This is completely under genetic control; that is, one is blood type A because he has inherited certain genes from his parents. But in what way, one may ask, does this come about? Or, how many different kinds of genetic determiners are involved in producing four types? It will be useful for overall understanding to digress here for a moment to consider the problem this represents. Our illustration will be the ABO blood groups, but the problem is common to all inherited traits. Consider for a moment a few possibilities: 1) *two alleles*. This cannot be the correct number, since, no matter how hard one might try, it is not possible to combine two things into more than three different pairs, AA, AB, BB, and the problem here involves the inheritance of four types. Thus, it is logical to conclude that more than two determiners are involved, but, without additional knowledge, it is not possible to tell if the ABO blood types are controlled either by: 2) *three alleles,* that is, three *different* determiners acting in pairs, or 3) *two separate genetic loci,* each with a pair of alleles. Table 8–2 illustrates the difference between these alterna-

TABLE 8–2

IMPLICATIONS OF COMPETING HYPOTHESES ON THE
INHERITANCE OF THE ABO BLOOD TYPES

Hypothesis #1 Three Alleles, One Locus				Hypothesis #2 Two Alleles, Two Loci				
Parent Sex ⟶ A	B	O		Parent Sex ⟶ AB	A′B	AB′	A′B′	
Cells Offspring Genotypes				Cells Offspring Genotypes				
↓				↓				
A	AA	AB	AO	AB	AABB	AA′BB	AABB′	AA′BB′
B	AB	BB	BO	A′B	AA′BB	A′A′BB	AA′BB′	A′A′BB′
O	AO	BO	OO	AB′	AABB′	AA′BB′	AAB′B′	AA′B′B′
				A′B′	AA′BB′	A′A′BB′	AA′B′B′	A′A′B′B′

tives; neither is immediately encouraging, since with three alleles there are six *different* possibilities, whereas with two loci there are nine, and our problem is to account for four and only four. The answer seems clearly to be dominance, but it is still not clear in which of the alternatives. Suppose, for example, that A is dominant over A′, and B over B′; this will produce four blood types, as follows:

$$AB = AABB, AABB', AA'BB, AA'BB'$$
$$A = AAB'B', AA'B'B'$$
$$B = A'A'BB, A'A'BB'$$
$$O = A'A'B'B'$$

That fulfills the requirements, but, then, so will three alleles when A and B are co-dominant and both are dominant to O, as follows:

$$AB = AB$$
$$A = AA, AO$$
$$B = BB, BO$$
$$O = OO$$

How can the correct possibility be determined? Only by empirical test. For example, in the first case, involving two pairs of alleles, it is possible for parents both of whom are AB to have an O child in the mating AA'BB' × AA'BB'; likewise O offspring could result from AB × A or AB × B marriages. The other model implies that whenever at least one of the parents is AB, the mating cannot produce an O child. On inspection of family blood groups it was discovered that AB parents never produced O children; thus the three-allele explanation is consistent with both logical and empirical demands. It tells us how the ABO blood groups are inherited.

The details of our knowledge of the ABO blood groups continue to expand rapidly. Some of the new information is of interest only to the specialist, but some has anthropological significance, and among the most important discoveries are the following: 1) There is a water-soluble form of the A and B antigens which can be detected in the saliva of some individuals, and this trait is itself under genetic control. This trait, known as the secretor factor, will be discussed in more detail later. 2) The antigenic substances are extraordinarily complex molecules known as mucopolysaccharides. 3) These substances, or others very much like them, are present in the composition of many plants. 4) Some diseases are more commonly found among persons of one blood type than they are in other blood types. Well-documented associations are summarized in Table 8–3.

TABLE 8–3

WELL-ESTABLISHED ABO BLOOD GROUP–DISEASE ASSOCIATIONS

Blood Group	Disease
A	Stomach Cancer
A	Pernicious Anemia
O	Ulcers, Gastric and Duodenal

5) ABO incompatibility can affect a couple's reproductive abilities, as can the better-known Rh incompatibility. 6) The A and B antigens have been found in monkeys and apes (Wiener and Moor-Jankowski, 1963).

These touch on some of the more striking things that have been learned about the ABO blood groups, and while they are perhaps intriguing on their own merits, the problem remains of dealing with the question of why physical anthropologists find the ABO blood groups particularly interesting: for many reasons over and above the general ones discussed earlier in connection with all blood groups. The ABO blood groups were the first to be discovered, and information on their frequencies in populations accumulated so rapidly that their distribution remains much better known than the distribution of any of the other blood types. Earlier they were of interest to scholars wishing to construct racial classifications, who presumed them to be unaffected by the environment and thus ideal racial tags. Ironically, perhaps, it is precisely because they appear now to be surprisingly sensitive to environmental influences that the ABO blood groups are a particularly informative genetic system in studies of evolution in contemporary populations. Their frequencies vary in puzzling ways that virtually cry out for explanation. Consider first the A allele. The highest frequencies of A are found among two widely separated groups, the Blackfoot Indians of the northern plains in North America and the Lapps of northern Scandinavia. High frequencies of A are also found among the aboriginal inhabitants of southern Australia and the peoples of Polynesia. It is low in frequency or entirely absent among Central and South American Indians. For most of the world, however, A gene frequencies range between .10 and .35.

The B allele is highest in central Asia with frequencies from .30 to .35. It is virtually absent, however, among American Indians and Australian aborigines. Its absence among American Indians has always posed a difficult problem for those wishing to use the ABO blood groups as indicators of racial affiliation, since on morphological and archaeological grounds it is clear that the American Indians are the descendants of migrants from Asia. Thus the morphological and archaeological evidence is not supported by this sharp discrepancy in the frequency of the B allele. The usual explanation given for this is genetic drift, implying that the gene frequencies of the early migrants were changed as a result of chance factors. Thus it is merely an accident that modern Indians do not reflect their degree of relationship to the modern Asians in this regard. This is a convenient explanation, but, in fact, little if any evidence exists to support it. The two groups could, for example, be closely related phylogenetically and yet, in recent generations, be affected differently by selective agencies. In this instance, their differences could provide a first clue in the solution of the problem of what environmental factors influence the frequencies of the ABO alleles. This is an interesting problem, and there is as yet no answer to it. Surprisingly, there are very few hypotheses attempting to explain it.

Among the rest of the world's populations the B allele ranges between .05 and .25. The frequencies of O, of course, are known when the frequencies of A and B are given.

What do these distributions mean to the anthropologist? The patterns do not correspond closely to any of the anthropometric distributions considered in the previous chapter. What do the variations in frequency imply about the histories of modern groups? Do they offer any new insights into the patterns' and dynamics of human evolution? Are they informative on the question of whether or not man is continuing to undergo evolutionary change? These constitute some of the core problems facing physical anthropologists today, as they confront the task of integrating and interpreting the vastly diversified ways in which human beings differ.

Perhaps these remarks about the ABO blood groups will underscore the differences between traits of known inheritance and those in which this information is lacking. From the point of view of classifying man's heterographic variation, the two kinds of traits are essentially of equal value, and in their taxonomic use they share the same deficiencies. However, from the standpoint of evolutionary dynamics, inherited traits appear to hold enormously greater potential. The most exciting part of this is the fact that this potential is only now beginning to be realized. Only now are the really interesting questions about the sources of man's variation beginning to be asked with some reasonable expectation of obtaining answers. Simply because we know more about them, the ABO blood groups are likely to receive the greatest amount of attention at the outset, but there is, of course, much more.

MN Blood Groups

The next blood types to be discovered were those of the MN system. These, too, were discovered by Landsteiner, together with his collaborator, Philip Levine, in 1927. This system was discovered as a result of some clever reasoning and the application of some elegant techniques. The reasoning proceeded from a hypothesis, which had been repeatedly demonstrated as correct in other contexts, that if you inject a protein substance (in this case red blood cells) into an animal, the animal usually develops antibodies to that substance. That is, if given an injection of type B cells, an organism might well form anti-B antibodies, and if these are removed from his serum and still agglutinated some B cells, then one possible reason for this would be that the animal had developed antibodies to an antigen not formerly identified. This is essentially how the MN blood groups were discovered. Landsteiner and Levine (1927) injected immunized rabbits with different ABO blood types and, after a time, obtained samples of the rabbits' blood, from which they drew off the serum. The expected antibodies (anti-A and anti-B) were removed by a technique known as absorption, and the serum was then tested against a variety of human cells. It was discovered by this process that individuals could be classified into three groups on the basis of their reaction to the rabbit sera: 1) those that reacted only to one type of antiserum (designated anti-M), 2) those reacting only with another type (designated anti-N), and 3) those reacting with both. The results are stated in Table 8–4.

Shortly after their discovery, the fact that these were inherited was established by investigation of families. The way they are inherited is entirely consistent with the model of two co-dominant alleles. Thus, unlike the situation in the ABO system, only three genotypes are possible,

TABLE 8–4

REACTIONS OF HUMAN CELLS TO RABBIT ANTISERA

The MN Blood Groups

Type	Antibodies*	
	Anti-M	Anti-N
1. M	+	−
2. N	−	+
3. MN	+	+

* + means agglutination.

and, since the alleles are not dominant to one another, there is a complete one-to-one correspondence between phenotype and genotype, thus:

Phenotype	Genotype
M	MM
N	NN
MN	MN

The MN system contrasts with the ABO system also in that human beings normally do not have antibodies to the MN antigens. Thus, the system lacks the medical implications for blood transfusions that the ABO types have. The MN locus is closely linked to one controlling the expression of another blood group antigen, the S locus. The significance of this linkage association is, of course, important in a number of ways to human geneticists confronted with the problem of interpreting the occurrence of the two traits in families, but for present purposes it is probably enough to point out that the most important implication has to do with the ways in which genes segregate and recombine before being transmitted from parents to offspring. Loci linked together on the same chromosome remain combined and thus are transmitted together. Loci located on separate chromosomes are transmitted independently to recombine in random associations in the offspring, and this is what is meant by independent segregation. Since one is either S-positive or S-negative, the two loci may be combined to form one blood group system with six phenotypes, as follows:

MS   Ms
MNS   MNs
NS   Ns

The S locus illustrates the very common mode of inheritance involving a pair of alleles, one of which is dominant over the other. Thus, while there are three genotypes (SS, Ss, ss), there are only two phenotypes, S-positive (SS, Ss) and S-negative (ss).

The highest gene frequencies of M, ranging from .75 to .90, may be found in American Indian populations. Lower frequencies, but still well above .50 (approximately .60–.70), characterize most of continental Asia with, in general, the frequencies increasing westward from the Pacific coast and dropping off at the Euro-Asian frontier. In Europe and Africa there is less variation, with the frequencies clustering around .50. The lowest frequencies of M are found among the Papuan peoples of New Guinea, aboriginal Australians, and Micronesians. The frequencies of M, of course, imply those of N; thus, the distribution of N is the reciprocal of that for M.

S is highest among Europeans, where it reaches a high of approximately .45. Very few reports exist on the distribution of S in central Asia. However, the frequencies for India are similar to those of Europe. American Indians likewise have not been tested extensively, but they appear to be similar to the Africans, with both showing frequencies from .10 to .30. As in the case of M, the lowest frequencies of S are found in aboriginal Australia, New Guinea, and Micronesia.

One further interesting feature of the MNS chromosome is the additional linkages with two antigens known as Hunter and Henshaw. Both are commonly found in African populations and rarely or never found in others.

The puzzling distribution of the MNS alleles, the recognizability of homozygous and heterozygous genotypes, and their linkage associations make these blood group systems interesting. As more is learned about their relationships to one another and about their distributions over the world, they have the potential to rival the ABO blood groups in the information they provide on the subject of human evolution and in improving our understanding of man's heterographic variation.

P Blood Groups

In the same studies that resulted in the discovery of the MN system, Landsteiner and Levine also discovered the P groups. The antibody was produced by immunizing rabbits, and it reacted with 78 percent of all human red cells in a way that crosscut the MN and ABO phenotypes, indicating a totally independent blood group system. At first it appeared to be a system inherited in a simple and straightforward way, controlled by a pair of alleles, with P dominant to p. Dominant homozygotes showed strong reactions, heterozygotes weaker ones. The weak reaction complicated the technical procedures to a degree that made it difficult to use this locus in describing differences between populations, for it was found that apparent differences were often due to mistakes in typing the weak P-positive reactions. This fact, taken together with the additional one that relatively few populations have been tested for the P antigen, makes it impossible to characterize its worldwide distribution with any confidence.

Enough is known, however, to say that its frequency does vary considerably, and thus the system should become of more importance to anthropological problems as more information becomes available.

The Rh System

The Rh system is interesting for three different reasons: 1) the precise way in which it is inherited remains an unresolved problem forming the basis of two competing theories; 2) pregnant Rh-negative females develop antibodies that can destroy the red blood cells of their unborn offspring; and 3) the Rh alleles show wide variation in their frequencies in samples drawn from populations all over the world. There are many other aspects necessary to obtain a reasonably complete understanding of the system and its history, but these will serve to direct attention to the features of greatest importance to physical anthropology.

Again it was Karl Landsteiner, collaborating on this occasion with A. S. Wiener, who in 1940 reported the initial discovery of an Rh antigen. They observed that rabbits immunized with red blood cells from rhesus monkeys developed an antibody that agglutinated the red blood cells of 85 percent of a sample of New Yorkers and failed to react with the cells of 15 percent. The experiment itself seems improbable and puzzling. Why inject rabbits with monkey blood cells and then test the rabbits' serum on the cells of human beings? However, one should recall that the M, N, and P factors had been discovered by immunizing rabbits with human cells. Moreover, Landsteiner and Wiener were deliberately trying to learn as much as possible about human blood groups. Furthermore, the reasoning behind the experiment becomes clearer in view of the observation that no additional systems had been disclosed in continued investigations of rabbit serum immunized with human cells. Why not inject cells from another animal, perhaps a taxonomic neighbor of man, and see what happens? Rhesus monkeys had been used regularly in medical research and thus provided convenient subjects, and it is, of course, from them that the Rh factor got its name. However improbable the experiment might seem, the consequences were far-reaching indeed, and it is this kind of response to an educated hunch that raises brilliant scientists above the level of run-of-the-mill scientists.

Initially, the antigen discovered by Landsteiner and Wiener appeared to be under the control of a single genetic locus that could be occupied by one or another of a pair of alleles with the positive condition dominant to the negative, and, in a sense, this remains a correct interpretation. Today, when we speak of a person as Rh positive or Rh negative, it is this antigen-antibody reaction that we are referring to, and the positive reaction is understood as dominant to the negative. However, two discoveries have greatly affected our views of this subject: 1) the demontration that Rh incompatibilities between mother and offspring can and often do produce serious defects in the newborn child (It was this clear medical implication that stimulated an intensive investigation of the Rh system. The details of this discovery will be discussed presently.), and 2) the discovery of five additional antigen-antibody relationships that, taken together with the first one, make up the totality of the Rh blood group system.

To understand the inheritance of the Rh system requires an understanding of these newer antigens and antibodies and how they are interrelated. To try to follow the historical development of this system involves a heavy commitment to a discussion of serological techniques, for many of the new antibodies were discovered as the consequences of applying some ingenious laboratory procedures which, while they are interesting in themselves, are nevertheless remote from the point of view of our objectives. So it seems reasonable to begin by giving the name of the original antigen discovered by Landsteiner and Wiener—it is called the D factor. Thus, positive reactions are genotypically DD or Dd, and negative results dd. One of the newer antibodies agglutinates the red blood cells of persons with the d factor,* and thus this system may be seen as similar to the MN blood types in the sense that all three genotypes are distinguishable, as shown in Table 8–5.

TABLE 8–5

The D Factor in the Rh System†

| Type | Antibodies | |
	Anti-D	Anti-d
DD	+	−
Dd	+	+
dd	−	−(?)

† + means a positive antigen-antibody reaction.

Another pair of antibodies and their antigens, designated as C and c, has also been identified, and for the moment these can be considered completely separately from the Dd antigens. The Cc system also consists of three phenotypes, and these imply the underlying genotypes, so that its reactions can be characterized as in Table 8–6.

If there were no more to it than the Cc and Dd systems, it would be simple and straightforward; but, in the inspection of data obtained on

* This bends the facts a bit. Anti-d was first reported in 1946. There are good reasons now for questioning the correctness of the results. In fact, there never has been a satisfactory demonstration of this antiserum, although, largely because of the symmetry of the rest of the system, many investigators believe that it exists. It has not been conclusively identified as yet.

TABLE 8–6

THE C FACTOR IN THE RH SYSTEM*

Type	Antibodies	
	Anti-C	Anti-c
CC	+	—
cc	+	+
Cc	—	+

* + means a positive antigen-antibody reaction.

families, it became clear that the Cc and Dd loci did not segregate; that is, the two loci are not independent, but rather are closely linked to one another. This, too, is similar to the MN system with the addition of the Ss locus closely linked together with it. The Rh system, however, is characterized by yet a third locus, Ee, closely linked together with the Cc, Dd loci. The Ee antigen-antibody relationships are analogous to the Cc, Dd loci (see Table 8–7) and, again, linked together with them. The five

TABLE 8–7

THE E FACTOR IN THE RH SYSTEM†

Type	Antibodies	
	Anti-E	Anti-e
EE	+	—
Ee	+	+
ee	—	+

† + means a positive antigen-antibody reaction.

additional antibodies are thus accounted for: d, C, c, E, and e. With the original D it is possible to identify all eight different kinds of arrangements as shown in Table 8–8. Thus, everyone's complete genotype for the Rh system is a pair (one chromosome from each parent) of these eight possible arrangements.

Consider for a moment the genetic implications of loci closely linked together on the same chromosome. Linked loci can be separated by a process known as crossover (see Chapter 3), wherein paired chromosomes exchange parts of themselves and thus break up former linkage associations. The likelihood that a linkage association between one locus and another will be destroyed by crossing over is proportional to the distance between them; the greater the distance, the more likely the crossover. Thus, loci linked on opposite extremes of a chromosome are more likely to be separated by crossover than two loci adjacent to one another.

TABLE 8–8

ANTIGEN-ANTIBODY REACTIONS IN THE RH SYSTEM*

| Type | Antibodies | | | | | |
	Anti-C	Anti-D	Anti-E	Anti-c	Anti-d	Anti-e
CDE	+	+	+	−	−	−
CDe	+	+	−	−	−	+
CdE	+	−	+	−	+	−
Cde	+	−	−	−	+	+
cDE	−	+	+	+	−	−
cDe	−	+	−	+	−	+
cdE	−	−	+	+	+	−
cde	−	−	−	+	+	+

* + means a positive antigen-antibody reaction.

How close together are the Cc, Dd, Ee loci? Apparently, very close. No case of their linkage being rearranged by crossing over has ever been conclusively proven. This in itself is interesting. If they are so close together that they never cross over, how is it that they can be called three separate loci? Is it not possible that the various reactions are the expressions of a single locus that can be occupied by any one of eight alternative alleles? Yes, indeed it is. These two alternatives have been the core of a long and heated controversy over the inheritance of the Rh system. The model employing three closely linked loci was proposed by R. A. Fisher and R. R. Race in 1948. The single-locus-multiple-allele model was put forth in 1949 by A. S. Wiener, Landsteiner's collaborator in the original experiments. Instead of chromosomes, Wiener's theory postulates eight alleles controlling the expression of eight antigens (agglutinogens in Wiener's vocabulary) and their reaction patterns with six antisera. Table 8–9 compares the essential features of each view. For our purposes the

TABLE 8–9

COMPARISON OF RH NOMENCLATURES

Three Closely Linked Loci Fisher–Race	Single Locus–Multiple Alleles A. S. Wiener
CDE	Rh_z
CDe	Rh_1
CdE	rh^y
Cde	rh'
cDE	Rh_2
cDe	Rh_o
cdE	rh''
cde	rh

models are equivalent. Each provides a logically consistent way of accounting for the empirical information known about the system. It is not, at this time, possible to choose one theory over the other on solid empirical grounds.

Today, most people are aware in a vague sort of way that the Rh blood types can be a source of difficulty in bearing normal children. Women particularly have become sensitive to the fact that if they are Rh negative they might well face the prospect of bearing moribund offspring. This general awareness arose as one consequence of the Landsteiner–Wiener discovery and another reported a year earlier by Levine and Stetson. As already noted, Landsteiner and Wiener (1940) discovered anti-D. Levine and Stetson (1939) noted that a woman who had delivered a stillborn child had an unusual antibody in her serum, and they proposed that it had been developed in response to an antigen introduced into her bloodstream by her developing child. The unusual antibody and anti-D were found to be identical, and further investigation established that children born with a disease known as *erythroblastosis fetalis* were the D-positive offspring of D-negative mothers and D-positive fathers. What Levine and Stetson had proposed for a particular case turned out to be of general validity.

Most commonly the incompatibilities arise as a consequence of the following conditions: 1) mother is D-negative (one could also say Rh negative); 2) father and child are D-positive; 3) the child's D antigen gets into mother's bloodstream and causes the reaction any foreign protein would—it stimulates anti-D antibodies; and 4) the antibodies contact the child's blood cells and destroy them. If the antibodies are few in number, as usually is the case in first pregnancies, often no effect may be seen in the child, or it may cause a mild anemia. Subsequent D-positive pregnancies are likely to increase the number of antibodies in the mother's bloodstream and thereby increase the severity of the condition in the offspring.

As mentioned, this is the most common way in which Rh incompatibility results in erythroblastosis fetalis, and the reason for this will become clearer presently in the discussion of the frequencies of the eight chromosomes. However, it is not the only way in which it can occur. The incompatible possibilities and the genotypes that can produce them are listed in Table 8–10.

This makes it appear that Rh incompatibility must be a common event, but in fact it is not as frequent as might be assumed, because antibodies, for reasons not at all well understood, often do not develop under circumstances where they might be expected to, and, in addition, chromosome frequencies are by no means equally distributed. In fact, four chromosomes (CDe, cDE, cDe, cde) make up over 95 percent of the eight possible types, and these four show striking and interesting patterns of variation over the world.

TABLE 8–10

MATERNAL-CHILD INCOMPATIBILITIES IN THE RH SYSTEM

Genotypes		Antibody Produced
Mother	Child	
ee	Ee	Anti-E
cc	Cc	Anti-C
dd	Dd	Anti-D
EE	Ee	Anti-e
CC	Cc	Anti-c
DD	Dd	(Anti-d)*

* The status of anti-d remains uncertain.

The CDe chromosome is the most common. It has a very high frequency in the Pacific islands, reaching as high as 90 percent in some populations. Europeans, North Africans, and Southwest Asians are alike in having high frequencies of CDe, but their frequencies are substantially lower than those in the Pacific, falling more between 40 percent and 60 percent, with the Chinese, Japanese, Korean, and Southeast Asian population frequencies even higher, but generally lower than those in the Pacific. American Indians have been found to have more variation in their frequencies, from approximately 30 percent to 70 percent, thus including the normal range of European variation and overlapping the northern to southwestern Orientals. Africans south of the Sahara have the lowest CDe frequencies in the world; the chromosome is entirely absent from some African populations and rarely exceeds 15 percent.

The European, North African, and Southwest Asian populations are remarkably homogeneous in the frequencies of their Rh chromosomes. In addition to sharing similar CDe frequencies, the populations in these areas are alike in having the highest cde chromosome frequencies of from 25 percent to 50 percent. Sub-Saharan Africans and the rest of the Asian peoples have lower frequencies of cde, the Africans with a range from approximately 5 percent to 25 percent, the Asians from zero to 10 percent. The cde chromosome is absent in the Pacific and among American Indians.

The cDe chromosome is common only in sub-Saharan Africa, where it regularly accounts for from 30 percent to 60 percent of the Rh chromosomes. It ranges from zero to 10 percent everywhere else. This is similar to the situation of the cDE chromosome, which is very common among American Indians (approximately 25 percent to 60 percent) and rare (zero to 20 percent) in all other groups. Table 8–11 provides a summary of the distributions of the common chromosomes in major parts of the world.

TABLE 8-11

SUMMARY OF THE DISTRIBUTION OF COMMON RH CHROMOSOMES

Chromosome	Europe, North Africa, Southwest Asia	Sub-Saharan Africa	Southeast Asia: China, Japan, Korea	Pacific	American Indian
CDe	high frequencies	lowest frequencies	marked variation; very high frequencies	highest frequencies in the world; not greatly varied, all high	marked variation; high frequencies
cDE	low frequencies	lowest frequencies	low frequencies	low to moderate frequencies	marked variation; highest frequencies
cDe	very low frequencies	marked variation; highest frequencies	very low frequencies	very low frequencies	very low frequencies
cde	highest frequencies	low to moderate frequencies	very low frequencies	absent	absent

Even from this brief summary, it should be clear that a great amount of information is known about the Rh system. We know a great deal about how it is inherited, even if it cannot be conclusively shown that it is controlled by one or three loci. Its relationship to erythroblastosis has been well documented and has become widely known among educated persons. Even though it was discovered forty years later than the ABO blood groups, we know nearly as much about its global distribution as we do that of the ABO blood groups. Yet, on reflection, it becomes evident that we are completely without well-documented answers to some of the most interesting, exciting, and basic questions regarding the system. For example, if three loci control the inheritance of the system, why is it that they have come to be so close to one another on the same chromosome? Or, on the other hand, if only one locus is involved, what, if any, is the special significance of several alleles? What factors account for the variations in the frequencies of the four common chromosomes? What is the relationship between the common combinations and the rare ones? And, most importantly, why is it that the cde chromosome, for which Rh-incompatible mothers are most frequently homozygous, is as common as it is in some populations of the world? Is it not reasonable to expect that if homozygous cde mothers have a greater likelihood of bearing defective offspring than mothers of any other type, the cde chromosome should be rare? Yet we have found it to be as high as 40 to 50 percent in some European populations and as high as 30 to 35 percent in some Asian populations. This raises a very interesting point which will be discussed presently.

Other Blood Group Systems

Since 1940, several other blood group systems have been discovered. As a group, these give the appearance of being of great potential value to the physical anthropologist, since in virtually every instance the alleles involved appear to vary sharply in their frequencies in different parts of the world. At this point, however, we are able to speak confidently only concerning their potential value, largely because, in most instances, only a comparatively small number of populations have been sampled. Moreover, in every case the inheritance of these systems was at first thought to be simple and straightforward, but subsequent discoveries have created much confusion. The confusion is only now beginning to be clarified, and we will have to wait until the antisera become more generally available to know with confidence the geography of these systems.

Reference is made here to the following systems: Lutheran, Lewis, Kell, Duffy, Kidd, and Diego. The Kell system is in many ways similar to the Rh system in that multiple alleles (at least four) are involved, and these are compatible with either a single-locus–multiple-allele model or a pair of closely linked loci that can be occupied by either of two pairs of alleles. The Lutheran, Lewis, Duffy, and Kidd loci have had remarkably similar histories. The first antigen-antibody reaction in each system to be discovered was followed by the discovery of its complementary antibody, and at this point the genetic determination appeared to be simple—two alleles determining three genotypes, which, in turn, produced three recognizable phenotypes. Each system was then shown to have a fourth phenotype, which was negative for the earlier two antigens. Thus, like the ABO blood groups, each has four phenotypes. The phenotype similarity is not, however, a basis for concluding that the inheritance of these four systems is like that of the ABO system. In the case of the Lewis system, for example, it appears now that this locus involves only two alleles, whose genotypic expression is modified by a totally independent genetic determiner, the secretor locus, which is discussed below.

The Diego system is new, and it may be that its inheritance will be further elucidated by discoveries similar to those that have taken place in the Lutheran, Lewis, Duffy, and Kidd groups. The attention of anthropologists has been directed rapidly to Diego because very early it became clear that it showed sharp variations between races. Diego positives are common among some American Indian groups and among the few populations tested from Southwest Asia, China, Japan, and Korea.

In 1962, the first report appeared of a sex-linked locus controlling the appearance of a blood group antigen. This is the Xg locus, and, at present, it is of primary interest to geneticists in learning more about the X chromosome and the arrangement of genes on it, and in testing genetic hypotheses on the role of the sex chromosomes. Its value to anthropological problems is uncertain.

These few remarks do not begin to do justice to the complexities of these systems. However, detailing these complexities would not, at this point in our knowledge of the systems, advance our general appreciation of the elements of physical anthropology.

SECRETOR

There are two forms of antigens in the ABO system: 1) an alcohol-soluble form that is found on the surface of the red blood cells, and 2) a water-soluble form which may be found in the tissues, saliva, and other body fluids of only some individuals. Except in very rare instances, all human beings have the alcohol-soluble antigens, but not everyone has the water-soluble form of the antigens. Moreover, whether or not a person has the ABO water-soluble antigens is genetically determined. Those who do are known as *secretors;* those who do not are *nonsecretors.* The secretor locus segregates independently of the ABO locus and can be occupied by either of a pair of alleles, Se or se. Secretors are either SeSe or Sese, and nonsecretors are all sese.

The existence of ABO antigens outside of the red blood cells had been recognized as early as 1910, and the manner in which the trait is inherited was worked out in 1932. The frequencies of Se and se were found to vary from place to place in no clear pattern, but apart from this, the trait was regarded for many years as little more than a genetic oddity.

Lewis antigens may also be found in a water-soluble form in saliva and other fluids, but their appearance in, say, saliva seemed to be completely independent of the secretor and ABO loci, since only some secretors have Lewis antigens in their saliva, whereas some nonsecretors do too. However, Grubb (1948) observed that the Lewis antigens, if any were present at all, were different in nonsecretors from those found in secretors. Specifically, nonsecretors had Le (a+, b−), and secretors Le (a−, b+). Recall that: 1) the ABO locus is independent of the secretor locus; 2) the secretor locus nevertheless determines whether or not the ABO substance is converted to a water-soluble form; 3) the secretor and Lewis loci are independent of each other, as both are of the ABO locus; and 4) the secretor and Lewis loci appear to interact in some way in their effect on the phenotype. To explain the relationships among these elements, Grubb proposed a theory which, at the time, seemed improbable and complex. However, subsequent work has demonstrated his view to be not only sound, but simplifying as well. In brief, the elements contained in his theory are as follows: 1) Everyone inherits the ability to produce a generalized polysaccharide known as a precursor substance. 2) The Lewis system involves only two alleles (Le^+ or Le^-). 3) Lewis positive genotypes (Le^+Le^+ or Le^+Le^-) convert the precursor substance to Le^a. The Lewis negative (Le^-Le^-) genotype does not modify it at all. 4) Secretors convert the precursor substance to the water-soluble ABO antigens and the Le^a to Le^b. The details of this are less important than the general realization that secretor and Lewis loci well illustrate an understanding that is becoming increasingly clear in genetics today: inherited traits can no longer be thought of as distinct and separate entities, to be taken up and analyzed one at a time, but rather as the products of interaction among the loci as well as between the genetic elements and the environment. To the physical anthropologist interested in the dynamics of human evolution this may mean that, for example, a simultaneous consideration of allelic frequency variations in the ABO, Lewis, and secretor loci will be more informative than a consideration of each one separately.

Inherited variations in the antigenic properties of the red blood cells in man have received much attention in physical anthropology for reasons which should by now be clear. It is, moreover, likely that they will continue to be of importance, although probably as applied to new and different problems, for many years to come. This emphasis tends to obscure the fact that the red blood cell antigens are but one of several classes of antigen systems that are known to exist in man and to show frequency variations in different populations. The white blood cells, for example, display antigen differences that make it possible to divide them into blood types. Likewise, there are interesting genetic variants of proteins that occur normally in human serum. Research into these areas is comparatively new and is likely to produce many insights in the future. At present, however, what we have learned about these traits tends to confirm rather than to add to the basic understandings provided by the red blood cell types. All are alike in the following features: 1) the various types are inherited; 2) the frequencies of the alleles controlling them vary among human populations; and 3) the causes for the frequency differences are largely unknown.

There is another class of inherited traits in man that deserves particular attention, for it does add to our fundamental knowledge of human heterography—the hereditary variations of hemoglobin.

HEMOGLOBIN

In Chapter 3, hemoglobin served as an illustration of the way in which the genetic material, DNA, is translated into the construction of a protein. In that context, there was no particular reason to call attention to the fact that different kinds of hemoglobin have been discovered, although it will be helpful to do so here. Before proceeding to investigate these variations, it will be useful to recall the following basic facts about hemoglobin: 1) hemoglobin is found within the red blood cells and functions to carry oxygen to cells throughout the body and to carry away carbon dioxide; 2) the hemoglobin molecule consists of four long chains of amino acids, or, more precisely, of two pairs of identical chains, two α and two β; and 3) the sequences of amino acids in both the alpha and beta chains are known. At the molecular level, it is clear that considerably more detail is known about hemoglobin than about the polysaccharides responsible for blood group factors. The functions of blood groups are not known, and, while a substantial beginning has already been made in this field, we know comparatively little about the structure of the blood group substances.

Hemoglobin variations can come about in three ways: 1) alterations in the normal sequence of amino acids in either α or β chains; 2) molecular modifications of the structure of hemes, the iron-bearing structures located in the interstices of hemoglobin which serve as sites for the attachment of oxygen; and 3) quantitative differences in the production of α and β chains. A change of any one of these is almost always harmful to the organism, varying in severity from mild anemias to fatal diseases. We shall largely ignore the quantitative differences and those arising as a result of structural modifications to heme and concentrate on changes in amino acid sequences of the alpha and beta chains. More particularly, our discussion will focus on an unusually interesting disease, sickle-cell anemia, which is a condition resulting from an alteration in the normal amino acid sequence of the beta chain.

Sickle-cell Anemia

Sickle-cell anemia has been recognized for a long time as a disease with high frequencies in parts of equatorial Africa, the Mediterranean, India, and southern Asia. It may also be found in derived populations, such as some groups of American Negroes, but is virtually absent everywhere else. It is a hemolytic anemia, that is, one characterized by the presence of free hemoglobin in the plasma. This is an abnormal condition, but not in itself sufficiently distinctive to distinguish sickle-cell anemia from other anemic conditions. Associated with this condition, however, is a most distinctive trait; the red blood cells of persons with sickle-cell anemia have a very characteristic shape. Figure 8–2 compares normal red blood cells with those from a patient suffering from sickle-cell anemia. The unusual shape is reminiscent of the form of the blade of a sickle, hence the name. The cells often become distorted and rupture, thereby emptying their contents, mostly hemoglobin, into the plasma. Thus the number of functional cells is reduced, but even more important is the fact that even the intact cells are unable to carry out efficiently their function of transporting oxygen and carbon dioxide, and, as a consequence, the victim almost always dies before he reaches maturity.

Analysis of the parents, brothers, and sisters of persons suffering from sickle-cell anemia resulted in two important observations: the disease is inherited, and there are three (rather than two) ways of classifying people with regard to this disease: 1) those with normal cells; 2) those with sickle cells; and 3) those whose cells are normal in shape in their bloodstream but fan out into sickle shapes when placed in a reduced-oxygen environment. These three were shown to be the phenotypic expres-

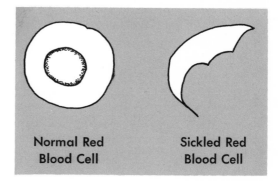

Figure 8–2. Comparison of a normal red blood cell with a sickle-shaped red blood cell.

Normal Red
Blood Cell

Sickled Red
Blood Cell

sions of the three genotypes expected in a trait controlled by a pair of alleles. Thus:

Homozygous normal	Hb^A Hb^A	no sickling
Heterozygous	Hb^A Hb^s	sickling in reduced-oxygen environment
Homozygous sickle cells	Hb^s Hb^s	sickling in blood-stream

However, another discovery, reported in 1949, resulted in a much wider interest in the disease and particularly in hemoglobin. The discovery, made by Linus Pauling and his co-workers, was that persons suffering from sickle-cell anemia had a different kind of hemoglobin from that of normal persons, and, furthermore, even though their red blood cells were normal in their bloodstreams, the heterozygotes had both normal and sickle-cell hemoglobin. In the years that followed, the molecular structure of hemoglobin was worked out in detail, and it became evident that sickle-cell hemoglobin (Hb^s) differed from normal hemoglobin in but one amino acid in the sequence of 146 that make up the beta chain. Homozygous individuals lack the ability to produce any normal beta chain sequences and, as a consequence, usually die during the first decade of life. Heterozygotes produce normal beta chains in equal proportions to the abnormal chains, and physiologically this is apparently sufficient to enable them to lead normal and healthy lives.

A curious sidelight to the sickle-cell anemia story is the fact that heterozygous individuals are highly resistant to malaria, a protozoan disease which has a high incidence in areas in which sickle-cell anemia is most common. Heterozygotes therefore have a substantial survival advantage over completely normal persons in malarial areas, and a hereditary disease that might otherwise slowly disappear is perpetuated.

Since 1949, over fifty other abnormal hemoglobins have been discovered. Clearly hemoglobin and its various abnormalities are, like the blood groups, extraordinarily interesting. On the one hand, we know much more about the molecular structure of hemoglobin than we do of the blood group substances. Perhaps this is due in part to the fact that, in spite of there being a large number of amino acids in a protein, they can be joined together by only one kind of bond, the peptide bond. There are comparatively few basic sugars that go into the makeup of the blood group polysaccharides, but they may be joined together in an almost endless variety of ways. On the other hand, a good deal more is known about the distribution of variation in the blood groups, and it is this fact particularly that makes the blood groups of greater value at the present time to anthropological problems.

Whatever the differences and whatever the advantages, the striking feature about both the blood groups and the hemoglobins is that we are only now at the threshold of understanding their significance and implications. As more is learned about the molecular structure and the geographical variation of the various forms of inherited traits as separate entities, more is also learned about interaction between and among them. This simplifies their interrelationships and thereby lays the foundation for the formulation of new and more profound questions about their evolutionary, historical, and ecological significance.

OTHER TRAITS

With the discovery of inherited variations in the structure of the hemoglobin molecule and the exciting consequences of the discovery, it is easy to understand why it was that other proteins soon began to be investigated in similar ways. Of those that show considerable variation, the most thoroughly investigated have been the proteins normally found in serum. Among the serum proteins, haptoglobin is perhaps the best known in terms of its geographic variation, and for this reason may serve as an illustration.

Haptoglobin

Haptoglobin is a protein that combines with free hemoglobin and prevents its passage into the kidneys, where it could cause damage to the tissues. Three common kinds of haptoglobin have been identified on the basis of differences detected in the electrical charges on the surface of the molecules. These have been shown to be the expression of a pair of alleles in the usual three possible combinations: *

$$Hp^1 Hp^1$$
$$Hp^1 Hp^2$$
$$Hp^2 Hp^2$$

Haptoglobin allelic frequencies vary considerably in an interesting way. Table 8–12 indicates that high frequencies of Hp^1 tend to cluster along the equator in both Africa and South America. From about 15 degrees north the frequencies of Hp^1 are intermediate, ranging from approximately .20 to .45, with exceptions on the high side noted among the Eskimo and Apache and on the low side the Asian Indians. The Bushmen of South Africa and some Australian aborigines have very low frequencies.

* Subsequent investigations have disclosed rarer variations which are ignored here.

TABLE 8–12*

DISTRIBUTION OF HAPTOGLOBINS IN VARIOUS POPULATIONS

(Hp⁰ individuals were subtracted from the total
population before computation of Hp^1.)

Population	N	Hp^1	Hp^0
Caucasian:			
United States White			
Ann Arbor	68	.43	0
Seattle	350	.38	.003
Canadian	49	.46	0
British	180	.43	.005
British	218	.39	.03
Australian White	100	.43†	0
Australian White	323	.38	.003
Swedish	160	.41	0
Swedish	220	.44	0
Norwegian	1000	.36	0
Danish	2046	.40	0
Finnish	891	.36	.002
Swedish Lapps	329	.32	.02
Greenlanders	74	.30	0
Bavarians	273	.46	0
Swiss	920	.40	0
French	406	.40	0
Italian			
Berra	120	.41	.01
Cologna	208	.35	0
Naples	93	.34	0
Sardinia	147	.37	0
Sicily	107	.40	0
Spanish Basques	107	.37	.01
Iranian	34	.25	0
Indian	74	.18	0
Indian	33	.17	0
Indian	219	.09	.02
Venezuelans ("hybrid")	208	.55	0
Mongolian:			
Orientals (Seattle, mostly Japanese)	242	.25	0
Japanese	349	.24	.01
Japanese	488	.27	
Japanese (United States)	23	.30	0
Malays	236	.24	.01
Chinese	167	.28	.01

* From H. E. Sutton et al., "Distribution of Haptoglobin, Transferrin, and Hemoglobin Types among Indians of Southern Mexico and Guatemala," *American Journal of Human Genetics,* 12 (1960): 342–343. Reprinted by permission. Readers interested in the original sources of the above information should consult the article.

† Based on paper electrophoresis only.

TABLE 8–12—*Continued*

Population	N	Hp^1	Hp^0
Mongolian—*Continued:*			
Alaskan:			
Eskimo	167	.33	.005
Eskimo	418	.30	0
Anaktuvuk	57	.52	.04
North Athabascan	202	.42	.01
Tlingit	82	.44	.02
Apaches	98	.59	0
Central American			
Non-Maya	170	.57	.01
Maya (less Lacandon)	414	.59	0
Lacandon	31	.93	.10
Peruvian Indians	173	.73	0
Oceanic:			
Borneo	22	.50	0
Micronesian (Marshall Islands)	52	.58	0
Tongans	200	.60	0
Negroid:			
American Negro			
Ann Arbor	43	.59	.10
Seattle	760	.54	.04
California	51	.61	.02
Nigeria:			
Yoruba	99	.87	.32
Yoruba	30	.72	.23
Habe	120	.60	.27
Fulani	111	.76	.37
Liberia, Ivory Coast	614	.72	
Gambia	157	.70	.40
Ibo	70	.49	.48
Congo			
Metropolitan	186	.60	.05
Nonmetropolitan	468	.57	.21
Pygmy	125	.40	.31
Cape Colored	88	.47	0
Hottentot	59	.51	0
Zulu	116	.53	.03
South African (Xhosa and Msutu)	315	.55	.05
Bushmen	113	.29	.02
Australian Aborigines			
Central Australia	100	.63†	0
North Queensland	123	.46†	0
Western Desert	133	.17	.01

† Based on paper electrophoresis only.

The significance of the variation is not known, and the interpretation is further complicated by the fact that, in some populations, a small proportion of otherwise normal individuals has been reported to lack haptoglobin entirely (Hp^o). Curiously, the highest frequencies of this phenomenon (ahaptoglobinemia) are associated with the highest frequencies of Hp^1.

Taster

There exists a group of substances that some persons identify as having a bitter taste, whereas others find them tasteless. This phenomenon has been recognized since 1931. Whether or not one is able to taste the substances is determined genetically by a pair of alleles (T, t), as follows:

TT taster
Tt taster
tt   nontaster

The heterozygote is indistinguishable from the TT homozygote; thus T is said to be dominant over t.

The geographic distribution of the alleles shows no correlation with gross climatic categories. High and low frequencies are found in the tropics, the temperate latitudes, and in the circumpolar region (see Table 8–13). In attempting to provide some explanation for this distribution, most investigations have proceeded from the observation that the substances (usually either phenylthiocarbamide—PTC—or phenylthiourea—PTO—are used) which distinguish tasters from nontasters are all known to suppress activity of the thyroid gland. Tasters could be expected to have some advantage over nontasters in resisting nodular goiter by rejecting these bitter-tasting thyroid-activity suppressors. Indeed, it has been demonstrated (Azevêdo, Krieger, Mi, and Morton, 1965) that nontasters are more commonly victims of nodular goiter than would be expected by chance.

The demonstrated relationship between taster status, thyroid function, and goiter is informative but fails to account, in any comprehensive way, for the geographic variations in allelic frequencies. The suggestion has been made that the taster locus might be associated with variations in body size. The reasoning behind this is simple: nontasters ingest thyroid-suppressing foods more commonly than tasters; the thyroid gland controls growth rates; therefore, the nontasters might be expected to be smaller than tasters. Only one preliminary study of the empirical basis for this has been undertaken (Johnston, Hertzog, and Malina, 1966), and, while its results are interesting and supportive, its design is awkward, and the conclusions are tentative.

TABLE 8–13*

THE INCIDENCE OF NONTASTER OF PHENYLTHIOCARBAMIDE AND
RELATED COMPOUNDS IN DIFFERENT POPULATIONS

Population	Number Tested	Percent Nontasters†
English	440	31.5
United States White	3643	(29.8)
Danes	314	31.8
Norwegians	266	30.5
Finns	202	29.2
Spaniards, Northeastern	306	24.8
Basques, Spain	98	(25.0)
Lapps, Norwegian and Swedish	140	6.9
Africans, mostly West African	74	2.7
Chinese (in London)	66	10.6
Chinese (in Malaya)	50	2.0
Japanese	295	7.1
Formosan "Natives"	1756	(1.8)
Malays	50	15.6
Tamils in Malaya	50	27.2
Bombay Indians	200	(42.5)
Ramah Navahoes	264	(2.0)
Cree and Beaver Indians, Northern Alberta	489	(2.0)
Eskimos, Labrador	130	(41)
Eskimos, Northern Alaska	68	25.8
Negritos, Malaya	50	18
Aborigines (Sēnoi), Malaya	50	4
Arabs, Assiut		(18)
Bantu, Kenya	208	3.8
Arabs, Kenya	63	25.4
Indians, Brazil	163	1.2
Welsh	203	17.24
Portuguese	454	24.0

* From A. C. Allison and B. S. Blumberg, "Ability to Taste Phenylthiocarbamide among Alaskan Eskimos and Other Populations," *Human Biology,* 31 (1959): 355. Reprinted by permission of Wayne State University Press. Readers interested in the original sources and testing procedures should consult the article.

† Parentheses indicate studies in which techniques other than selection were used.

INHERITED DISEASES

Even one with only a vague awareness of genetics is likely to feel that something is missing on completing a section dealing with inherited traits in man that deals exclusively with blood types, hemoglobin varieties, serum proteins, and a few other factors. What of the many other disorders known to be inherited in man, such as hemophilia, phenylketon-uria, albinism, etc.? To be sure, there are many such traits of known inheritance. These are the rare, usually pathological traits that constitute the major area of interest in the subdivision of genetics called medical genetics. Physical anthropology is less concerned with these traits simply because they are very rare in frequency whenever they occur and, for this reason, are uninformative in assessing degrees of relationship among modern populations. The genes responsible for these rare conditions are maintained by mutation, and the frequency of a particular condition appears to be a result of both the mutation rate and the degree of inbreeding, and no good reason exists that would lead one to believe that these variables reflect the degree of relationship. Since research on these rare inherited pathologies requires the development of mathematical models for the calculation of mutation rates and inbreeding coefficients, these pathologies have been given a great deal of attention in population genetics as well as in medical genetics.

The primary objective of this and the preceding chapter is to summarize man's heterographic variation, emphasizing, on the one hand, a selected group of traits of unknown inheritance and, on the other, some of the better-known characteristics for which the mechanisms of inheritance are known. In discussing the latter, it has been necessary to deal with a large number of details concerning the genetic aspects of the traits, and in doing so a more comprehensive understanding should result. It is now time to reconsider the distributions of both categories of traits to determine as well as possible whether the traits cluster together. If they do, are similar clusters indicators of racial affiliation or common adaptation, or do the traits vary in their distributions in a crazy-quilt pattern with little or no indication of overall distributional regularities suggesting underlying common adaptations or close common descent? In short, what, if anything, does the present-day spatial distribution of man's formal variations imply about his past? This is the main question considered in the next chapter.

REFERENCES AND
SUGGESTIONS FOR ADDITIONAL READING

ALLISON, A. C.
   1954   Protection afforded by sickle-cell trait against subtertian malarial infection. *British Medical Journal* 1:290–294.
   1955   Aspects of polymorphism in man. *Cold Spring Harbor Symposia on Quantitative Biology* 20:239–255.
   1964   Polymorphism and natural selection in human populations. *Cold Spring Harbor Symposia on Quantitative Biology* 29:137–149.

ALLISON, A. C., AND B. S. BLUMBERG
   1959   Ability to taste phenylthiocarbamide among Alaskan Eskimos and
          other populations. *Human Biology* 31:352–359.
AZEVÊDO, E., H. KRIEGER, M. P. MI, AND N. E. MORTON
   1965   PTC taste sensitivity and endemic goiter in Brazil. *American Jour-
          nal of Human Genetics* 17:87–90.
BEARN, ALEXANDER G., AND W. CAREY PARKER
   1965   *Genetics and evolution in three human serum proteins.* Birth De-
          fects Original Articles Series, vol. 1. New York: National Founda-
          tion—March of Dimes.
BRUES, ALICE M.
   1963   Stochastic tests of selection in the ABO blood groups. *American
          Journal of Physical Anthropology* (n.s.) 21:287–299.
COON, CARLETON S., WITH EDWARD E. HUNT, JR.
   1965   *The living races of man.* New York: Alfred A. Knopf.
GARN, STANLEY M.
   1965   *Human races.* 2d ed. Springfield, Ill.: Charles C. Thomas.
GRUBB, R.
   1948   Correlation between Lewis blood group and secretor character in
          man. *Nature* 162:933.
JOHNSTON, FRANCIS E., KEITH P. HERTZOG, AND ROBERT M. MALINA
   1966   Phenylthiocarbamide taste sensitivity and its relationship to growth
          variation. *American Journal of Physical Anthropology* (n.s.) 24:
          253–255.
KELSO, A. J.
   1962   Dietary differences: a possible selective mechanism in ABO blood
          group frequencies. *Southwestern Lore* 28:48–56.
KELSO, A. J., AND GEORGE ARMELAGOS
   1963   Nutritional factors as selective agencies in the determination of
          ABO blood group frequencies. *Southwestern Lore* 29:44–48.
LANDSTEINER, K.
   1900   Zur Kenntnis der Antifermentativen, Lytischen, und Agglutinie-
          renden werkungen des Blutserums und der Lymphe. *Zentralblatt
          für Bakteriologie, Parasitenkunde, Infektionskrankheiten, und
          Hygiene* 27:357.
LANDSTEINER, K., AND P. LEVINE
   1927   A new agglutinable factor differentiating individual human bloods.
          Proceedings of the Society for Experimental Biology 24:600.
LANDSTEINER, K., AND A. S. WIENER
   1940   An agglutinable factor in human blood recognized by immune sera
          for rhesus blood. *Proceedings of the Society for Experimental Bi-
          ology* 43:223.
LEVINE, P., AND R. E. STETSON
   1939   An unusual case of intragroup agglutination. *Journal of the Ameri-
          can Medical Association* 113:126–127.
LIVINGSTONE, FRANK B.
   1958   Anthropological implications of sickle cell gene distribution in West
          Africa. *American Anthropologist* 60:533–562.

1960   Natural selection, disease, and ongoing human evolution, as illustrated by the ABO blood groups. *Human Biology* 32:17–27.

MANN, J. D., A. CAHAN, A. G. GELB, N. FISHER, J. HAMPER, P. TIPPETT, R. SANGER, AND R. R. RACE

1962   A sex-linked blood group. *Lancet* 1:8.

MOURANT, ARTHUR E.

1954   *The distribution of the human blood groups.* Springfield, Ill.: Charles C. Thomas.

MOURANT, A. E., C. KOPEĆ, AND K. DOMANIEWSKA-SOBCZAK

1958   *The ABO blood groups.* Springfield, Ill.: Charles C. Thomas.

OTTEN, CHARLOTTE M.

1967   On pestilence, diet, natural selection, and the distribution of microbial and human blood group antigens and antibodies. *Current Anthropology* 8:209–226.

PAULING, LINUS, HARVEY A. ITANO, S. J. SINGER, AND IBERT C. WELLS

1949   Sickle cell anemia, a molecular disease. *Science* 110:543–548.

RACE, R. R.

1948   The Rh genotypes and Fisher's theory. *Blood* 3, suppl. 2:27–42.

RACE, R. R., AND R. SANGER

1962   *Blood groups in man.* 4th ed. Oxford: Blackwell.

SUTTON, H. E., G. A. MATSON, A. R. ROBINSON, AND R. W. KOUCKY

1960   Distribution of haptoglobin, transferrin, and hemoglobin types among Indians of southern Mexico and Guatemala. *American Journal of Human Genetics* 12:338–347.

WIENER, A. S., EVE B. GORDON, AND LILLIAN HANDMAN

1949   Heredity of the Rh blood types. *American Journal of Human Genetics* 1:127–140.

WIENER, ALEXANDER S., AND J. MOOR-JANKOWSKI

1963   Blood groups in anthropoid apes and baboons. *Science* 142:67–69.

CHAPTER 9

IMPLICATIONS OF HUMAN
HETEROGRAPHY

INTRODUCTION

If physical anthropology were concerned solely with describing man's variation, its future could be expected to be simply the expansion and refinement of the information presented in the last two chapters. The future would be secure, for as new traits were discovered or as more was learned about old ones, specialists would continue to have the task of determining the range and location of their variation. But, of course, physical anthropology is interested in much more, specifically, in what the variation implies. The question of interest at this point, then, is: How is it possible to learn from the facts of variation? The answer necessarily depends on what one is interested in learning more about (for example, evolutionary history or taxonomy). Progress along either line will, however, first require that the facts of variation be organized in some useful way; that is, a classification is called for, since (no matter how often one hears the contrary) facts simply do not speak for themselves.

The first step, then, in learning more about human variability is to classify it. In this chapter three different kinds of classifications of human heterographic variation are discussed: 1) typological, 2) populational, and 3) clinal. Many other kinds are logically possible, but these three are in common use today. Indeed, much of the confusion that exists today could be obviated if those involved could be made to realize that any type of classification may improve our understanding, and that no one classification is *the* correct one. The particular way of grouping human variation that one may select should be governed exclusively by the kind of understanding one hopes to obtain from the distribution of variation.

Any classification, then, should serve a purpose, and at the present time there are three fundamental biological reasons for constructing a classification of man's heterographic variation: 1) to identify clusters of attributes; 2) to reflect common phylogenetic histories, or, in other words, close biological relationship; and 3) to delineate integrated evolutionary units. When a taxonomist classifies a group of organisms into a species and species into higher categories, these purposes are satisfied simultaneously. However, when a classification is devised for specific subgroupings, there is no reason to conclude that a scheme satisfying the requirements of one necessarily satisfies the requirements of the others. Failure to realize this has been a basic source of confusion and controversy.

In addition to the biological purposes, economic competition among distinguishable groups of human beings provides sociological reasons for classifying man's heterographic variation. The biological basis of such classifications is often incidental and accidental, or, on occasion, entirely lacking, as in the classification that divides people into groups on the basis of political boundaries or linguistic distinctions. When the biological component appears more readily identifiable, as, for example, in the distinction between white and colored in the United States, it turns out, on closer inspection, to be arbitrary, accidental, and incidental to the more obvious sociological purpose. Many illustrations of the arbitrary character of such a classification could be used. A simple one is the observation that several years ago, in many parts of the country, persons regularly identified and treated as Negroes found that if they wore a fez, they would often be identified as Near Eastern and thereby be able to participate more fully in activities that ordinarily would not be available to them.

To say that the biological component is arbitrary and incidental to the purpose of a sociological classification is not, however, to claim that the units identified are arbitrary and incidental. They are social realities that have provided a basis for suspicion, hatred, segregation, suffering, degradation, violence, and even death. Nor does it mean that such a classification has no significant biological implications; indeed it has. The subject is generally thought to be the academic property of sociology and will not be explored here in any detail. Instead, the types of classifications commonly used in physical anthropology will be discussed here, with illustrations using the traits discussed in Chapters 7 and 8 whenever possible.

TYPOLOGICAL CLASSIFICATIONS

A typological classification divides human beings into geographical groups on the basis of the regular occurrence together of distinctive heterographic traits. This definition makes it appear a relatively simple and straightforward problem to obtain a complete typological classification. Apparently all that is involved is investigating man's formal variation, deciding on where traits tend to occur together, and drawing a boundary line around the area. Yet there are a number of implications not made explicit in the definition in the interest of keeping it general and clear. First, since the classes include human beings in particular geographical areas, it is clear that both spatial and formal factors are involved in the classification. Space is, however, a function of the range over which the morphological traits occur together, and therefore the limits of the geographical area depend on the kind and, to some extent, the number of traits considered to be distinctive. Secondly, even though it is not stated, there is an implicit element of time generally involved in typological classifications, amounting to something very much like what the ethnologists call the ethnographic present. In cultural anthropology, an analogous typological classification divides the totality of cultural variation into culture areas (see Figure 9–1). Culture areas provide a means of summarizing and identifying the fundamentally similar cultural features of, say, the Plains Indians and of distinguishing these from those features distinctive of another area, such as the Arctic Eskimo. By using the notion of the ethnographic present, cultural anthropologists make it clear that culture areas are temporary and, furthermore, come together at different times and hold together for different durations. To use the Plains Indians of North America as an example, they developed their distinctive features, flourished, and died out all within the nineteenth century. The Arctic Eskimo, on the other hand, has been adapted to his environmental requirements in ways that extend back over one thousand years or more and which may still be seen today. So the ethnographic present refers to a relative point in time. It usually corresponds closely to the time when the particular area begins to be regularly affected by the spread of Western civilization.

Typological classifications imply a heterographic present, that is, the period prior to the massive migrations of people into, or even out of, the particular area under consideration. For most parts of the world, the ethnographic and heterographic presents will correspond closely, since both are usually due to the same technological and economic factors. They differ only in that the ethnographic present refers to assemblages of cultural traits, and the heterographic present to assemblages of morphological traits. Whatever the time period selected, it should be kept clearly in mind that it is representative itself of but one instant in man's phylogeny that was preceded by a long, complex, but essentially unknown history that must have involved extensive migrations, countless adaptations and re-adaptations, and continual fluctuations in population size, density, and structure, all occurring within a perpetually changing environment. The decision to deal with a heterographic present is one of convenience;

Figure 9–1. Culture area map of North and Central American indigenous peoples. (After A. L. Kroeber.)

SUBAREAS
1A *High Culture*
1B *Subnuclear*
2A *Hohokam Sphere*
2B *Anasazi Sphere*
3A *California*
3B *Intermountain*
5A *Eastern*
5B *Northern*
5C *Plains*

it makes easier the task of describing contemporary human variation and constructing a typological classification.

This leads to another part of the definition that is not entirely clear: *distinctive heterographic traits.* Distinctive is perhaps clear enough; it restricts attention to variable traits that occur together and thus may serve as a basis for distinguishing one area from another. For example, hearts, lungs, stomachs, and intestines are traits that occur together, but they always do so and thus fail to distinguish one group from another. If these attributes varied from one area to another, they could be regarded as distinctive, and in fact they may indeed show some consistent variation, but, at present, this is difficult and impractical to demonstrate. There remain, however, an infinite number of characteristics that distinguish groups from one another. In principle, these include both traits of known and unknown inheritance, although the use of traits of known inheritance is more recent. In fact, typological classifications most commonly use a rather small number of visually perceptible, readily observable, somatic characteristics, such as skin color, stature, hair form, nose form, limb proportions, etc. However, there is no valid reason for not using blood groups, serum proteins, taster, secretor, etc., in typological classifications. Indeed there is no logical reason for excluding tactile, olfactory, auditory, or even gustatorial distinctions, but they are not made and probably will not be, since we are primates, and, as everyone knows, primates rely very heavily on vision.

A practical question to raise at this point is: Into how many groups does a typological classification divide mankind? The answer is perhaps by now obvious—it all depends. Ideally, perhaps, the number of groups should depend solely on the distribution of heterographic variation. If attribute clusters were tightly restricted and clearly distinctive within a well-defined area, there would be little or no problem. In practice, however, human variation is distributed in such a way that the range of variation within a typological unit is greater than the variation distinguishing one unit from another. Thus the number of groups is not a simple function of the distribution of traits; it depends as well on: 1) the number and, to some extent, the kinds of traits employed in the classification, and 2) the degree of refinement used in evaluating "distinctiveness." The first of these can be readily illustrated. Consider, for example, a typological classification based solely on one trait, dark skin color. A typological classification using this trait alone would require placing together in the same group peoples from Africa, Asia, Indonesia, and parts of Oceania. Add to dark skin color another attribute, say a broad nose, and the group would include fewer people within each area. If kinky hair is then considered, the group of dark-skinned, broad-nosed, kinky-haired people will include some Africans and the Negritos of New Guinea and the Philippines. Short

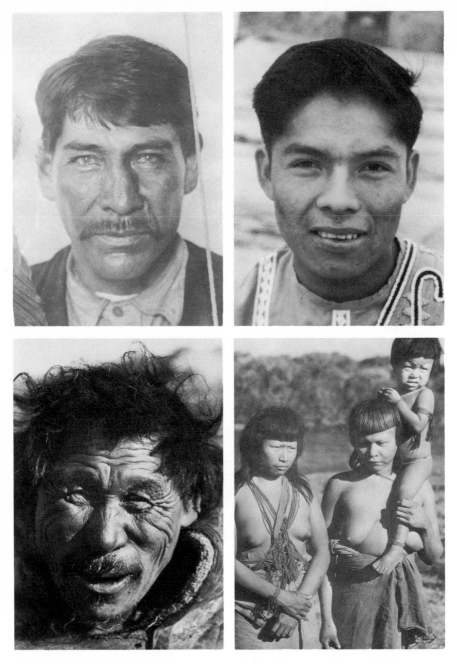

Figure 9–2. American Indians. Top: Left, Iroquois. (Courtesy The University Museum of the University of Pennsylvania.) Top: Right, Choctaw. (Courtesy Carleton S. Coon.) Bottom: Left, Eskimo. (Courtesy National Film Board of Canada, photo by G. Gely.) Bottom: Right, Bororo Indians of South America. (Courtesy The University Museum of the University of Pennsylvania.)

stature as a characteristic will provide a basis for distinguishing the Negritos from other dark-skinned, broad-nosed, kinky-haired people. Thus, by using a minimum of four traits, it is possible to identify a cluster of traits concentrated in parts of Africa south of the Sahara. Certainly, many persons included within this region are not dark-skinned; some have narrow noses, others wavy hair, and in some areas there are whole populations of quite short people. Yet, recognizing these exceptions—even recognizing them to be common—does not invalidate a broad generalization intended only to summarize some of the major features of variation that tend to cluster together in this part of the world. A more adequate description would include more traits. The effect of adding more traits is to increase the general background of information on the inhabitants of the area as well as increase the number of individuals that are "exceptions" for one or more traits. In fact, if one were to describe any of the heterographic areas of the world in terms of from ten to fifteen distinctive features, it is likely that few, if any, persons within the area would possess all the traits.

The degree of refinement used in evaluating distinctiveness is likewise of crucial importance in determining the number of groups in a typological classification. A crude scale, for example, may distinguish only between, say, tropical and nontropical peoples, or, as is done more commonly, between the major continental groupings of mankind. A more refined scale might distinguish within the tropical group those living at high altitudes from all others, or, within the European continental division, between Mediterraneans and Scandinavians. Even more refined restrictions on distinctiveness can, of course, be imposed, and, clearly, as this is done, the number of groups increases. Stanley Garn (1965) has recognized this effect and attempted to formalize levels of distinctiveness into groups he calls geographical races, local races, and micro races. These are in the order of crude to refined in evaluating distinctiveness.

If the construction of a typological classification rests so heavily on these external factors that the number of groups identified is almost arbitrary, then one may reasonably inquire as to the value of a typological classification. This problem can be considered in the context of the purposes of a heterographic classification, which (as discussed earlier) are to: 1) group together clusters of attributes, 2) reflect biological relationship, and 3) identify integrated evolutionary units. Does a typological classification fulfill one or more of these functions? A typological classification fulfills one and only one of these functions: it groups together clusters of attributes. The clusterings may in some instances be due to a common phylogenetic history, and thus may reflect biological relationship, but whether or not they are is a problem to be solved, not a solution implicit in the classification. The problem may be stated simply: Is the fact that

two or more populations share a number of characteristics in common evidence of close biological relationship? The answer is—perhaps, but not necessarily. Similarities between two or more populations may be due to other factors. For example, two groups that are not closely related in their evolutionary histories may be similar because each has adapted to common environmental requirements. This phenomenon, known as *convergence*, would seem to be at least partly responsible for some of the similarities between the South African Bushmen and the aborigines of Australia. Furthermore, as has been noted earlier, human beings have a reserve of adaptive potential that permits them to adjust to environmental changes. This *physiological plasticity* may be responsible for the clustering together of characteristics. Thus it is, for example, that persons living at high altitudes share a variety of characteristics in common that do not imply close relationship. Finally, *chance factors* may act to produce similarities; such factors appear to have been responsible for producing some of the similarities between Polynesians and American Indians.

One might also consider the problem of whether or not groups delineated by a typological classification constitute evolutionary units. That is, do they correspond to integrated units of evolutionary change, to groups that are undergoing common selective pressures distinguishable from those affecting other parts of the world? The answer to these fundamental questions of evolutionary integrity is—not necessarily. For example, the area designated as Africa south of the Sahara and described as inhabited by dark-skinned, broad-nosed, kinky-haired, tall (as opposed to Pygmy) people contains many identifiable groups experiencing sharply contrasting ecologies, competing for different resources, and thus subjected to different evolutionary forces. One may feel that Africans south of the Sahara are distinct as an evolutionary unit from, say, the Asians north and east of India, since they contrast in the inventory of traits clustering in each. There is no question that these differences exist, but their existence alone does not imply some present-day evolutionary integrity. The clusterings may be due to the fact that each group has descended from separate and contrasting breeding units. Thus, the ancestral populations may have been integrated units that diverged and ramified into several descendant units, each one continuing to display features that attest to their common origin in the past, but modified by the processes that caused the diversification and by the subsequent evolutionary factors imposed on the populations adapting to new ecological requirements. In any event, it should be clear that a typological classification results in

Figure 9–3. (Opposite Page) Africans. Top: Left, Tunisian. (Courtesy J. H. McCullough.) Top: Right, Bedouin. (Courtesy William M. Shanklin.) Middle: Left, Hausa; Right, Batonga. Bottom: Left, Bushman; Right, Zulu. (Courtesy Carleton S. Coon.)

groups that are not logically equivalent to integrated evolutionary units. Whether any particular group is empirically equivalent is a problem to be solved through empirical investigation.

From this discussion, it may be seen that typological classifications are useful devices in summarizing the complex distributions of man's heterographic variation. They may be useful in suggesting hypotheses concerning possible relationships between attribute clusters and the environments in which they are located, and in offering convenient units for instructors to use in presenting the material on man's heterographic variation.

Traditional racial classifications are, of course, typological classifications, but an effort has been made deliberately to avoid these until this point, for racial classifications have usually implied much more about the units classified than typological ones. As we have noted, typological classifications attempt to reflect nothing more than the ways in which human variation is distributed at some point in time, whereas racial classifications tend also to imply phylogenetic relationships and evolutionary integrity. This is unwarranted, and failure to separate these various implications has been a basic source of misunderstanding and confusion in the dialogue on race in the professional journals. The situation is analogous to that of a cultural anthropologist drawing the conclusion from a culture area classification that, since the societies grouped together in an area are similar in many traits, they must therefore be derived from the same cultural antecedents. For example, all the societies within the Plains culture area would be presumed to have emerged from a common cultural source. Likewise, if culture areas were the logical equivalent of races, then, by implication, the groups within an area would be presumed to form an integrated unit of cultural evolution.

Typological classifications divide mankind into units, the composition of which is determined largely by the distribution of heterographic variation. The size of the units can, however, vary, depending on the number of characteristics and how refined the classifier chooses to be in regarding one unit as distinct from another. The essential value of such a classification is to provide information which can facilitate communication and an empirical background to the formulation and testing of specific hypotheses. Investigators with specific hypotheses may wish to classify segments of the variation in different ways that are necessary to the resolution of particular problems. Thus, typological classifications can result in groups and areas of varying sizes and compositions. It is not a question of which one is the most nearly correct, but rather which is most useful, and that is determined by the specific purposes the classifier has in mind.

But what of the other purposes for constructing classifications of human variation? Is it possible, for example, to divide mankind into units with evolutionary integrity? Such a system could be very useful in adding to our understanding of evolutionary processes affecting man at the present time, and indeed might imply biological relationship as well, thereby fulfilling the requirements for classifying human biological variation. Physical anthropologists have recognized the deficiencies of racial classification and have attempted to resolve them in a variety of ways. Some, as we have seen, have proposed a hierarchical arrangement of races (geographical races, microgeographical races, local races, etc.); some have discarded the term *race* entirely; some say that races do not exist (they really mean that the group brought together for descriptive purposes does not correspond to an evolutionary unit); and some continue to be confused. But the most common reaction among professionals has been to draw upon the theory of population genetics that contends that breeding populations qualify as minimal integrated units of evolutionary change.

POPULATIONAL CLASSIFICATIONS

Recall the discussion of population genetics presented in Chapter 3. From this it may be seen that a division of mankind into breeding populations apparently bypasses the problem of *discovering* evolutionary units as implications of a racial classification by *specifying* what these units are. A breeding population is the basic unit of evolutionary change—the unit that, regulated by the Hardy–Weinberg law, tends toward equilibrium in the composition of its genetic structure—the unit whose structure changes in response to the action of the mechanisms of evolution.

The population as a unit of classification has been increasing in popularity among physical anthropologists and human geneticists during the last twenty years. It has, in fact, served as a kind of basic distinction between the approaches of the younger generation and the "typological" approach characteristic of their teachers. Prior to this time, classification of human variation had been based solely on traits of unknown inheritance and was found repeatedly to lack the conclusive evidence required to reconstruct the myriad of events through which the "types" had passed. The first effect that genetics had on the problem of reconstructing racial histories was simply the addition of inherited traits, such as the blood groups, to the others with the expectation that the inherited traits might produce more definite bases for reconstructing racial histories. Since then two things have become clear: 1) traits of known inheritance are no more informative in solving the problem of racial history than others; 2) they are, however, of much greater value than other attributes in learning further about the processes of evolution, but traditional typological classifications are of no use in realizing this potential. If, as implied in the Hardy–Weinberg law, evolution is change in the genetic structure from one generation to the next, then the logical unit of evolutionary analysis is a reproductive unit, a group of individuals that mate and produce a subsequent generation, or, in other words, a breeding population. It will be recalled that for the equilibrium specified by the Hardy–Weinberg law to be attained, the following conditions within the population are necessary: 1) it must be large; 2) individuals must mate randomly with respect to the alleles involved; and 3) the locus should not be affected by the mechanisms of evolution. These formed a basic core of problems which population geneticists have continued to be concerned with right up to the present. That is, they have wanted to know what happens when populations are small, when the locus is controlling a feature that influences the choice of a mate. What are the consequences of inbreeding? How can selection or mutation alter the equilibrium? General answers to these questions must be made deductively by means of the techniques of mathematics, since human populations rarely, if ever, satisfy these conditions, and experimental populations are too artificial to extend results obtained on them to all populations.

The mathematics was simple and crude by comparison with more advanced sciences, but the results were compelling and dramatic. It would seem that the urge to try them out on real populations was perhaps overwhelming, and, as we have already seen, the result was a rapid accumulation of gene-frequency data. The effect of these advances on the subject of human variation was to focus attention on breeding populations as biologically and evolutionarily integrated units and to describe them in terms of their gene frequencies. Yet, as implied earlier in the chapter, substantial confusion resulted. Races, for example, were defined variously as synonymous with a breeding population (a race is a breeding population), or as groups of breeding populations (a race is a group of breeding populations with the same gene frequencies), or as nonexistent superstitions (there are no races, just breeding populations). Clearly, the population, and particularly the breeding population, had passed from the abstract unit existing under ideal conditions suitable only for mathematical or experimental manipulation to a real, finite, and discoverable thing. That substantial confusion existed on this issue is implicit in the fact that gene frequencies have been obtained on such strikingly heterogeneous "breeding populations" as Spaniards, Negroes, Americans, Russian mothers, Ethiopians, Sea Dyaks, and Blackfoot Indians. The effect on physical anthropology has been basic, extensive, and permanent. The entire focus of attention and the fundamental reason for studying human variation has shifted from an almost exclusive concern with racial history to an almost exclusive concern with human evolution. Correspondingly, the traditional traits used to characterize typological units, traits such as stature, skin color, and hair form, are becoming more and more confined to the elucidation of specific problems in which their use is immediately applicable. Blood groups and other inherited characteristics are, however, used more and more by physical anthropologists to characterize man's general heterographic variation.

Some authorities have attempted to integrate the typological and populational approaches, but up to now their efforts have been little more than verbal, and the effect has probably been to create more confusion. For example, races have been defined as breeding populations differing in their gene frequencies. On closer inspection, this definition raises some serious difficulties in practical situations. Does it mean, for example, that two populations with the same gene frequency for one locus are to be included in the same race? If so, then absurd results follow: the Ainu of Japan belong to the same "race" as the Berbers of northwestern Africa if only MN frequencies are considered. One group of Berbers sampled would, however, be in a race apart from another. Does the definition mean, on the other hand, that populations with many of their genetic loci occupied by alleles in the same frequencies are to be considered groups within the same race? But no two populations have an identical array of gene frequencies; so empirically there would be as many races as populations. Moreover, the units usually specified by the term *race* are not equivalent to the units specified by a populational classification. To fail to recognize that typological and populational classifications are fundamentally different is to add to an already confusing situation.

What are the distinctive characteristics of a populational classification of human variation? First the units of classification are necessarily *groups* of individuals. In a typological classification, it is possible in principle to classify individuals without knowing where they reside. That is, if one is familiar with the criteria on which a classification is based, he should be able to classify any individual into one and only one of the classes. To be sure, mistakes will occur, for, as we have already noted, exceptions within an area are common. In a population classification, however, it is not possible to assign an individual to a class by inspection of his features. Even though a complete knowledge of his inherited characteristics may be available, it would not be possible to do so. (He might have a trait, however, that is very rare and known to occur only in a very restricted area, and this could provide a basis for concluding that he belonged to a particular population. This foreknowledge would, however, be rare.)

An individual may be assigned to a populational class only by identification of the marriage or breeding group to which he belongs. This implies the second distinctive characteristic of a populational classification: the boundaries between one class and another are fixed by mating practices. It will be recalled that in a typological classification the boundaries between the classes are fixed essentially by the actual distribution of the traits. Classifiers using the same criteria can arrive at larger or smaller units depending on their bias, but nonetheless the limits of the classes remain a function of the distribution of traits. In a populational classification, traits serve simply as the basis of description; that is, differences and similarities between breeding populations may be noted by comparing the traits that occur within them. For example, a particular group of persons, all of whom select their mates from within the group, can be identified as a breeding population. Now such a class can be compared to another on structural grounds alone and without reference to physical differences between the membership; that is, they can be compared on the basis of such things as population size, age and sex distributions, whether or not internal subdivisions exist, etc. Likewise, the classes can be compared in terms of physical differences and similarities found among the persons identified (on other grounds) as belonging to one or the other breeding population. Ideally, in a typological classification, the procedure is reversed; after inspecting the distribution of traits, the classifier identifies clusters, and these serve to distinguish between classes. Finally, descriptions of breeding populations are presented almost exclusively in terms of gene frequencies. There is no reason for excluding the traditional measurements and observations of physical anthropology as bases for describing breeding populations, but they are rarely included.

In summary, then, a populational classification is distinctive in the following ways: 1) the units classified are of necessity *groups* of individuals; 2) one group is distinguished from another on the basis of breeding isolation; and 3) the classes are usually described in terms of the frequencies of genes. By contrast, in a typological classification: 1) individuals are the basic units of classification; 2) one class is distinguished from another largely on the basis of differences in the distribution of heterographic variation; and 3) the classes are usually described in terms of traits of unknown inheritance. So much for the formal differences between these two kinds of classifications. Two practical questions remain for consideration in this discussion of populational classifications: How many breeding populations are there? And to what extent do populational units satisfy the reasons for constructing a classification of man's heterographic variation?

How many breeding populations are there within the human species today? If mankind were neatly divided into isolated breeding populations, the answer to this question would be readily ascertainable. As it is, however, the actual fabric of human mating behavior today is made up of such a complicated and continually changing weave that not only is a simple count impossible, but even an estimate is a deception. It is at this point that attention is readily drawn to some of the basic problems associated with applying a populational approach to heterographic variation in man. For example, is Denver, Colorado, properly identified as a breeding population? An inspection of the situation in Denver or in any urban center would reveal that the parents have been drawn from all over the world, and that, as they mature, their offspring marry persons from all over the world. Thus, in one sense, Denver is but one part of an "isolate" that is worldwide. But, one may argue, there is a clear tendency for Denverites to marry other Denverites, and this tendency diminishes as distance from Denver increases. In arguing this way, one might conclude that for practical purposes it can be considered as a breeding population. Indeed Sewall Wright (1943) over twenty years ago presented a model (the isolation by distance model) for "isolating" such populations by statistical means. But the very same inspection of the actual marriage practices would reveal that Denver can be internally subdivided into many reproductive units. Whites tend to marry whites, Negroes to marry Negroes, and even within these social divisions smaller groups with imagined or real common economic and ethnic backgrounds tend to choose marriage partners from within the group. Thus, in another sense, Denver is the location of several breeding populations. Additionally, as if the problem of trying to deal with these difficulties by the standard means were not enough, the situation is made more complex when primitive societies are considered. Are the Bushmen of South Africa an isolate? Are they part of a larger reproductive unit? Are they divisible into several such units? As in the case of Denver, the answer to each of these questions is probably yes, although the composition and structure of each population are very different. Again, one can find a comparable problem in cultural anthropology, and that is the question of deciding on the limits of a society. Does Denver constitute a social system? Is it part of a larger whole that is integrated socially? Are there several systems within the geographical limits of the city? As above, the answer to each of these questions is yes.

Considering the specific question of how many breeding populations there are raises some doubts about the validity of applying the populational classification to the human species, but before any general conclusion is reached, some attention should be given to the question of the value of a populational classification: 1) in identifying clusters of heterographic attributes, and 2) in delineating evolutionarily integrated units.

If the objective of a heterographic classification is simply to discover types, that is, to locate clusters of distinctive traits, then a populational classification is wholly inappropriate and inefficient as a typological classification. As noted previously, the process by which an investigator identifies a breeding population is the antithesis of the process involved in arriving at a typological class (usually called a race). The attributes in a populational classification are the means by which breeding populations are described and compared. Thus it is that, except for unusual situations, all breeding populations have the same characteristics—the same blood groups, the same serum proteins, etc. They differ from one another in the frequencies of the alleles controlling these traits. In a typological classification, the traits and their distributions are the primary factors used to identify a class.

It is indeed possible that frequencies of two or more alleles vary in systematic ways from one population to the next. Thus it may be shown that frequencies cluster together as in the case of the S and M alleles in

Australia, Micronesia, and New Guinea. These associations would seem more likely to be forthcoming from a third way of ordering heterographic data, by the clinal approach, which is becoming more popular in physical anthropology, and which is discussed in the next section.

As far as "delineating evolutionary units" is concerned, the breeding population as a unit of study meets every logical requirement. It is, by definition, a reproductive or generational unit, and, again by definition, any change in the genetic structure of the unit is an evolutionary change. The problem associated with the use of the breeding population as a basis for improving our understanding of the significance of heterographic variation in man is not, however, a logical one; it is a practical one. Today human beings live in groups that rarely, if ever, even remotely approximate the requirements of any breeding-population model. In most cases this discrepancy between the real situation and the theoretical model has simply been ignored, and investigators have presumed the limits of a breeding population rather than determined them. From these "isolates," painstakingly chosen random samples of persons have been tested and the results reported in gene frequencies. One may well ask what such frequencies imply. Suppose, for example, that random samples of equal size are selected from two communities, and each is tested for several traits of known inheritance. On the basis of these determinations, gene frequencies are calculated and the results tabulated. It is not obvious what these frequencies imply. Many factors can affect any gene-frequency estimate; among the most important are the following: 1) *Sampling error.* One sample may include more relatives, thereby increasing the likelihood that the same alleles will be counted more than once. 2) *Population structure.* One population may be subdivided into several more or less isolated reproductive units, whereas another may not. The error inherent in any estimate may be greatly different in these two situations. 3) *Mating practices.* In Chapter 3, the effects of various forms of nonrandom mating on the genetic structure of a population were demonstrated. Since nonrandom mating affects the distribution of genotypes, and since gene frequencies are calculated from genotype frequencies, it should be clear that different mating practices can affect gene-frequency estimates. This would be particularly the case in gene-frequency estimates for traits in which a heterozygote is indistinguishable from a homozygote. 4) *Evolutionary mechanisms.* Two or more populations may be the same or different in their array of gene frequencies because of the action of one or more of the mechanisms of evolution. How these exert their influence was also dealt with in Chapter 3.

Since any one or all of these things can influence any gene-frequency estimate, then any array of frequencies is not a reliable indication of the degree of relationship between the two populations. As stated above, with all these contingencies it is not at all clear what these frequencies imply.

In summary, a populational classification is inefficient as a means of identifying attribute clusters, impractical to apply to processual problems in human heterography, and inappropriate as a basis for assessing degrees of relationship between and among subspecific groupings in man. This view is by no means a generally accepted one among physical anthropologists today, and that, more than any other, is the reason for dealing so laboriously with the issue here. Physical anthropologists continue to take random samples and report gene frequencies as though the units were equivalent and the meaning of the figures were obvious. While this effort has resulted in very little progress in solving the usual problems approached by investigations of human variation, it has yielded a considerable quantity of gross and unrefined descriptive information on the distribution of genes throughout the world. These data, together with those already available on phenotypic traits of unknown inheritance, form the basis for the clinal approach, another method of dealing with human variation, and one which orders the variations in still another way.

CLINAL CLASSIFICATIONS

Breeding populations and the races of a typological classification are in reality transitory, continually changing units that provide vague and fleeting glimpses of history and evolutionary processes. In any particular classification, however, they must be dealt with as finite, and, with the limitations discussed above, are able thereby to add to our general knowledge of how traits and the genes that control them vary in form and frequency. A different kind of classification is possible if attention is focused on the distribution of individual traits and gene frequencies. A particular trait, whether its inheritance is known or unknown, may be thought of as infinite in its possible expressions, but if, as we know already, the real variation is limited at any one point in time, then the distribution of identical forms can be grouped together into zones and separated from other areas by boundaries that are determined by the ranges over which a particular trait may be found to have a common expression. The delimited zones are called *clines* (see Figure 9–4).

The theoretical background necessary for dealing with clines and relating them to evolutionary theory is still in a crude state. If the initial assumptions prove to be correct, such classifications hold out new possibilities for understanding the evolutionary fine structure of traits and their variations. The assumptions are simple and stem from evolutionary theory and the more special axioms of population genetics. In simplified form, a clinal analysis assumes that: 1) traits vary; 2) systematic variations in the traits are due to systematic forces; 3) the systematic forces may be due

Figure 9–4. Clinal map showing altitude variation.

either to an evolutionary mechanism, such as selection or migration, or to other factors, such as physiological plasticity; 4) the two kinds of systematic forces are, in principle, separable; and 5) trait distributions offer an alternative way of relating the facts of heterographic variation to the theory of evolution.

The clinal approach has a familiar ring to anthropologists. For many years, cultural anthropologists sought to obtain detailed lists of trait distributions for the purpose of studying diffusion and ultimately for reconstructing the histories of particular peoples. It is today generally recognized that trait distributions only accidentally provide useful information for historical reconstruction. There does seem to be considerable potential insight to be gained by attempting to learn about evolutionary process in the biological sphere, and there are indications that cultural anthropologists are studying processes of adaptation and evolution just as the biologist wishes to do.

The theoretical foundation for the interpretation and analysis of clines is only now beginning to be formulated. To appreciate the value of such an approach requires the development of analytical models very different from those presently available for the study of finite populations. The work needs to be done.

SUMMARY

A comparison of typological, populational, and clinal classifications may clarify their differences. Table 9–1 presents a summary of the essential

TABLE 9–1

COMPARISON OF THREE WAYS OF GROUPING
HETEROGRAPHIC VARIATION

Type of Classification	Criteria	Resulting Units
Typological	Trait clusters	Races and other "types"
Populational	Mating systems	Breeding populations
Clinal	Individual trait distributions	Clines

features of each. The trait clusters of typological units can and do cross-cut the reproductive boundaries of mating systems. Likewise clines may vary independently of races and breeding populations.

THE CONCEPT OF RACE

Geographical areas can be characterized by the presence within them of clusters of traits, and the people included therein may be said to be members of the same race. However, if a race is delineated in this way, one should keep in mind that similarities within such races may be due to: 1) close common ancestry, 2) similar adaptive responses to common evolutionary forces, or, in some cases, 3) the direct influence of the environment on the inhabitants. In almost every case, it is impossible with present information to know the sources of the observed similarities, and it may never be possible to do so. The mechanisms of evolution and of physiological plasticity operating over time with changing ecological conditions act to cover up the phylogenetic tracks that might otherwise indicate the relationships between and among the groups included within such races. Evolutionary integrity, and thus biological meaning, is not a characteristic of such races. Furthermore, the traits that cluster together have, when taken individually, much broader distributional ranges continuing well outside the area. Dark skin color may well cluster together with broad noses and kinky hair in Africa south of the Sahara, but it continues as a trait within a broad belt along both sides of the equator. Its distribution crosscuts and varies independently of many other racial characters, suggesting that to the extent that these traits are due to evolutionary mechanisms, they are the consequences of separate factors operating at varying intensities over variable durations. Thus, such classifications not only fail to imply phylogenetic relationships among the groups that make them up, but may serve to *obscure* the adaptive (or nonadaptive) significance of the traits on which they are based as well.

Why, then, is it that these descriptive geographic "races" are considered at all? Because, even with the above limitations, they continue to be useful. They identify trait clusters within continuous geographic areas among groups of people who have been isolated in varying degrees for unknown periods of time. They are useful for two main purposes: in providing a broad range of background information on the distributions of human variation, and also as a basis for determining the effects that might be due to long-term geographical isolation. As may be seen from the preceding discussion, these "races" are not self-evident, natural units; they are merely useful and convenient ways of dividing up human variation. Any "natural" or "real" qualities they might have remain to be demonstrated.

The entire subject is confusing, but the confusion is itself a healthy sign that scientific usage of the word *race* and the concept to which it refers is changing from the old, standard, "typical" view into new ways of regarding human variation that appear to have greater scientific potential. The term *race* is ambiguous; the units to which it has been applied are not at all equivalent, and they have been established to achieve different objectives. In attempting to increase our understanding of human variation, the result has been confusing and unproductive.

The purpose of this discussion is unusual in that it is not primarily intended to inform the reader, nor to provide him with new information on the subject of race. There is, rather, an opposite objective that is being sought: to take away the comfortable feeling that most people in our society have when they use the term *race*. They know what they mean, and, further, there is something "out there" that corresponds to what they mean. If you started to read this chapter with a knowledge of what race is, and you are no longer sure of that knowledge, then the discussion has served a useful purpose. Consider, if you will, how your answers to the following questions might now be different: How many races are there? When did each begin? Is it harmful for two persons of different races to marry? Are the Jews a race? In all likelihood, if you try these questions out on others, you will find that the only persons with ready answers are those who have not thought very much about the subject.

REFERENCES AND
SUGGESTIONS FOR ADDITIONAL READING

BRACE, C. LORING
　　1964　A nonracial approach towards the understanding of human diversity. In *The concept of race,* ed. Ashley Montagu. New York: Free Press.

COON, CARLETON S.
  1962   *The origin of races.* New York: Alfred A. Knopf.
COON, CARLETON S., WITH EDWARD E. HUNT, JR.
  1965   *The living races of man.* New York: Alfred A. Knopf.
COON, CARLETON S., STANLEY M. GARN, AND JOSEPH B. BIRDSELL
  1950   *Races: a study of the problems of race formation in man.* Springfield, Ill.: Charles C. Thomas.
DOBZHANSKY, THEODOSIUS
  1962   *Mankind evolving.* New Haven: Yale University Press.
GARN, STANLEY M.
  1965   *Human races.* 2d ed. Springfield, Ill.: Charles C. Thomas.
HULSE, FREDERICK S.
  1955   Technological advance and major racial stocks. *Human Biology* 27:184–192.
  1962   Race as an evolutionary episode. *American Anthropologist* 64:929–945.
KELSO, A. J.
  1967   The concept of race. *Improving College and University Teaching* 15:95–97.
KROEBER, A. L.
  1948   *Anthropology: race, language, culture, psychology, prehistory.* Rev. ed. New York: Harcourt, Brace & World.
LIVINGSTONE, FRANK B.
  1964   Human populations. In *Horizons of anthropology,* ed. Sol Tax. Chicago: Aldine.
MONTAGU, ASHLEY, ED.
  1964   *The concept of race.* New York: Free Press.
MORTON, N. E., AND N. YASUDA
  1962   The genetical structure of human populations. In *Les déplacements humains,* ed. J. Sutter. Paris: Hachette.
WASHBURN, SHERWOOD L.
  1944   Thinking about race. *Science Education* 28:65–76.
  1963   The study of race. *American Anthropologist* 65:521–531.
WRIGHT, S.
  1943   Isolation by distance. *Genetics* 28:114–138.

CHAPTER 10

NATURAL SELECTION IN MODERN HUMAN POPULATIONS

The Problem

Is man continuing to undergo evolutionary changes today? If in 1940 one had gathered together into one room all the specialists in human biology and asked them this question, about half would have answered yes, and about half would either have answered no or maintained that the answer is not known. If one had asked why it was that they disagreed, he would have found that those scientists who had answered in the affirmative would have emphasized that man is an animal and subject to the same laws as all other life forms, that paleontology has produced solid evidence for the existence of trends that continue right on up to the present, and that one can readily demonstrate the presence of adaptive characteristics among contemporary populations. Those persons answering otherwise would have argued that, while it is certainly true that man is an animal, he has culture which functions as a protective screen providing him with an extrasomatic means of adapting to his environment and thereby the means of escaping the ruthless screening process of evolution that continually confronts all other animals and plants. They would have pointed to the many apparent nonadaptive traits that may be found in man, and would have concluded their stand with the disclaimer that trends and adaptive traits do not conclusively prove the existence of evolution in human populations today. If one were to bring together specialists in human biology today, those answering the question with a confident *yes* would be an overwhelming majority.

To understand what caused the change, it will be helpful to consider each of the arguments presented above and determine what, if anything, has happened to alter its forcefulness today. Before turning to these arguments, two points should be discussed. First, even though the question is often asked in reference to the operation of evolution, it is almost always understood to refer specifically to natural selection. One can readily point to the occurrence of mutations and migration in today's populations and readily admit that genetic drift, even though its role may be considerably less significant today, must have been an important force in the recent past. So the question under consideration is really: Is natural selection operative in human populations today? The arguments offered above by both sides refer specifically to natural selection.

Second, one must consider a preliminary problem that has to be resolved before any progress can be made on the main question. Consider the question of what kind of evidence constitutes proof that evolution is operating in human populations today. It is here that the reader should recall the material from Chapter 3 on population genetics. Evolution alters the genetic structure of populations, and thus any such change is an evolutionary change. If one can demonstrate that the genetic composition of a population changes from one generation to the next, he has perforce provided reasonably conclusive proof for the operation of evolution. Becoming more precise and providing a convincing case that such a change is due specifically to natural selection is more difficult. Evolutionary changes due to the action of natural selection must be systematic, that is, not due to chance, and must be reflected through differential reproduction. Some people, or, more precisely, some combinations of genotypes, must contribute disproportionately to the number of viable offspring in the next generation.

SOURCES OF EVIDENCE

These are the basic criteria that may be used to evaluate the evidence bearing on both the general question of the continuation of evolution and the more specific one of the operation of natural selection in the human species today. Consider now the ways in which the question has been argued on both sides.

Logic

If the only basis for a decision were logic, then the issue would be irreconcilable, since conclusions supporting both points of view can be arrived at by valid arguments. In support of the stand that man is presently undergoing evolutionary change, one might begin with the proposition that evolutionary processes are detectable throughout the universe, and conclude from this that they must therefore be affecting the human species. If matter is divided into three levels of organization—inorganic, organic, and extrasomatic—evolution may be seen in operation at each level. On the inorganic level, it is becoming more and more comprehensible to speak of the evolution of matter and of the universe. At the organic level it is, of course, commonplace to accept evolution, and at the extrasomatic, or cultural, level of organization, an evolutionary perspective is essential to the understanding of the different forms of cultural variation. Or, heading toward the same conclusion, it could be pointed out that man is a highly variable, highly mobile species occupying an enormous range of adaptive zones. All of these are features that one would expect to find as ideal grist for the mill of natural selection.

There is nothing particularly wrong with these arguments. They reason, in effect, that since evolution is all around man, and since man has all the characteristics for the effective operation of natural selection, therefore he is indeed undergoing evolutionary change by means of natural selection. One could argue just as reasonably that in man's case it is culture that makes the critical difference—that as culture has evolved, the effectiveness of natural selection has been reduced to nothing. Evidence in support of this position may be obtained from two sources: 1) the many diseases and defective conditions that survive in modern society imply that as man and culture evolve, the effect of selection is reduced; and 2) the same observation used to support the opposite conclusion, that of man's wide range of variation, may be offered as evidence for the ineffectiveness of natural selection. In recent years, this view has lost some of its forcefulness as it has become more evident that, while culture may indeed alter the effectiveness of natural selection, it may as well generate new adaptive requirements of its own. The following quotation from White (1959) is submitted as an illustration of how all-pervasive culture is in man's life:

> The purpose of culture is to serve the needs of man. These needs may be divided into two categories: (1) those that can be served only by exploiting the resources of the external world; and (2) those that can be served by drawing upon the resources of the human organism only. Man needs food and materials of many kinds for clothing, utensils, ornaments, etc.; these must be obtained, of course, from the external world. But man has inner, psychic, social, and 'spiritual' needs that can be fed and nourished without drawing upon the external world at all. Man needs courage, comfort, con-

solation, confidence, companionship, a feeling of consequence in the scheme of things that life is worthwhile, and some assurance of success. It is the business of culture to serve these needs of the 'spirit' as well as the needs of the body.

Life is continued only by effort. Pain, suffering, lonesomeness, fear, frustration, and boredom dog man's steps at almost every turn. He requires companionship, courage, inspiration, hope, comfort, reassurance, and consolation to enable him to continue the struggle of life. Cultural devices serve man here. Mythologies flatter, encourage, and reassure him. By means of magic and ritual he can capture the illusion of power and control over things and events: he can 'control' the weather, cure disease, foresee the future, increase his food supply, overcome his enemies. Various devices relate him to the spirit world so that he may enjoy the blessings and avoid the wrath of the gods. Cosmologies give him answers to all fundamental questions, of life and death and the nature of all things. Thus culture gives man a sense of power and of confidence. It assures him that life is worth living and gives him the courage to endure it. It comforts and sustains him when he meets defeat or frustration. It provides him with companions, divine as well as human. It attacks boredom and manages at times to make life pleasurably exciting and of fine flavor. In short, culture gives man the illusion of importance, omnipotence, and omniscience. These inner spiritual —or *intraorganismal*—needs of man are of course as real as those for food, shelter, and defense; in fact, they might be felt even more keenly. And these needs must be served if man is to succeed in the struggle of life.*

As culture evolves, the means of satisfying these needs change. Culture elements combine in ways that generate new adaptive challenges to mankind. Again the argument sounds reasonable, and sufficiently so to forestall acceptance of the conclusion that man is not at present undergoing evolutionary change. But at this point, something more than a logical argument is required. The problem requires more information; specifically, it requires data to answer the significant and fundamental question: Do these culturally induced situations create a systematic selective pressure on the genetic structures of one or more subdivisions of the human species? What other sources of evidence are available that might have a bearing on this issue?

Trends

One category of evidence frequently used in support of the stand that man is continuing to undergo evolutionary change is the existence of trends extending back over a long part of the paleontological record as well as others with much more recent origins. The basis of their applicability in

*From *The Evolution of Culture*, by Leslie A. White. Copyright, 1959, by the McGraw-Hill Book Company. Reprinted by permission of McGraw-Hill Book Company.

the present problem is simple and perhaps obvious; changes, presumed to be evolutionary changes, begun in the past and continuing up to the present must still be going on and probably will continue into the future. Most commonly cited as illustrations of evolutionary trends are: 1) *Brachycephalization of modern man.* Once anatomically-modern man is clearly established as the only hominid form on earth, there begins a trend from narrow-headed to broad-headed that may be found, wherever the paleontological evidence is abundant, throughout both the New and the Old World. 2) *Reduction in the size of third molars (wisdom teeth).* One of the contrasts between modern man and the fossil hominids that preceded him is that modern man has smaller teeth. Thus it would appear that reduction in tooth size is a general trend in man's phylogeny. More particularly, however, there are some indications that since man obtained his modern anatomical form, the last two molars, and, of these, particularly the last, or third, molar, have been greatly reduced in size. Indeed, many human beings today completely lack third molars. This lack of a third molar is itself occasionally claimed as a trend. As time passes, the proportion of persons without third molars increases, but the paleontological evidence to support this contention is meager and ambiguous. 3) *Increasing stature.* The belief that mankind has been getting taller over the last several thousand years is very widespread indeed, but, as it turns out on closer examination, probably not true. E. A. Hooton (1947) has discussed the bases for this belief as follows:

> There are two tales respecting alleged increases in stature during historical times that are always being dinned into the ears of anthropologists. One is that of the tourist who attempts to seat himself in one of the seats in the Colosseum where the sporting populace of the ancient Romans used to be entertained by watching lions lunching upon obstinate Christians. This tourist invariably reports that the seats are scarcely large enough to accommodate a single modern buttock. My reply to this is: firstly, that Italians are still small people, used to living in cramped quarters; secondly, that one has only to arrive late at a football game to discover that modern builders of concrete stadia are none too liberal in allotting space where pinched posteriors mean extra dollars. The seat of the latecomer has to be discovered by a process of long division, and he then has to be driven into it like a wedge.
>
> The other tale, involving a supposition that our forebears were smaller men, is also purveyed by tourists who gape at empty suits of armor and simply cannot understand how a normal-sized man could be fitted into one. To these, I would point out that a metal suit standing alone in the middle of the floor is necessarily somewhat telescoped and does not attain the altitude of the person it was supposed to fit. Again I would suggest that these extant suits may have survived because they were outgrown by their owners, like the dress suits of our youth. Odd sizes are generally numerous

in bargain basements. And, finally, our own ancestors may have been big even in those days, but perhaps they were churls and thralls and varlets and knaves who could not afford or did not rate suits of mail.*

To be sure, the average stature of adults has increased dramatically in European and American populations over the past fifty years. There are conflicting opinions among experts concerning the causes of this trend, and, at present, there is no way to resolve the conflict. A scientific conservative could claim that, as far as it provides evidence for the effect of selection in human populations today, resolving the conflict is immaterial. Even if it were shown to be the result of selection, who knows if it is continuing at the present time?

The last illustration of evolutionary trends is: 4) *Gerontomorphism to paedomorphism.* Consider for a moment the distinctive differences in appearance between very old (gerontomorphic) persons and infants (paedomorphic). A number of investigators have pointed out that in the course of human evolution, the phenotypic differences between the two extremes are diminishing, as paedomorphic traits become more and more commonly characteristic of adults. At first, this trend seems simply to be a curious oddity. Why, as time passes, should youthful characteristics be retained more and more commonly among adult human beings? However, if this is indeed an evolutionary trend, then it implies that selection opposes early maturation in favor of the retention of youthful characteristics into later years. As pointed out by Sir Gavin De Beer, in his interesting book *Embryos and Ancestors* (1958), this can provide a means by which phylogenetic lines involving species with highly specialized features in the adults can give rise to more generalized descendant lines. Even so, the interesting questions remain unanswered; assuming the trend is indeed a real one, what factors are responsible for it? Why does selection operate to increase paedomorphism in man? Does culture have anything to do with this trend?

These are a few of the many trends that have been cited as evidence to support the position that man continues to be modified by selective pressures. Taken as a whole, they do indeed point to that conclusion, but a skeptic would see that the evidence they provide is inconclusive and equivocal. The existence of temporal trends may imply the action of natural selection, but these trends are not proof of such action. To what extent, for example, might the changes in the dentition be influenced in nongenetic ways by cultural factors such as improved cutting tools, cooking techniques, grinding implements, and, more recently, industrial food processing, canning, and artificial water fluoridation? Moreover, even

---

* From *Up from the Ape,* by Earnest Albert Hooton. Copyright, 1947, by the Macmillan Company. Reprinted by permission of the Macmillan Company.

granting that these trends result from selection, the development of trends through the past does not *prove* that they are continuing today. Recall that the proof demanded is a demonstration of a systematic change in the genetic structure of a population. Paleontological evidence clearly demonstrates the existence of systematic changes, but it fails to show conclusively that they are due to selective forces that continue to operate.

Adaptive Characteristics

Another source of evidence for continuing evolution is the existence of adaptive characteristics among contemporary groups of human beings. To illustrate, adaptive characteristics might include the following: 1) the morphological features which enable Eskimos to adapt more readily to extreme cold than other groups; 2) traits found among tropical peoples that provide for more efficient heat dissipation than found in nontropical groups; or 3) the distinctive attributes possessed by peoples living at high altitudes that physiologically compensate for the lower concentration of oxygen in the atmosphere.

One can argue, for example, that many of the differences between groups adapted to contrasting environments and those that are not are the results of selective factors. If one accepts this proposition and recognizes that the relevant environmental conditions still prevail, then it is a small logical step to conclude that the fact of adaptive characteristics is proof of the continuing action of natural selection. But should we accept the initial proposition? Perhaps we should, but if we do, we do so partly on faith, for the only basis on which we can accept the stand that adaptive characteristics are the result of selective factors is by presuming that we know that the differences are not due to physiological plasticity, which, as indicated in Chapter 7, is simply not justified.

In the earlier discussion, trends were regarded as systematic changes over time, and the evidence for them was, thus, paleontological. Analogously, adaptive traits may be thought of as systematic variation through space, and the evidence for them is heterographic. As the temperature gets cooler, the elevation higher, and the atmosphere more humid, there is often a systematic increase in the frequencies of the relevant adaptive characteristics. As in the case of trends, adaptive traits may in fact be due to the continuation of selective agencies, but they do not prove the existence of such agencies, since any one or all of them might be due to plasticity.

As Stanley Garn (1957) has said:

> . . . it is one thing to prove either logically or experimentally that a given trait may be beneficial, and another thing to demonstrate survival value. Given a sunlamp and a timer one can easily show that the Negro is slower to reach erythema and subsequent discomfort. Given a tank of cold water and a thermocouple it is no trick to show that Eskimo skin temperatures

remain higher and that peripheral blood flow is twice that of whites (Brown, Hatcher, and Page, 1953). But to clinch the argument, selective survival must be demonstrated; the possessors must be differentially represented in the next generation.

Trends and adaptive traits, then, provide suggestive but equivocal evidence on the issue.

Inherited Traits and Disease Susceptibility

Trends and adaptive characteristics constituted the only source of evidence thirty years ago, and this makes more clear why it was that specialists were divided on the issue of man's continued susceptibility to the effects of selection. Two lines of investigation have been taken up since then, and each has added support to the stand that selection continues to affect human populations. One of these is the increasing number of demonstrations of systematic associations between inherited traits and diseases, such as those noted in Table 8–3 on page 273. What do these associations mean? An association between blood type A and stomach cancer simply means that there is a higher percentage of blood type A persons among stomach cancer patients than there is in the total population. How might this be interpreted? One obvious way to view these associations is to interpret them as direct evidence of the action of natural selection. That is to say, one might reason that if persons who are blood type A are more likely to die from stomach cancer than persons who are some other blood type, then blood type A must be selected against. Again recall, however, that while such a view may be reasonable enough, it is not the kind of evidence we have demanded; it does not of itself provide proof that a change in the genetic structure of the population is under way. For example, stomach cancer is a disease that characteristically has a late onset, and people who die from it usually have completed their reproductive periods. And since, as we have seen, selection may act only through differential reproduction, it is entirely possible that such an association may have no effect whatever on the genetic structure of the resulting generation. To prove the point that blood type A is at a selective disadvantage, one would have to show that type A parents contribute proportionately fewer type A offspring to the next generation, and this has not yet been shown, nor has the comparable demonstration been made for any of the associations. In any attempt to analyze the effects of selection among human beings today, there are two interesting problems to be resolved. First of all, one must, of course, solve the problem of whether or not selection is active. Then secondly, if it is, what factors in the environment are responsible for the action? In demonstrating associations between diseases and inherited traits, it is the second problem that is at issue, but what needs to be done is to solve the first.

Polymorphisms

The situation regarding inherited traits is, like trends and adaptive traits, strongly suggestive of the action of selection. It differs as a source of evidence in that the associations provide a better opportunity to show the action of selection, but as yet that proof is lacking. The best evidence has come from the separate but related study of genetic polymorphisms, sets of alleles with frequencies more common than idiomorphs. Traits of this kind have been known for a long time and include, for example, all of the traits of known inheritance discussed in Chapter 8.

The common logical view of selection implies that it acts largely by reducing variation; that is, in any particular environment the prevailing conditions will create, for any particular gene, a favorable situation for one allele, and thereby greatly reduce in frequency or eliminate completely its alternates. Polymorphisms seem at first to contradict this; their existence proves that two or more alleles can be and often are found together in the same population, and, moreover, they can be in very high frequencies. Now the question of interest is, how is this possible? If selection acts continually to favor one allele or one genotype, then is it not odd that polymorphisms are so common? One solution to the problem could be that all alleles presently identified as polymorphs are simply caught in the evolutionary act of becoming idiomorphs or monomorphs. These unstable systems are known as *transient polymorphisms*. If this were the case, then the existence of polymorphisms, far from offering contradictory evidence, would provide ideal illustrations of the classical view. But such is not the case; in man there are many polymorphisms that show no indication whatever of being transient. On the contrary, they appear to be completely stable. These are known as *balanced polymorphisms*, and they do, at first, create some problems.

How is it that the existence of balanced polymorphisms in human populations may be used as evidence in support of the view that man is continuing to undergo evolutionary change? In fact, not all of those that are known have offered such evidence, but one in particular has: the hemoglobin polymorphism. In particular, the best-documented instance is the situation involving Hb^s, the abnormal hemoglobin allele that in homozygous form results in sickle-cell anemia.

The distribution of Hb^s reveals one of the most intriguing problems ever to come up in the study of human evolution. As indicated in Chapter 8, persons who are homozygous for the Hb^s allele fail to produce any normal hemoglobin and usually die from the resulting anemia before they reach maturity. Genetically, the condition is lethal—homozygotes leave no offspring. Under the classical evolutionary view, the normal expectation from conditions like this would be to find the allele, wherever it occurs, in very low frequencies. Yet in some African populations, the

Hb^s allele reaches frequencies as high as .40. That is to say that 40 percent of all the genes responsible for producing the beta chains of hemoglobin in these populations produce an abnormal chain which in homozygotes is lethal. How is it possible for an allele with such obviously harmful effects to be present in such high frequencies?

In Chapter 3, attention was given to the means by which the genetic structure of a population may be changed by the mechanisms of evolution. Are there any means by which an allele with extremely harmful effects can be maintained at high frequencies? Indeed there is at least one way that could fit this situation: selection favoring the heterozygote. Recall that one of the unusual features of this particular form of selection was that by this means selection could act to maintain variation, or, as we might wish to say at this point, to generate and maintain a balanced polymorphism.

So much for the logical possibility. What, if any, empirical evidence exists in the case of sickle-cell anemia? In the case of Hb^s, the answer is reasonably well known: heterozygous individuals enjoy a selective advantage over homozygous normals in that the heterozygotes resist malaria more effectively than persons with completely normal hemoglobin. This relationship was first suggested by the concordance between the distribution of sickle-cell anemia and the distribution of malaria and was subsequently confirmed in an experiment by A. C. Allison (1954).

Thus, the Hb^s allele with lethal effects on homozygotes reaches and is maintained at high frequencies in malarial areas by providing heterozygotes with a survival (thus reproductive) advantage over the normal Hb^A homozygotes, thereby assuring the retention of Hb^s in high frequency. The demonstration of this relationship implied that as the likelihood of contracting malaria increased, the frequency of the Hb^s allele should likewise increase, and Frank B. Livingstone (1958) showed that this is indeed the case. The particularly elegant feature about Livingstone's article is that in it he integrates the distributions of sickle-cell anemia with the intensity of malaria by bringing to bear linguistic, archaeological, and ethnographic detail. In doing so, he illustrates how physical anthropology is able to bridge the gap between the strictly biological and strictly cultural realms of man's variation.

The confirmation of the relationship between malaria and Hb^s provides a sharp insight into the way in which man has adapted genetically to his environment and has resulted in a reevaluation of the distribution of other inherited traits in an effort to relate them to diseases and other selective agencies in their environments. Malaria, for example, appears to be at least partly responsible for the distribution of the inherited conditions thalassemia and glucose-6-phosphate dehydrogenase deficiency, although the evidence bearing on the relationships is less conclusive than in the case of Hb^s. Thalassemia is a general term for several hereditary anemias resulting from a deficiency of a particular kind of hemoglobin chain. Glucose-6-phosphate dehydrogenase (G6PD) is a red cell enzyme inherited as a sex-linked trait. The red blood cells of persons deficient in this enzyme will break open when such persons are given certain drugs (primaquine, sulfonamides) or, curiously, when they inhale the pollen from, or eat, the fava bean. In other respects, the cells of these deficient individuals are normal. Both traits are distributed over the same region as Hb^s and are rare or absent outside this area. Although the picture is as yet unclear, perhaps Hb^s, thalassemia, and G6PD may represent phenotypic interaction similar to that discussed earlier for independently segregating blood group loci.

SEGREGATION ANALYSIS

The very existence of balanced polymorphisms has been enough to convince almost all human biologists that man is still very much an object of natural selection's action. But even evidence of polymorphism is not completely conclusive. No one has as yet demonstrated unequivocally that in areas where malaria is common, sickle-cell heterozygotes do in fact possess some systematic advantage with respect to reproduction over the homozygous normal individual.

The critical experiments are yet to be carried out. The design of such an experiment is comparatively simple and, as pointed out earlier, involves the acquisition of genetic data on nuclear families; that is, on both parents and the offspring they produce together. If data on a sufficiently large sample of nuclear families can be obtained, then the distribution of genotypes among the offspring can be compared with the distribution predicted by Mendel's laws, and any systematic differences between the observed and expected distributions can be noted. Is one particular mating type more fertile than any other? Do marriages, for example, where both parents are heterozygous produce one-quarter *AA*, one-half *Aa*, and one-quarter *aa* genotypes in the children? Or is there some systematic tendency for one genotype to be more frequent than expected? This analytical approach, known broadly as segregation analysis, has been applied extensively to a human population only once. N. E. Morton and his co-workers (1966) collected data on a large number of nuclear families in Brazil. The most surprising feature about the results of segregation analysis on this Brazilian data is the fact that Morton found very few differences between the observed distribution of genotypes and that expected under Mendel's laws. That is to say, for almost all of the genetic loci tested, the various mating types were, in fact, producing the expected proportions of genotypes among their children. On the one hand, this may be deceiving; natural selection may be acting too gently or too subtly to be detected by segregation analysis. On the other hand, it could very well mean what it appears to mean; the traits may be selectively neutral and thus represent instances of the equilibrium specified by the Hardy–Weinberg law. If this latter interpretation is correct, it raises once again the problem of nonadaptive traits. At one time selectively neutral, or nonadaptive, traits were taken for granted as self-evident facts of life. More recently the opposite view has been considered as self-evident: there are in reality no selectively neutral traits. Morton's data indicate that perhaps it would be best to forgo any definite decision until more information is available.

Conclusion

All sources of evidence considered point toward the same conclusion: human populations continue to be under the influence of natural selection. To reject this conclusion or even to remain uncommitted on the issue would be unnecessarily conservative. The problem is, in general, resolved. However, in every particular case where the action of natural selection can be shown, there remains a secondary problem: What elements of the environment cause selection to act the way that it does? Except for sickle-cell anemia and a few other malaria-dependent polymorphisms where this secondary question was first resolved, virtually nothing is known on this question. As our knowledge improves, there are more and more reasons to believe that the significant environmental factors responsible for directing natural selection in human populations are cultural factors. In contrast to the view that culture shields man from selection, this implies that cultural elements impose unique selective requirements on man. If this is correct, then man's biological future might best be predicted by a knowledge of cultural events.

References and Suggestions for Additional Reading

ALLISON, A. C.
    1954   Protection afforded by sickle-cell trait against subtertian malarial infection. *British Medical Journal* 1:290–294.
BIELICKI, TADEUSZ, AND Z. WELON
    1964   The operation of natural selection on human head form in an East European population. *Homo* 15:22–30.
BROWN, G. M., J. D. HATCHER, AND J. PAGE
    1953   Temperature and blood flow in the forearm of the Eskimo. *Journal of Applied Psychology* 5:410–420.
CHAMLA, MARIE-CLAUDE
    1964   L'Acrroissement de la stature en France de 1880 à 1960: comparaison avec les pays d'Europe occidentale [The increase in

stature in France from 1880 to 1960: a comparison with the countries of western Europe]. *Bulletin Société Anthropologie de Paris* 6:201–278. English translation by John Robert Kane in *Yearbook of Physical Anthropology* 12:146–183.

DE BEER, GAVIN
1958   *Embryos and ancestors.* 3d ed. London: Oxford University Press.

DOBZHANSKY, THEODOSIUS
1960   The present evolution of man. *Scientific American* 203, September, pp. 206–217.

GARN, STANLEY M.
1957   Race and evolution. *American Anthropologist* 59:218–224.

HOOTON, EARNEST ALBERT
1947   *Up from the ape.* Rev. ed. New York: Macmillan.

LIVINGSTONE, FRANK B.
1958   Anthropological implications of sickle cell gene distribution in West Africa. *American Anthropologist* 60:533–562.

MEDAWAR, P. B.
1960   *The future of man.* London: Methuen.

MORTON, N. E., H. KRIEGER, AND M. P. MI
1966   Natural selection on polymorphisms in northeastern Brazil. *American Journal of Human Genetics* 18:153–171.

MULLER, HERMAN J.
1965   Means and aims in human genetic betterment. In *The control of human heredity and evolution,* ed. T. M. Sonnenborn. New York: Macmillan.

SIMPSON, GEORGE GAYLORD
1950   Some problems of historical biology bearing on human origins. *Cold Spring Harbor Symposia on Quantitative Biology* 15:55–66.

WHITE, LESLIE A.
1959   *The evolution of culture.* New York: McGraw-Hill.

Glossary

Adaptability: Among evolving units (populations, species), the capacity to make successful adjustments to environmental changes.

Adaptation: The adjustment made by an evolving unit (population, species) to a particular set of environmental requirements.

Aegyptopithecus: A late Oligocene primate form from the Fayum deposits in Egypt. The fossil evidence consists of five lower jaws and an almost complete skull.

Agglutination: The process of forming clumps of red blood cells. A consequence of antigen-antibody incompatibility.

Agnatha: A class of vertebrates to which the primitive jawless fishes belong.

Alcaptonuria: A hereditary disease of human beings caused by the absence or malfunction of an enzyme. The urine of affected individuals turns black on exposure to air.

Allele: An alternate form of a gene. For example, A^1 and A^2 designate alleles of gene A.

Allen's rule: Notes that in the colder regions of a mammalian species' range, the parts of the body most susceptible to frostbite tend to be shorter than they are in members of the same species situated in warmer areas.

Alpha chain: A particular sequence of amino acids linked together by peptide bonds and forming one of two kinds of polypeptide chains found as part of hemoglobin. The other kind of chain is called the beta chain. In any molecule of hemoglobin the alpha and beta chains occur in pairs.

Amphibia: A class of vertebrates transitional in their adaptation. Characteristically Amphibia occur both on land and in water, but ultimately depend on water as a medium for laying their eggs.

Analogies: Similarities among organisms that result from similar functions. Analogies imply similar adaptations, but not close biological relationship.

Angiosperms: The flowering plants.

Animalia: The kingdom of living organisms to which man belongs.

Antibody: A protein substance formed in the plasma as a defense mechanism against attack by a foreign protein.

Antigen: Protein substance that stimulates the production of antibodies.

Apidium: An early Oligocene primate from the Fayum deposits in Egypt. See *Parapithecus.*

Arboreal: Adapted to living in trees.

Archaeology: A subdivision of cultural anthropology which investigates the forms of cultural variability along the dimension of time.

Archaeozoic: The first era of paleontological time. Begins with the origin of life (about three billion years ago) and ends rather vaguely with the appearance of many-celled organisms.

Australopithecus africanus: The smaller and apparently earlier variety of the *Australopithecus* genus. Possibly representative of the ancestor of *Homo erectus.*

Australopithecus robustus: The larger, more recent variety of the *Australopithecus* genus. Status in man's evolution is in dispute. Some authorities maintain that *Australopithecus robustus* became extinct, others that he is transitional between *Australopithecus africanus* and *Homo erectus.*

Aves: The class of vertebrates to which birds belong.

Bergmann's rule: States that among mammals, the larger animals within a species tend to be found in the colder regions of the species' range.

Beta chain: See **Alpha chain.**

Biochemical genetics: A subdivision of genetics that deals with the influence of heredity on metabolism.

Biogenesis: In accounting for the origin of life, the view that maintains that life on earth is the product of preexisting life.

Blade tools: One of five basic kinds of stone implements from the Paleolithic. Blade tools are usually well-made flake implements, usually elongated with both edges sharpened. Blade tools are characteristic of the Upper Paleolithic.

Brachiation: A form of locomotion. The ability to get from one location to another by means of swinging by the forelimbs.

Brontosaurus: A herbivorous dinosaur form which lived during the Mesozoic and grew to lengths up to eighty feet and developed bulks weighing forty tons.

Cambrian: The first period of the Paleozoic era, beginning approximately one-half billion years ago.

Carbon 14 (C^{14}) dating technique: A method used in estimating the age of a fossil. The proportion of C^{14} to C^{12} begins to decline at a known rate at the time an organism dies, and thus a measure of the proportion is an indication of the amount of time that has elapsed.

Carboniferous: A period of the Paleozoic that began approximately 280 million years ago. Divided by some geochronologists into two periods: the Mississippian and the Pennsylvanian.

Catarrhinae: A suborder of the order Primates. Includes the Old World monkeys, apes, and man.

Ceboidea: Taxonomic designation for the only superfamily in the platyrrhinae suborder or the primate order. It consists of two families, Callithricidae and Cebidae.

Cenozoic: The geological era in which we are now living. It began approximately 75 million years ago.

Cephalic index: A numerical expression of head form:

$$\text{Cephalic index} = \frac{\text{head breadth}}{\text{head length}} \times 100.$$

Cercopithecoidea: One of two superfamilies of the suborder Catarrhinae. It consists of the Old World monkeys.

Chelles-Acheul tradition: An Old World archaeological sequence of paleolithic core-tool implements. The distinctive feature of sites included in the sequence is the presence of hand axes.

Chondrichthyes: A class of vertebrates to which the sharks and their relatives belong.

Chopper-chopping tools: One of five basic kinds of stone implements from the Paleolithic. Chopper-chopping tools are rather crudely made and have been found in eastern Asia.

Chordata: A phylum of the animal kingdom that includes a diverse group of forms, all of which have at some time during their life cycle a notochord, gill slits, and a dorsal tubular nerve cord.

Choukoutienian industry: The chopper-chopping tool assemblage found in association with the Chinese *Homo erectus.*

Chromosome: The structure in the cell nucleus which contains a discrete set of genes arranged in linear order.

Clactonian-Levalloisian tradition: An Old World archaeological sequence of Paleolithic flake tools.

Class: A major taxonomic category ranking above the order and below the phylum.

Clinal classification: A classification of the varieties of a heterographic trait based on systematic variation of the trait geographically.

Clines: Systematic changes in the distribution of a trait. The word is also used to designate the zones in which similar or identical forms or frequencies occur.

Core tools: One of five basic kinds of stone implements from the Paleolithic. Core tools have been found over a broad area of the Old World. They are large implements, also known as hand axes, made by striking pieces from a rock until it has the desired shape.

Cretaceous: The most recent period of the Mesozoic era, beginning approximately 145 million years ago.

Crossover: A process which separates linked genetic loci by the exchange of segments between homologous chromosomes.

Cross-sectional sampling: A technique used in studies of growth involving the selection of several persons at each of several age groups, therefore drawing inferences about growth regularities.

Culture: The primary means by which man adapts to requirements of the environment.

Deoxyribonucleic acid (DNA): The hereditary material of genes; a doubly coiled helix consisting of a chain of nucleotide pairs.

Devonian: The fourth period of the Paleozoic era, beginning approximately 335 million years ago.

Diploid number: One complete set of pairs of chromosomes. In man the diploid number is 46 chromosomes.

Down's syndrome: A genetic disease associated with the occurrence of an extra chromosome. Also called mongolism.

Dryopithecus: Genus of Miocene apes known from a large number of fossils found throughout the Old World.

Empiricism: The philosophical view that correct knowledge about nature can be obtained only through correct reasoning and by testing the results of reasoning against experience.

Eocene: The second epoch of the Tertiary period, beginning approximately 60 million years ago and lasting approximately 20 million years. In the primates there is considerable evidence of the proliferation and diversification of the prosimians during this epoch.

Epicanthic fold: A skin fold on the eyelid that, when the eye is open, comes down over and runs on a line with the edge of the upper eyelid.

Eutheria: The subgrouping of mammals to which man belongs; Eutherian mammals are distinguished by the fact that mothers carry their young within the uterus until an advanced state of development is reached.

Family: A taxonomic category ranking above genus and below order.

Fauresmith: Stone tool assemblage from South Africa consisting of small hand axes and flake implements. Associated with the tropical variant of Neanderthal.

Flake tools: One of five basic kinds of stone implements from the Paleolithic. Flake tools are small stone implements made by striking flakes off a larger stone (core). Techniques of manufacture vary from a crude trial-and-error procedure to the careful and deliberate shaping of a flake on the core and its removal in a single blow.

Fluorine dating technique: A method used to assess the relative ages of two or more fossils from the same deposits which involves the measurement of the amounts of fluorine they contain.

Formal genetics: A subdivision of genetics that deals with determining the precise modes of inheritance of traits.

Frequency: The number of times an event occurs out of the total number of occasions it could have occurred. Can be expressed as a fraction (e.g., 50/100), a proportion (.50), or a percentage (50 percent).

Gene: The physical structure in the cell nucleus which transmits hereditary potential from one generation to the next.

Genetic code: The messenger RNA triplet sequences that specify particular amino acid units in the synthesis of a polypeptide chain.

Genetic drift: Change in the genetic structure of a population caused by chance factors. Also known as the Sewall Wright effect.

Genetic linkage: Genetic loci situated on the same chromosome. Linked loci are transmitted together as a unit.

Genotype: For any individual, the complete set of allelic pairs he inherits from his parents. For any locus, the particular pair of alleles that has been inherited.

Genus. A taxonomic category ranking above species and below family.

Gloger's rule: Darkly pigmented varieties within a species are found in the warmer, more humid parts of the species' range.

Günz: The earliest of four glacial periods in Europe occurring in the Pleistocene.

Haploid number: One complete set of chromosomes; as distinct from one complete set of pairs (diploid number). In man, the haploid number of chromosomes is 23.

Haptoglobin: A protein found in serum that is believed to combine with hemoglobin and prevent its passage through the kidneys.

Hardy–Weinberg law of genetic equilibrium: Gene and genotype frequencies will reach and remain at a stable equilibrium after one generation of random mating in a large population that is not being affected by the mechanisms of evolution.

Haversian canals: The longitudinal channels in the matrix of bone through which pass blood vessels and nerves.

Hemoglobin: A protein normally present within red blood cells which carries oxygen to the cells of the body and carries away carbon dioxide.

Heterography: The description and investigation of biological variation among living populations.

Heterozygous: Possessing, in the genotype, two different allelic forms of a gene.

Hominoidea: One of two superfamilies of the suborder Catarrhinae. It consists of three families—Hylobatidae, Pongidae, and Hominidae—composed of the apes and man.

Homo erectus: The genus and species designation used to identify the Middle Pleistocene hominids that appear to precede Neanderthal man and to follow the australopithecines.

Homologies: Detailed structural similarities built upon a basic morphological pattern and which therefore indicate close relationship among the forms that share them.

Homo sapiens: The genus and species designating modern man.

Homozygous: Possessing in the genotype the same allelic forms of a gene.

Idiomorph: A rare allele, i.e., one whose frequency is less than 2 percent.

Interphase: A stage in the life cycle of a cell that begins when the cell is formed and lasts until it begins to divide. This has been called the "resting phase," but it is becoming clearer that considerable activity is going on during interphase.

Ischial callosities: Distinctive calloused areas on the buttocks of Old World primates. May be an adaptation to sleeping sitting up in trees.

Jurassic: The second period of the Mesozoic era. The Jurassic began approximately 170 million years ago.

Karyotype: A classification of chromosome pairs according to number and form.

Kingdom: A taxonomic category; the primary subdivision of living forms.

Klinefelter's syndrome: In males, the assemblage of moderately developed female traits together with sterility. The syndrome is associated with an abnormal karyotype containing two X chromosomes together with one Y.

Lamellae: In bone, the concentric deposits of minerals, particularly calcium and phosphorus.

Lemuroidea: One of the four superfamilies of the suborder Prosimii of the order Primates; consists of three families: the Lemuridae, Indridae, and Daubentonidae.

Locus: The position a gene occupies on a chromosome.

Longitudinal sampling: In growth studies, the ascertainment of information on the same individuals at intervals throughout their lifetime.

Lorisoidea: One of four superfamilies of the suborder Prosimii; consists of two families, the Lorisidae and Galagidae.

Lumpers: One of two categories (see also **Splitters**) into which taxonomists may themselves be classified. This group tends to regard differences as less important and thus lumps together the forms displaying these differences.

Mammalia: The class of vertebrates which includes man.

Meiosis: The cellular process that produces sex cells, i.e., cells with the haploid number of chromosomes.

Meiotic drive: The production by heterozygotes of unequal proportions of homologous chromosomes. Also known as prezygotic selection.

Mendel's first law of inheritance: Specifies that whereas an individual has a pair of alleles determining his genotype for all loci, he transmits only one member of each pair to his offspring. Also known as the law of genetic segregation.

Mendel's second law of inheritance: Specifies that genetic loci assort independently in the process of inheritance. Also known as the law of independent assortment.

Mesopithecus: Fossil primate form represented by several remains from the Miocene and Pliocene of Europe and East Africa that may be an ancestral stage in the evolution of the Colobinae.

Mesozoic: A geological era also called the Age of Reptiles. It began approximately 200 million years ago and ended approximately 75 million years ago.

Messenger RNA (ribonucleic acid): A nucleic acid that may be found in both the nucleus and the cytoplasm. It is made by the DNA and plays a fundamental part in protein synthesis.

Metatheria: A subgrouping of mammals distinguished by the fact that the females bear their young in an immature condition and provide for their continued development in pouches. Also called pouched mammals.

Mindel: The second of the four Alpine glaciations during the Pleistocene.

Miocene: The fourth epoch of the Tertiary period. The Miocene began approximately 28 million years ago and lasted for approximately 16 million years. During this epoch it appears that the hominoids become differentiated into pongids and hominids.

Mississippian: See **Carboniferous.**

Mitosis: The process that produces body cells, i.e., cells with the diploid number of chromosomes.

Molecular genetics: A subdivision of genetics that deals with the structure of the materials of inheritance.

Monogenesis: The view that all the races of man share a single origin.

Monomorph: Any allele with a frequency higher than 99.9 percent.

Mousterian industry: A Middle Paleolithic assemblage of archaeological materials including scrapers, flake tools, and, in some instances, hand axes. The Mousterian is commonly found in association with the temperate Neanderthals.

Mutation: A change in the structure of a gene.

Nasal index: A numerical expression of nose form:

$$\text{Nasal index} = \frac{\text{nasal breadth}}{\text{nasal length}} \times 100.$$

Natural selection: The mechanism of evolution proposed and documented by Darwin which implies that the environment imposes requirements on a species which can be met effectively by only some members of the species, which thus are the ones who survive and produce the subsequent generation.

Neanderthal man: A highly varied, late Pleistocene, Old World hominid that may be in modern man's ancestry.

Neurospora: An organism responsible for some types of bread mold and used for some of the basic investigations in biochemical genetics.

New World monkeys: The Platyrrhinae.

Nonrandom mating: Any departure from random mating in a population. May be a tendency for likes to mate (positive assortative mating), for likes to avoid one another as mates (negative assortative mating), or a tendency for biological relatives to mate (inbreeding).

Nonsecretor: One who lacks the ABO substances in water-soluble form in his body fluids. The nonsecretor trait is homozygous recessive.

Nontaster: An individual who is unable to taste certain substances, such as phenylthiocarbamide (PTC), which to others (tasters) has a vividly bitter taste. The nontaster is homozygous (recessive) for the locus determining this trait.

Notochord: An elastic tubular structure situated along the dorsal surface. It is present at some time during the life cycle of all members of the phylum Chordata.

Nucleotide: The basic molecular unit of nucleic acids; it consists of a sugar molecule, a phosphate group, and a base of purine or pyrimidine.

Occipital crest: A ridge of bone running transversely across the lower part of the back of the skull. It serves as an area of muscle attachment for many of the muscles that move the neck.

Oldowan industry: The oldest known assemblage of Paleolithic implements. The Oldowan is a pebble-tool assemblage from Africa.

Olduvai Gorge: Location in Tanzania, East Africa, which has produced an extraordinary amount of paleontological and archaeological evidence bearing on man's origin and evolution.

Old World monkeys: A designation commonly used in place of Cercopithecoidea, the proper taxonomic term.

Oligocene: The third epoch of the Tertiary period. The Oligocene began approximately 40 million years ago and lasted for approximately 12 million years. During this epoch the higher primates (monkeys and apes) make their first appearance in the paleontological record of the Old World.

Order: A taxonomic category ranking above family and below class.

Ordovician: The second period of the Paleozoic era, estimated to have begun approximately 435 million years ago.

Osteichthyes: One of the classes of vertebrates—the fishes with bony skeletons.

Osteocytes: Cells imbedded in the matrix of bone.

Paleocene: The earliest epoch of the Tertiary period. Probably the epoch in which the primates first became clearly distinct as an order of mammals. It began approximately 75 million years ago and lasted approximately 15 million years.

Paleontology: A subdivision of biology that concerns itself with the ancestral forms of modern organisms. Its primary source of data is fossils.

Paleozoic: The geological era lasting from approximately 520 million years ago to about 200 million years ago, in which may be found the first abundant fossil record of the evolution of life.

Pangenesis: A defunct theory proposed by Darwin to accommodate some logical implications of the theory of the inheritance of acquired characteristics. Pangenesis postulates the presence in all body cells of gemmules, which are modified by the way of life an organism leads, and which can then alter the individual's hereditary potential.

Pantotheria: Jurassic reptilelike mammals which, by the close of the Mesozoic, gave rise to the marsupial and placental mammals.

Parapithecus: An early Oligocene primate from the Fayum deposits in Egypt. The evidence consists mostly of a fragmentary jaw, and its significance has been in dispute for some time. The most common interpretation regards *Parapithecus* (together with *Apidium*) as the earliest known Old World monkey.

Pebble tools: One of five basic kinds of stone implements from the Paleolithic. Pebble tools are the earliest Paleolithic implements and were made by the simple process of striking two rocks together until a sharp edge was obtained.

Pennsylvanian: See **Carboniferous.**

Permian: The final period of the Paleozoic era; it began approximately 225 million years ago.

Phenotype: In reference to an individual, the sum total of the effects of interaction between that individual's genotype and the environment. Thus an individual's phenotype is what we call vaguely his appearance and includes his morphology and behavior.

Phenylketonuria (PKU): An inherited disease that results in mental deficiencies. It is the result of the absence of a single enzyme.

Photosynthesis: The process by which green plants utilize the sun's energy for their own life processes.

Phylum: A taxonomic category that serves as the major subdivision of the kingdom category; thus it ranks above the class and below the kingdom.

Physiological plasticity: The ability of organisms to adapt during their lifetimes to changing environmental conditions.

Piltdown: The name of a peculiar assemblage of supposedly ape and modern man skull remains from England that was shown to be a deliberate fraud.

Placodermi: One of eight classes of the vertebrates—the archaic jawed fishes.

Platyrrhinae: A suborder of the primates consisting entirely of New World monkeys.

Pleistocene: The most recent epoch of the Cenozoic era. The Pleistocene began over 2 million years ago and contains within it the paleontological and archaeological record of man's evolution.

Plesiadapis: The only primate fossil known from both the New and the Old World. A Paleocene form transitional in its morphology between insectivore and primate characteristics.

Pliocene: The fifth epoch of the Tertiary period, beginning approximately 12 million years ago and lasting approximately 10 million years.

Polygenesis: The view that maintained that the races of man had separate origins.

Polymorphism: A trait controlled by two or more common alleles.

Populational classification: A system used by physical anthropologists and human geneticists which is designed to divide human groups into breeding isolates.

Population genetics: A subdivision of genetics that deals with the determination of the genetic structure of natural populations and the factors that maintain or alter that structure.

Potassium-argon (K-A) dating technique: A rate-quantity dating technique. K^{40} disintegrates to A^{40} at a known rate. In volcanic rock the Argon is trapped as it is formed; thus by measuring the ratio of K^{40} to A^{40} one may estimate the age of the volcanic rock.

Primates: An order of the class Mammalia; the order to which man, the apes, the monkeys, and the prosimians belong.

Proconsul: An African Miocene primate group known from several fragmentary fossil remains displaying considerable variability. It is perhaps more accurate to consider *Proconsul* as the African variety of *Dryopithecus*.

Propliopithecus: Generic name given to a lower jaw and some teeth from Oligocene deposits in Egypt. There is disagreement over the taxonomic status of this form within the order Primates.

Prosimii: A suborder of the order Primates. Members of this suborder were the first of the primates to appear.

Proterozoic: The geological era between the Archaeozoic and the Paleozoic. The paleontological record from the Proterozoic is sparse, but the presence of highly developed life forms within it is clearly indicated from the Ediacara Hills in Australia.

Prototheria: A subgrouping within the class Mammalia. These mammals lay eggs, but, like other mammals, feed their newborn by means of mammary glands.

Quaternary: The later period of the Cenozoic era, beginning approximately 2 million years ago.

Ramapithecus: The earliest known hominid. The fossil material consists of fragmentary fossil jaws and teeth that have been dated at from late Miocene to early Pliocene. *Ramapithecus* remains are known from India and Africa.

Random mating: System of mating within a population wherein any individual has an equal probability of mating with any other individual in the population.

Rationalism: The view that truth about nature can be reached by means of correct reasoning alone.

Rensch's rule: Specifies that, in mammals, the members of a species adapted to hot climatic conditions have localized deposits of fat.

Replication: The process of copying or duplicating; the process by which DNA copies itself.

Reproductive isolation: A situation in which one group of organisms cannot or does not interbreed with another group.

Reptilia: A class of vertebrates. The reptiles of modern and ancient times.

Rh factor: A red blood cell antigen that, when it is present in an unborn child, can stimulate the production of antibodies to itself in the plasma of mothers that lack it, with serious consequences to the child.

Ribonucleic acid (RNA): A nucleic acid similar in structure to DNA, but differing from DNA in three basic ways: RNA 1) contains a distinctive sugar; 2) lacks the base thymine and has uracil, which DNA lacks; and 3) consists of a polynucleotide chain—not a pair of chains, as in DNA. RNA functions in the cell to make proteins.

Riss: The third of four Alpine glaciations during the Pleistocene.

Sagittal crest: A bony ridge running from front to back along the top of the skull. It serves as an area for the attachment of the muscles that move the jaw.

Sangoan: An archaeological assemblage from forested regions of central Africa consisting of picks, cleavers, and crude hand axes.

Secretor: One who has ABH antigens in water-soluble form in his body fluids. Whether or not a person is a secretor is genetically determined.

Sewall Wright effect: See **Genetic drift.**

Sex chromatin body: A mass of chromatin material that may be found in the nuclei of female mammalian cells. The belief is common that this body is an inactive X chromosome.

Sex chromosomes: The pair of chromosomes genetically differentiating males and females. In man and many other animals the female has two X chromosomes; the male has one X and one Y chromosome.

Shovel-shaped incisors: Our front teeth are called incisors. In some instances these fold backward at the sides and thereby increase the size of the chewing surface without increasing the width of the tooth. Such teeth are called shovel-shaped incisors.

Sickle-cell anemia: A hereditary disease caused by an abnormality in the sequence of amino acids in the beta chain of hemoglobin. Individuals unable to make normal beta chains (homozygotes for the trait) have grossly distorted red blood cells and commonly die before maturity.

Silurian: The third period of the Paleozoic era, beginning approximately 375 million years ago.

Soluble or transfer RNA (sRNA or tRNA): Short, twisted strands of RNA present in the cytoplasm that activate and position amino acids in the process of protein synthesis.

Species: A taxonomic category ranking below the genus and commonly identified (for bisexually reproducing organisms) as the total group of organisms capable of interbreeding and producing fertile offspring.

Splitters: One of two categories (see also **Lumpers**) into which taxonomists may themselves be classified. Splitters tend to regard small differences as of greater taxonomic significance and thus split similar forms into distinct taxonomic categories.

Spontaneous generation: The view that life arose from nonliving matter.

Steatopygia: A trait characterized by an extraordinary accumulation of fat on the buttocks.

Swanscombe: The name given to three skull bones from Mindel-Riss interglacial times. The bones are like those of modern man and suggest that modern man's antiquity is very great.

Tarsioidea: One of the four superfamilies of the suborder Prosimii, represented today by only one living family and genus, the tarsiers.

Taster: An individual able to taste certain substances such as phenylthiocarbamide (PTC) which others (see **Nontaster**) are unable to taste. The trait is inherited, and the allele determining taster status is dominant to that determining nontaster; thus the taster may be homozygous or heterozygous.

Tertiary: The earlier period of the Cenozoic era, beginning approximately 75 million years ago.

Thecodonts: Small, terrestrial reptiles of Triassic times.

Thompson's rule: Refers to nose breadth and states that in cold climates, noses tend to be narrow, whereas in hot climates they tend to be broad.

Triassic: The earliest period of the Mesozoic era. It began approximately 200 million years ago.

Trilobite: A widely diverse group of invertebrates common throughout the fossil record of the Paleozoic.

Tupaioidea: One of four superfamilies of the suborder Prosimii. The tupaiids display an assemblage of primate and insectivore traits, and, indeed, some taxonomists place them in the order Insectivora.

Typological classification: A classification of variability that divides human beings into groups on the basis of the regular occurrence together of distinctive heterographic traits.

Tyrannosaurus: Enormous carnivorous Mesozoic reptile. This dinosaur was bipedal and is believed to be a descendant of the early Mesozoic thecodonts.

Uniformitarianism: The belief that geological phenomena of the past are the result of processes that are observable today.

Villafranchian: The Old World mammalian faunal assemblage used in some areas as a means of identifying the beginning of the Pleistocene.

Würm: The most recent of the four Pleistocene Alpine glaciations.

Zinjanthropus: Name assigned by L. S. B. Leakey to a skull discovered in 1958 in East Africa. It has subsequently been recognized as a member of the already established genus *Australopithecus.*

Index